the Forth
Naturalist
*and*Historian

Volume 36 2013

1-3 Prelims

4 Author Addresses

Naturalist Papers

Historical Papers

Published by the Forth Naturalist and Historian, University of Stirling – charity SCO 13270.

ISSN 0309-7560

ISBN 978-1-898008-71-2

Supported by INEOS and Scottish Natural Heritage.

Cover: front– The doocot or former gun bastion on Stirling town wall at Allan's school (photograph by John Harrison).

Printed by Meigle Colour Printers Ltd., Tweedbank Industrial Estate, Galashiels. Set in Zapf Calligraphic on 115 gsm Silk and cover 300 gsm Silk.

THE FORTH NATURALIST AND HISTORIAN

The Forth Naturalist and Historian (FNH) is an informal enterprise of Stirling University. It was set up in 1975 by several University and Central Regional Council staff to provide a focus for interests, activities and publications of environmental, heritage and historical studies for the Forth area, comprising now local authority areas Stirling, Falkirk and Clackmannanshire.

Since then the organisation of an annual environment/heritage symposium called *Man and the Landscape* has been an important feature.

The annual *Forth Naturalist and Historian* has published numerous papers, many being authoritative and significant in their field, and includes annual reports of the weather, and of birds in the locality, plus book reviews and notes. These volumes provide a valuable successor to that basic resource *The Transactions of the Stirling Field and Archaeological Society*, 1878-1939. Four year contents/indexes are available, and selected papers are published in pamphlet form, while others are available as reprints.

In addition a 230 page book *Central Scotland – Land, Wildlife, People*, a natural history and heritage survey, was produced in 1994 and is available in the form of a CD-Rom, *Heart of Scotland's Environment* (HSE).

Other FNH and associated publications still in print include – *Mines and Minerals of the Ochils, Airthrey and Bridge of Allan, Woollen Mills of the Hillfoots, The Ochil Hills* – landscape, wildlife, heritage – an introduction with walks, *Alloa Tower and the Erskines of Mar*, and the *Lure of Loch Lomond* a journey round the shores and islands. Several of these are in association with Clackmannanshire Field Studies Society.

FNH publications are listed on the internet British Library (BLPC) and by booksellers e.g. Amazon, Bol, Barnes and Noble.

Offers of papers/notes for publication, and of presentations for symposia are ever welcome. **Visit website for instructions to authors.**

Honorary Secretary Marilyn Scott,
Computer Services, University of Stirling, FK9 4LA.
E-mail: fnh@stir.ac.uk
Web: http://www.fnh.stir.ac.uk

Author Addresses

Nick Aitchison, 22a Snowdon Place, Stirling FK8 2JN

Neil Bielby, 56 Ochiltree, Dunblane FK15 0DF

Stephen Digney, Flat 2/2, 810 Crow Road, Glasgow G13 1LY

John Harrison, 14a Abercrombie Place, Stirling FK8 2QP

Euan Hills, Clackmannanshire Countryside Rangers, Greenside Street, Alloa FK10 1EB

Peter Maitland, Fish Conservation Centre, Gladshot, Haddington EH41 4RN

Roy Sexton, 22 Alexander Drive, Bridge of Allan FK9 4QB

John Simpson, 3 Mitchell Drive, Cardross, Argyll and Bute G82 5JJ

Michael Usher, Dept. of Environmental Science, University of Stirling FK9 4LA

Dan Watson, NTS, Lynedoch, Main Street, Killin FK21 8UW

POWAN *COREGONUS LAVARETUS* INTRODUCED TO CARRON VALLEY RESERVOIR: A CONSERVATION EXERCISE

Peter S. Maitland and Alex A. Lyle

'... it was an interesting sight to behold this brilliantly shining specimen,
iridescent with the most delicate colours,
as it lay on the grass just after it was taken out of the water.'

Houghton (1879)

Introduction

The powan *Coregonus lavaretus* is one of three rather similar species of fish which occur in the British Isles (the other two are vendace *Coregonus albula* and pollan *Coregonus autumnalis*) and there is some confusion among them because of the various common names which these fish have acquired. Sometimes called the freshwater herring, the powan is also known as gwyniad in Wales (where it occurs naturally in just one lake) and as schelly in England (where it occurs naturally in four lakes). In Scotland, the powan occurs naturally in just two waters – Loch Lomond and Loch Eck.

The powan has a well-built body, elongate and laterally compressed (Plate 5). The head is small, as is the mouth, which has no teeth. The head and back are dark bluish grey which grades to greenish grey along the sides and eventually to a silvery whitish yellow on the belly. The body is covered by large shiny scales. The characteristic adipose fin is large and fleshy whilst the paired fins are well-developed. The adult size of powan is normally some 30-35 cm in length and 300-400 g in weight. The present British rod-caught record is 950 g for a fish caught in 1986 in Haweswater (Cumbria), but recording has been discontinued because it is now illegal to catch this species intentionally in Great Britain (Wildlife and Countryside Act, 1981) without a permit from the appropriate country conservation agency – Scottish Natural Heritage in the case of Scotland.

Like some other species (for example the sparling or smelt *Osmerus eperlanus* and the grayling *Thymallus thymallus*), the powan is remarkable for its smell. Brown (1891) describes the powan as having a strong odour like the sparling, so that in the summer and autumn when they float in large shoals at the surface the surrounding air for a distance is tainted with their scent. Writing some years later, Lamond, in 1931, seems to agree: While alive, and even when cooked, the fish seems to have a scent and flavour faintly reminiscent of cucumber. Over many years, the authors have handled thousands of these fish and they certainly have a characteristic odour, which always seems fresh and pleasant.

Although rare in Scotland, the powan is widespread across much of north-west Russia, Finland and Sweden. It occurs also in several other countries (Norway, Switzerland, Germany, Poland and France) but only in certain areas – usually in mountainous alpine lakes. Typically, powan occur in relatively large deep lakes with clear well-oxygenated water. During daylight, outwith the breeding season, adult fish stay in relatively deep water – on the bottom if they are near the shore, or at depths of 20-30 m if in deeper water. At dusk they rise into shallower water, often coming right up to the surface and in to the shore. At dawn a reverse migration takes place.

Threats

Although the powan normally occurs in large numbers in both Loch Lomond and Loch Eck, the fact that it occurs in just these two lochs, out of thousands in Scotland, makes it very vulnerable. Numbers mean little in the face of catastrophe, and security for the species lies in the numbers of populations rather than the total numbers of fish in one or two places. Potential catastrophies have taken place in Loch Lomond in the past, where there have been several major incidents affecting powan.

In Loch Lomond, powan have several natural predators, one of the most important of these being pike *Esox lucius*, which prey on them especially during their spawning period when they are very vulnerable in shallow water (Shafi and Maitland, 1971). Fewer powan are eaten by pike during the summer months, but they are then attacked in large numbers by river lampreys *Lampetra fluviatilis* which leave characteristic oval flesh wounds along the backs (Maitland *et al.*, 1994).

Powan eggs too have many predators, including adult powan themselves. In some areas large caddis larvae have been shown to be significant predators (Slack, 1955). A relatively new threat is that of ruffe *Gymnocephalus cernuus*, which were introduced to Loch Lomond about 1980 and are now one of the commonest fish species there (Maitland *et al.*, 1983, Adams and Maitland, 1998). Examination of the stomachs of ruffe during the spawning season of powan (January) confirmed that powan eggs are a major item of ruffe diet at this time (Adams and Tippett, 1990).

During the Second World War the heather in the Ben Lomond area was set alight at night to confuse the Luftwaffe into thinking this was a town. Several bombs were delivered there and at least one of them fell into the loch and exploded. Next morning there were hundreds of powan (as well as Atlantic salmon *Salmo salar*, brown trout *Salmo trutta* and other fish species) floating in the water – a welcome addition to the rations of local people at that time.

During both World Wars, powan were fished commercially in Lochs Lomond and Eck and several hundred thousand fish were taken at these times, Lamond (1931) noted that: During the closing months of the War, when there was a shortage in the food supplies of the country, powan fishing was intensively prosecuted by request of the Government. The minimum annual catch between 1916 and 1926 was 10,000 fish (1916), the maximum catch 51,500 (1918).

During the late 1960s, powan started dying in large numbers and could be found dead all along the shoreline. The reason was found by Roberts *et al.* (1970) to be due to a disease called 'bald spot', which caused lesions on the skin, particularly on the head, and was obviously fatal to many fish. In June, 1968, during this mass mortality of powan, when thousands were washed on to the shore, buzzards *Buteo buteo* were coming down regularly to the edge of the loch and feeding on dead powan there (Mitchell, 1984).

Over the years, Loch Lomond has been subjected to a number of engineering impacts. In 1859 the construction of the water supply from Loch Katrine to Glasgow resulted in the diversion of water away from the Loch Lomond catchment. In 1948, the Loch Sloy Hydro-Electric Scheme, incorporating large volumes of water from outside the Lomond catchment started discharging to Loch Lomond. There are now plans to convert this to a pumped-storage scheme. In 1970, a barrage was built on the River Leven to control the surface level of Loch Lomond so that water could be reliably pumped from the south end of the loch at Ross Priory to Glasgow.

Research on powan in Loch Lomond was started by Slack (1957) and colleagues, and has been continued since then by various workers (Maitland, 1967, 1969; Brown and Scott, 1994; Adams and Tippett, 1990; Etheridge, 2009). One aspect of particular relevance to subsequent translocation projects was the initial development of techniques to collect fertile eggs and incubate these in the laboratory (Maitland, 1967).

Conservation

The powan and a few other fish species were given legal protection by their inclusion in Schedule 5 of the Wildlife and Countryside Act 1981 and eventually in Annex 5a of the EC Habitats Directive 1992 and in Appendix III of the Bern Convention. However, though this was welcome recognition of the vulnerability of the species, it did little to help it, for the problem was not that people were catching and killing the powan, but that it was vulnerable to pollution and other threats – especially so since it occurred in only two lochs.

Because of such substantial threats, it was decided to consider an innovative conservation project for powan which would involve creating new populations in suitable waters. Such a project was not undertaken lightly and the authors developed a set of criteria for such translocations (Maitland and Lyle, 1990; 1992). In summary, these emphasise that any translocation must not threaten the parent stock (in this case, powan) nor the ecology of the introduction site. The introduction site must be suitable ecologically and ideally should be in the same catchment. Permission must be sought from owners and other appropriate authorities. Stock may be transferred at any life stage but maximum genetic diversity should be aimed at by selecting material widely in space and time. Now, international guidelines are available (IUCN, 1987) for such transfers.

Translocation to create refuge populations was considered to be a feasible option to safeguard the Loch Lomond powan stock. Two apparently suitable waters were available, both in the Lomond catchment. Loch Sloy, originally a natural loch but impounded and greatly enlarged as a hydro–electric reservoir in 1948, sits at an altitude of 247 m, it has a surface area of 116 ha and a maximum depth of 57 m. Carron Valley Reservoir, opened in 1939 as a water supply for central Scotland, actually sits astride the Lomond/Forth watershed and has a dam at either end. At an altitude of 225 m it has a surface area of 390 ha and a maximum depth of 12 m. Conditions in both reservoirs were regarded as appropriate for powan. and permission to carry out the experiment was obtained from the then owners, North of Scotland Hydro-Electric Board (Sloy) and Central Regional Council (Carron).

Spawning of powan takes place during winter, usually between late December and early February. At that time the fish move much nearer to the shore and shoal over the areas of coarse gravel there. They are vulnerable to netting at this time and thus it is relatively straightforward to obtain ripe adult females and strip them of eggs which are then fertilised by milt from males. These eggs are then incubated in hatcheries for many weeks (the time dependent on temperature), hatching usually in March or April (Figure 1), when they can be easily transferred to a new site as unfed fry.

Translocations

As an initial experiment, in 1964, one of the authors released a few hundred powan fry to a small pond near Milngavie. The intention was not to start a permanent population, for there was no suitable spawning habitat, but just to gain some experience of the rates of growth and the way in which these fish might adapt to this new habitat. The fish grew well and were actually in much better condition than fish from Loch Lomond, for, having been introduced as unfed fry, they had no internal parasites, nor had they any scars from attacks by lampreys. Additionally, and much to the author's surprise, some young fish appeared each year, for in spite of there being no spawning gravels there, it appeared that a few eggs managed to survive after spawning by being caught up in submerged plant growths. Unfortunately, this experiment was brought to an end a few years later when anglers introduced tench *Tinca tinca* to the pond (Burkel, 1971), after which the powan died out.

Starting in 1988, sampling of adult powan at Loch Lomond was kept to the minimum consistent with obtaining reasonable numbers of eggs for the conservation-management programme. In January of each of the years 1988,

1989 and 1990, ripe adult powan were collected from their spawning grounds. Gill nets were set out in the evening and lifted next morning. Fish were removed from the nets and held in large containers of loch water.

Also in 1988, adult powan in good condition and undamaged by netting were transported directly to Loch Sloy only, where they were carefully released. Thus the introduction here (but not at Carron Valley Reservoir), of a total of 85 adult powan, was assumed to be carrying a normal load of parasites from Loch Lomond (see below).

Over the three spawning seasons, 22 ripe female powan were netted at Loch Lomond, stripped there and fertilized by milt from many ripe males. The total number of eggs collected was 60,565. After hatching in March, batches of fry were introduced at each site. At Loch Sloy, a total of 12,227 fry was introduced over the three years, 1988-90. At Carron Valley Reservoir, 13,123 were introduced over the 2 years 1989 and 1990.

After some years, it was clear that powan had done well in their new habitats, for fine adult fish which had grown well were netted by the authors in Loch Sloy in 1991 (Plate 6). These fish were in three distinct groups (Figure 2). The four largest, from their ages, must have been fish originally transferred from Loch Lomond in 1988 and the guts of all four carried the characteristic cysts of the trematode parasite *Cotylurus erraticus* (Copland, 1957). The two smaller groups were fish which had hatched in Loch Sloy in 1988 and 1989. The smallest group were all immature fish and none of these two groups carried parasitic cysts.

After a few years, anglers started to catch well grown fish in Carron Valley Reservoir (Plate 7). It is now known from netting carried out in 2006 by Etheridge *et al.* (2010) that powan have had established populations in both Loch Sloy and in Carron Valley Reservoir for over 20 years. This was confirmed by the hydroacoustic survey there by Winfield *et al.* (2008).

Discussion

It appears that transferring powan to new waters is not a new idea, for they were at one time cultivated in ponds at Rossdhu estate on the west shores of Loch Lomond. During the fifth annual excursion of the Scottish Arboricultural Society on the morning of Tuesday 8 August, 1882, it was recorded that: A short visit was then made to the fish ponds, very neatly laid out and surrounded with flowered terraces and lawns. In these ponds are preserved and bred the powan or fresh-water herring, a beautiful silvery fish something like the herring in shape. It seems unlikely that this was a conservation exercise but rather more likely as ensuring something additional for the laird's table!

Over the years of translocation work by the authors, practical methodologies have improved. With experience, greater site-specific knowledge of spawning timing and locations has been achieved, and enabled a move to the use of fewer nets but of meshes specific to mature adults of the target species. Egg stripping and fertilization techniques have improved to increase both egg fertilization and survival rates, and the genetic diversity of the translocated stock. Egg incubation performance in hatcheries has been significantly enhanced by moving from a tray system to a bottle system and incubation mortality is now much less than previously. Adjusting hatchery water temperature can control egg incubation rates so that hatching occurs when food production in the recipient sites is favourable. The preferred method of introduction to new sites is by transferring unfed fry directly from the hatchery as was done at Carron Valley Reservoir where the resulting self-sustaining populations has demonstrated the success of this method. However, circumstances, logistics and budgets may not always allow this and transfers have been made to new sites by distributing eggs (both freshly collected and at the pre hatching stage) directly onto suitable substrata and by the direct transfer of adults as was done at Loch Sloy.

When asked recently about powan at Carron Reservoir, the fishery director there commented: "The powan on Carron are doing extremely well. Last season (2012) over 300 powan were caught and released by anglers (Plate 7); some were up to three pounds in weight. … I remember them getting put in around 1989 so in the space of 23 years they have established very well and are an asset to our fishery. The anglers are sometimes puzzled by the fish thinking they are grayling. The Carron powan are the biggest in size compared to Loch Eck and Loch Lomond, so there is something in the feeding in Carron that suits them."

The translocations of powan to Carron Reservoir and Loch Sloy can be regarded as a conservation success story. Instead of just one population of the Lomond stock there are now three, all within the Lomond catchment. The biodiversity of the new waters concerned, which are both artificial, has been enhanced by the introduction of powan and there seem to have been no negative effects, rather the contrary; so much so that one of the authors has been involved recently in further powan translocations from both Loch Lomond and Loch Eck to four hydro-electric reservoirs in Argyll (Adams *et al.*, 2009, Lyle *et al.*, 2010). Hopefully, such transfers will ensure the survival in Scotland of this rare and attractive fish species.

Acknowledgements

We thank Neville Dix for useful comments on this paper. We acknowledge advice and support from Colin Bean, Colin Adams, and from the owners of sites used for translocation: Central Regional Council (now Scottish Water), and North of Scotland Hydro-Electricity Board (now Scottish and Southern Electricity). Financial support for the project was received from Scottish Natural Heritage. We thank Elizabeth Brown for her analysis of the early Sloy data and Jimmy Coyne for recent reports of powan caught at his fishery at Carron Valley Reservoir.

References

Adams, C.E., Lyle, A.A., and Wilson, S. 2009. Establishment of conservation refuge populations of powan (*Coregonus lavaretus*). Phase I. Report to Scottish Natural Heritage.

Adams, C.E. and Maitland, P.S. 1998. The Ruffe population of Loch Lomond, Scotland: its introduction, population expansion, and interaction with native species. *International Association for Great Lakes Research* 24, 249–262.

Adams, C.E. and Tippett, R. 1990. Powan ova (*Coregonus lavaretus*) predation by introduced Ruffe (*Gymnocephalus cernuus*) in Loch Lomond, Scotland. *Aquaculture and Fisheries Management* 22, 261-267.

Brown, A. 1891. The fishes of Loch Lomond and its tributaries. *Scottish Naturalist* 10, 114-124.

Brown, E.A.R. and Scott, D.B.C. 1994. Life histories of the powan, *Coregonus lavaretus* (L.) (Salmonidae, Coregoninae) of Loch Lomond and Loch Eck. *Hydrobiologia* 290, 121-133.

Burkel, D.L. 1971. Introduction of fish to new water. *Glasgow Naturalist* 18, 574-575.

Copland, W.O. 1957. The parasites of Loch Lomond fishes. In: *Studies on Loch Lomond. 1.* (ed. H.D. Slack) pp. 128-133. Glasgow: Blackie.

Etheridge, E.C. 2009. *Aspects of the conservation biology of* Coregonus lavaretus *in Britain.* PhD Thesis, University of Glasgow.

Etheridge, E.C., Bean, C.W., Maitland, P.S. and Adams, C.E. 2010. Morphological and ecological responses to a conservation translocation of powan (*Coregonus lavaretus*) in Scotland. *Aquatic Conservation* 20, 274-281.

Houghton, W. 1879. *British Freshwater Fishes.* London: Mackenzie.

IUCN. 1987. *IUCN position statement on translocation of living organisms: introductions, reintroductions and re-stocking.* Gland: IUCN.

Lamond, H. 1931. *Loch Lomond.* Glasgow: Jackson.

Lyle, A.A., Adams, C.E., Wilson, S. and Dodd, J. 2009. Establishment of conservation refuge populations of powan (*Coregonus lavaretus*). Phase II. Report to Scottish Natural Heritage.

Maitland, P.S. 1967. The artificial fertilisation and rearing of the eggs of *Coregonus clupeoides* Lacepede. *Proceedings of the Royal Society of Edinburgh* 70, 82-106.

Maitland, P S. 1969. The reproduction and fecundity of the powan, *Coregonus clupeoides* Lacepede, in Loch Lomond, Scotland. *Proceedings of the Royal Society of Edinburgh* 70, 233-264.

Maitland, P.S., East, K. and Morris, K.H. 1983. Ruffe *Gymnocephalus cernua* (L.), new to Scotland, in Loch Lomond. *Scottish Naturalist* 1983, 7-9.

Maitland, P.S. and Lyle, A.A. 1990. Practical conservation of British fishes: current action on six declining species. *Journal of Fish Biology* 37A, 255-256.

Maitland, P.S. and Lyle, A.A. 1992. Conservation of freshwater fish in the British Isles: proposals for management. *Aquatic Conservation* 2, 165-183.

Maitland, P.S., Morris, K.H. and East, K. 1994. The ecology of lampreys (Petromyzonidae) in the Loch Lomond area. *Hydrobiologia* 290, 105-120.

Mitchell, J. 1984. Common Buzzards feeding on fish carrion at Loch Lomond. *Scottish Birds*, 13, 118.

Roberts, R.J., Leckie, J. and Slack, H.D. 1970. Bald spot disease in powan. *Journal of Fish Biology* 2, 103-105.

Shafi, M. and Maitland, P.S. 1971. Comparative aspects of the biology of Pike, *Esox lucius* in two Scottish lochs. *Proceedings of the Royal Society of Edinburgh* 71B, 41-60.

Slack, H.D. 1955. Factors affecting the productivity of *Coregonus clupeoides* Lacepede in Loch Lomond. *Verhandlungen der Internationalen Vereinigung fur Theoretische und Andewandte Limnology* 12, 183-186.

Slack, H.D. 1957. (Ed.) *Studies on Loch Lomond. 1.* Glasgow: Blackie.

Winfield, I.J. and Fletcher, J.M. 2008. Hydroacoustic assessment of the introduced powan populations of Carron Valley Reservoir and Loch Sloy. Final Report. Lancaster: NERC/Centre for Ecology and Hydrology.

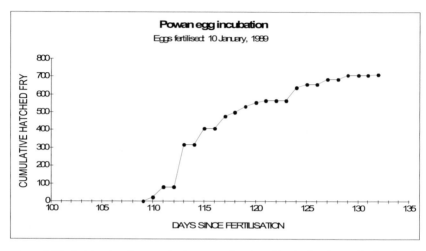

Figure 1. The hatch rate of powan fry from eggs incubated in the hatchery. The first hatch occurred 110 days after the eggs were taken from Loch Lomond.

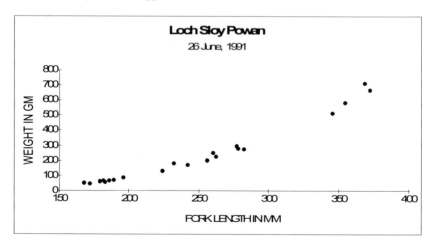

Figure 2. A length/weight diagram showing three different age groups of powan caught in Loch Sloy. The four largest fish (right hand group) are from the batch transferred from Loch Lomond in 1988. The two other age groups are fish hatched in Loch Sloy from eggs transferred there, or laid there by the translocated powan, in 1988 (middle group) and 1989 (left hand group). See Plate 6.

PLANT REPORT 2013
Schleicher's Thread-moss:
Stirlingshire's National Rarity Faces Extinction

Roy Sexton

In May 2007 while surveying the site of a proposed wind farm in the Touch Hills John Mitchell offered to show me Schleicher's Thread Moss (*Bryum schleicheri* v *latifolium*) which grows in a spring and associated flush near the Drumshogle Burn on Shielbrae Farm. I was surprised to learn that this moss only grows at this one spot in the British Isles and as a result it was not only classified as a Red Data Book critically endangered species but was designated (or named) in Schedule 8 of the Wildlife and Countryside Act 1981. In view of its rarity it seemed odd that the site had no statutory protection.

Apparently in the 19th century Scheicher's Thread Moss was found at five sites in the Breadalbane Hills including Ben Chonzie where it was collected by A.O. Black in 1853. Targeted surveys attempting to relocate it there since have failed. The moss was first recorded on Touch Moor by G.A. Holt in 1880 and was re-found there by John Mitchell and G. Rodway in October 1968. Nineteen years later in 1987 John Mitchell and N.G. Hodgetts revisited the colony and found an increase in the number of plants.

The site is located 1.4 km south of the Lower Touch Reservoir. It is at the bottom of a north facing slope covered in coarse grass with clumps of rushes and bracken. The small spring is found on the south side of the upper reaches of Drumshogle burn (also referred to as Berryhill burn) and is easily recognized by the vivid green vegetation of its associated flush (NS 7368 9005) (Plate 1). In 2007 this 3 x 3 m spongy mat of plants was largely composed of water blinks *(Montia fontana)* and opposite-leaved golden saxifrage (*Chrysosplenium oppositifolium*). In amongst these could be seen considerable numbers of the robust upright pale green stems of the Thread Moss (Plate 9) and although we did not count the stems there were certainly hundreds present. Because it was confined to such a small area the whole population appeared very vulnerable to grazing livestock and the local Scottish Wildlife Trust added it to the list of sites they try to monitor. This proved more difficult than usual since it required a competent moss taxonomist and a return trip was not arranged until Gordon P. Rothero (GPR) a consultant botanist from Dunoon volunteered to help in November 2011.

It transpired that GPR had been active at the site since 1988 when the moss was present not only at its current site but also in an adjacent flush 30 m downstream. By 1993 a survey by R. Allen revealed it had been lost from the lower flush but 854 stems were still found at the main site. A search of all the similar springs in the area found no further colonies. GPR's next visit was in

2003 when he was distressed to find a suckler herd had badly trampled the area and only 372 stems were found. Urgent action was required and after consultation with the Conservation Committee of the British Bryological Society it was agreed that Scottish Natural Heritage would finance an attempt to reintroduce the moss into the downstream flush. This involved a novel strategy. Three stems were taken from Touch and cultured in Petri dishes on Phytogel by Prof. Jeff Duckett and Silvia Pressel of Queen Mary College, London University. Within 3-4 weeks the stem fragments produced a mass of thread like protonema which started bearing young shoots. These cultures were placed in 12 muslin bags and pegged out in the lower flush during September 2004 by GPR. Ten of these were still alive in March 2005 and some had grown robust stems. Only four cultures survived the full year but encouragingly one had produced 120+ stems. The cattle trampling that provoked these measures far from damaging the colony was apparently beneficial and in April 2004 there were approximately two thousand stems in the recovered main spring.

Our combined visit in November 2011 revealed a disaster. The whole area had become so overgrown in waist deep rushes (*Junucus acutiflorus*) that neither flush could be immediately recognised. Fortunately GPR found a few Thread Moss stems (Plate 9) amongst the bases of the rush plants at the original main upsream flush site. He immediately sought the license required to manage a Statute 8 species. The following March 2012 we returned and carefully pulled the rush rhizomes from the mud under the moss and cut back the vegetation at the margins of the flush. For safety two more plants were sent to the Natural History Museum to be put in culture. Throughout 2012 and 2013 the local group of the Scottish Wildlife Trust has visited the site every month and kept the rushes cut down to ground level. As a result of this and a perfect moss summer with practically daily rain the colony has continued to increase. By October 2012 there were approximately 1,400 stems and by May 2013 the stem count was over 4,000.

References

Allen, R. 1993. A study of the distribution and habitat requirements of *Bryum schleicheri* var *latifolium*. Unpublished MSc project, SNH Stirling Office.

Rothero, G.M., Duckett, J.G. and Pressel, S. 2006. Active conservation augmenting the only British population of *Bryum schleicheri var. latifolium* via in vitro cultivation. *Field Bryology* 90; 12-16.

WATER QUALITY IN THE FORTH ESTUARY

Judy Dobson

The Forth estuary extends approximately 55 km from the tidal limit at Stirling to the Rail Bridge at Queensferry. It is narrow and winding from Stirling to Kincardine then widens and straightens between Kincardine and Queensferry. The varied topography provides a range of habitats which host a variety of wildlife, ranging from saltmarshes in the upper estuary to mudflats in the lower estuary.

The estuary has been used for centuries by man for food, transport and the disposal of waste. In the mid 20th century uncontrolled disposal of waste into the estuary led to the degradation of water quality which threatened wildlife. By the middle of the 20th century the salmon and sea trout fishery in the estuary was in danger of being wiped out by extensive mortalities of smolts and adult fish (Collett, 1972).

The introduction of the Control of Pollution Act in 1974 helped the regulatory agencies to impose standards on waste water discharges to reduce pollution and further legislation (e.g. the Urban Waste Water Treatment Directive 91/271/EEC) tightened these standards. The introduction of the Water Framework Directive (200/60/EC) in 2000 widened the focus of environmental legislation from protecting water quality to encompass the protection of wildlife. The ultimate aim of the Water Framework Directive (WFD) is achieving at least 'Good Ecological Status'. Good Ecological Status is described as a low level of disturbance to the ecosystem resulting from man's activities compared to undisturbed conditions. Unlike previous legislation the WFD takes account of the impact on wildlife of the physical modification of the estuary in addition to water quality.

The WFD classifies water bodies into five classes: High, Good, Moderate, Poor and Bad. The classification is based on measurements of water quality and various aspects of ecology including assessments of phytoplankton, macroalgae, fish and benthic invertebrates. The overall class defaults to the lowest class for each measurement.

Under the Water Framework Directive the Forth estuary is sub divided into three water bodies (Figure 1) which are based on their physical, ecological and chemical differences:

1) The upper estuary extends from the tidal limit at Stirling to Kincardine Bridge. This section of the estuary is predominantly narrow and meandering. Salinity is relatively low as a result of freshwater input from the rivers Forth, Teith, Allan, Devon and Black Devon. Much of the shore

line of the upper estuary has been claimed for agricultural land with a subsequent loss of the natural saltmarsh habitat.

2) The middle estuary extends from Kincardine Bridge to a line between Carriden and the eastern edge of Torry Bay. The estuary is wider and straighter here and the water is more saline although there are freshwater inputs from the Rivers Carron and Avon at Grangemouth. The middle estuary is fringed with mudflats, which are important feeding grounds for fish and wading birds. However, much of the intertidal land in the middle estuary has been lost to industrial land claim at Bo'ness, Grangemouth and Longannet. Intertidal land has also been lost to agriculture, especially along the banks of the Carron and Skinflats mudflats (Figure 1).

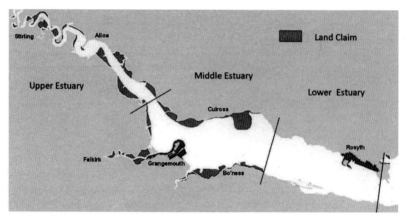

Figure 1. Assessment and land claim areas (dark grey) along the Forth estuary.

3) The lower estuary extends from the middle estuary to the seaward limit just downstream of the rail bridge at Queensferry. This part of the estuary is wide and deep with a strong marine influence. The shoreline has been modified by ports and the large harbour at Rosyth.

The loss of natural habitat in both the upper and middle estuary means that they are designated as heavily modified. Heavily modified water bodies cannot reach Good Ecological Status, therefore the aim is for them to reach Good Ecological Potential. The lower estuary is less impacted by land claim so it can be expected to achieve Good Ecological Status.

The upper Forth estuary is currently classed as Poor Ecological Potential due low dissolved oxygen concentrations which develop during the summer months when the water is warm and freshwater input is low. Lowest dissolved oxygen concentrations typically occur on Spring tides when there are high levels of suspended particulate matter in the water. The high levels of suspended particulate matter result from turbulent mixing between the flooding tide and freshwater flow in the narrow upper estuary. This mixing causes the muddy bed of the estuary to be mixed into the water column. This zone of muddy water, called the turbidity maximum, extends for 10 km and moves up and down the estuary from Stirling to Kincardine with the tide. Oxygen entering the estuary from the rivers is consumed by bacteria attached to the particulate matter as they metabolise organic matter. As a result water passing through the turbidity maximum becomes increasingly depleted in oxygen resulting in the characteristic oxygen sag.

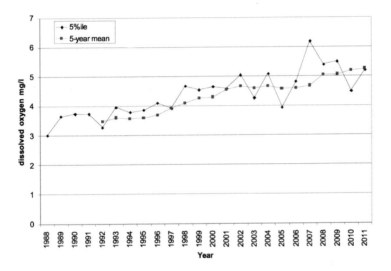

Figure 2. Long term trend in dissolved oxygen (mg/l) in the upper Forth estuary, 1988-2011. The 5 percentile is the value exceeded by 95 percent of the data. It represents the lowest values recorded.

Dissolved oxygen has been monitored at 30 minute intervals throughout the year by in situ monitoring equipment since 1988. The 5 percentile value of this data has increased from 3 mg/l to 5 mg/l although there has been substantial interannual variation in recent years (Figure 2). This interannual variation is a result of changes in climate, dissolved oxygen concentrations are higher in wet summers as the supply of oxygen is increased by higher river flows. The 5 year mean of this data smooths out the interannual variation.

Oxygen is also removed from the water by the decomposition of organic waste discharged to the estuary. The oxygen consumed by organic waste is estimated from the biological oxygen demand (BOD) of the discharges. The BOD is defined as the oxygen removed from a waste water sample incubated at 20°C for 5 days. Dissolved oxygen concentrations in the upper estuary have increased (Figure 2) as the BOD of waste water discharges to the estuary have decreased (Figure 3).

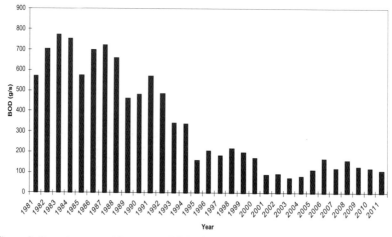

Figure 3. Long term trend in average BOD g/s (Biological Oxygen Demand) of inputs to the Forth estuary from 1981 to 2011.

Despite the reduction in discharges of organic waste, the upper estuary has not achieved good ecological potential because there are sufficient organic residues present in the turbidity maximum to continue to consume oxygen. However, as water quality has improved the number of fish found in the estuary has increased (Figure 4). The return of the sparling to the estuary in 1989 was a significant indicator of the improvement in water quality because it is an oxygen sensitive fish which lives in the estuary and migrates to freshwater to spawn (Maitland, 2010).

The middle Forth estuary is classed as Moderate Ecological Potential. Although water quality in the middle estuary is good, the benthic invertebrate population of the subtidal sediments is impacted by historical discharges of industrial waste. The sediments of the middle Forth estuary were contaminated by a discharge of mercury in the 1970s. This was substantially reduced in 1985 and has now ceased however it was estimated that 90 % of the mercury discharged was retained in the sediments. Mercury binds to organic matter in preference to remaining in solution so the concentration of dissolved mercury was always relatively low, despite the volume of the discharge. Annual monitoring of mercury in sediments, fish and mussels show that the concentrations have decreased, however they are still elevated compared to background levels (Figure 5).

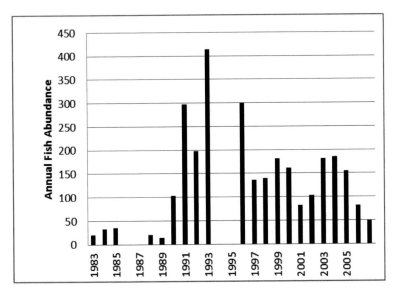

Figure 4. Annual fish abundance (number of fish caught in beam trawls) in the upper Forth estuary 1983 to 2007 of the eight most common species. These in approximate order of abundance are: flounder, goby, sprat, smelt, place, herring, whiting, cod. Data have been normalised for number of trawls per year. Surveys were not carried out in years 1986-7 and 1994-5.

The benthic invertebrate population of subtidal sediments of the middle Forth estuary are showing recovery from pollution following the Species-Abundance-Biomass model of macrobenthic succession described by Pearson and Rosenberg (1978). Sediments impacted by pollution are populated by a high abundance of opportunistic species, typically oligocheate worms. As the sediments recover these opportunistic species are replaced by a variety of larger longer lived species so the abundance drops but the number of species and biomass increases. The benthic invertebrate population in the middle Forth estuary is at different stages of recovery depending on the distance from discharge sites. The sites closest to the discharges are still more impacted than the sites furthest from them.

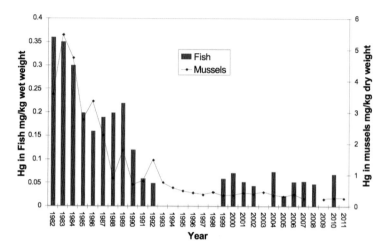

Figure 5. Long term trends in mercury in fish and mussels from the middle Forth estuary.

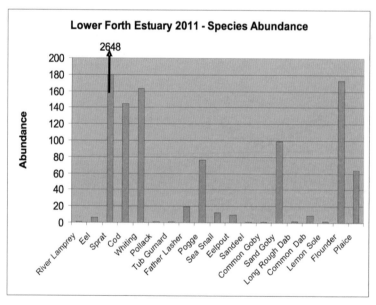

Figure 6. Species and number of fish caught in the lower Forth estuary in 2011.

The lower Forth estuary, which extends from the middle Forth estuary to the estuarine limit just downstream of the rail bridge, is Good Ecological Status. This water body is less influenced by freshwater input and is more marine in nature. Water quality is good and the benthic invertebrate population is less impacted by discharges than in the middle estuary. Fish population studies have revealed that the lower Forth estuary supports a good variety of fish with representatives from different functional groups and feeding guilds (Figure 6).

Summary:

- The upper and middle Forth estuary from Stirling to Torry Bay cannot achieve Good Ecological Status as defined by the Water Framework Directive because the shoreline has been extensively modified by agricultural and industrial land claim. The best that can be achieved is Good Ecological Potential.

- Currently the upper estuary is classified as Poor Ecological Potential. The efforts to control waste discharge have had a beneficial effect on the dissolved oxygen concentrations but there is still sufficient organic matter in the river bed to produce an depletion of oxygen particularly when the turbidity increases during the summer spring tides.

- The middle estuary from Kincardine Bridge to Torry Bay is classified as Moderate Ecological Potential but is still impacted by historical discharges of mercury. The subtidal benthic invertebrate populations are at different stages of recovery dependent on their distance from discharge sites.

- The lower estuary from Torry Bay to downstream of the rail bridge is classified as Good Ecological Status and supports a variety of fish.

References

Collett, W.F. 1961. *A Preliminary investigation of the pollution of the upper Forth Estuary*. The Institute of Sewage Purification. Glasgow.

Maitland, P. 2010. The Sparling *Omerus Esperlanus* in the Forth. *Forth Naturalist and Historian* **10**, 79-91.

Pearson, T.H. and Rosenberg, R. 1978. Macrobenthic succession in relation to organic enrichment and pollution of the marine environment. *Oceanography and Marine Biology: an Annual Review* **16**, 229-311.

DUNBLANE WEATHER REPORT 2012

Neil Bielby

The weather station is my suburban back garden in Ochiltree, Dunblane. This is situated 50 m to the east of the Dunblane Hydro ridge, 100 m a.s.l., in a shallow, sheltered valley. (GR NN 78990143).

I have been recording the weather since 1995 and all averages etc. refer to the last 18 years. (Note: because there is much variation from year to year in Britain in the parameters used to define climate, climatological averages are usually taken over periods of 30 years for temperature and 35 years for rainfall. Therefore, all averages in this report should be viewed with some caution). I am indebted to Dr. John P. Holland for providing Met. Office and additional weather records from Kirkton Farm, Strathfillan (NN 359283; 170 m a.s.l.) and Killin. Weather recording began in 1991 at Kirkton Farm and means etc. for this site date from that year. Killin means date from 2000. The data from Kirkton allows for some interesting meteorological comparisons between the far north-west and central areas of our region.

Daily rainfall (> 0.2 mm), maximum and minimum temperatures, barometric pressure, cloud cover, wind direction and speed (Beaufort scale) are recorded. All except the maximum daily temperature are recorded at 09.00 hours. A brief description of the day's weather is also noted along with exceptional and unusual weather phenomena across the UK. Unless indicated otherwise, daily (24 hour) rainfall amounts are measured from 09.00 hours on the date mentioned until 09.00 hours the following morning.

2012 was **cooler** and **wetter** than normal. The mean temperature of 7.94°C was 0.52°C below the norm. The maximum temperature was 28.2°C (24th May) and the minimum temperature was –8.0°C (11th Dec.). There were 81 air frosts (mean 71) and snow lay on the ground at 09.00 on 14 occasions. Precipitation of 1262.5 mm was 12 % above the norm with measurable amounts on 214 days (mean 208). Turning to the seasons: Winter (December-February) was warmer and slightly wetter than normal while spring (March-May) had temperature and precipitation values close to the means. The mean summer temperature (June-August) was close to normal but rainfall was 60 % above average. The mean temperature in autumn (September-November) was 1.45°C below the mean while the rainfall amount was normal. Across the UK the mean temperature was 8.8°C, 0.1°C below the 1981-2010 average. Mean rainfall of 1331.0 mm was 15 % above the average.

January was a little warmer and drier than usual. The mean temperature of 2.35°C was 0.09°C above the average. There were 17 air frosts and snow lay on the ground at 09.00 hours on three occasions. Precipitation of 111.7 mm was

93 % of the average with measurable amounts occurring on 21 days, the average for the month. The average pressure was 1013 mb with a high of 1031 mb (29th) and a low of 958 mb (3rd). Over Scotland as a whole temperatures were 0.8°C above the 1971-2000 average and while the north of the country received around 150 % of normal precipitation, Fife and the eastern Borders had only half the norm. It was the second sunniest January (in a series dating back to 1929) for eastern Scotland.

Wet snow during the night of the 1st/2nd produced a light covering. A deep depression (958 mb at Strathallan airfield, Perthshire at 09.00 hours) moved across northern Scotland from east to west during the morning of the third. The winds were at their strongest across the Central Belt from 07.00 hours to 11.00 hours with gusts of 102 mph and 91 mph recorded in Edinburgh (Blackford Hill) and Glasgow respectively. These were the result of a 'sting jet' which formed round the rear of the depression. The Forth, Tay, Erskine and Kingston bridges were closed to all traffic. Several high-sided vehicles as well as trees were blown over and there was structural damage. Ferry and train services were also disrupted. Up to 160,000 homes were without electricity at any one time and the Isle of Bute had their supplies cut for 3 days. Tyndrum recorded 52.6 mm of precipitation. The 4th was a day of continuous raw rain (23.9 mm, 48.0 mm Tyndrum). Another deep low (985 mb) crossing Scotland during the night of the 4th/5th produced more gales (82 mph on Islay). The 5th was a rare cloudless day as the northwesterly winds slowly eased. As high pressure built over Scotland from the 8th the weather became more settled with the occasional day of unbroken sunshine (12th & 13th). There were night frosts from the 13th to the 17th with the –7.3°C recorded at 09.00 hours on the 16th being the lowest of the winter to date (–10.5°C, Aboyne). As the high pressure system decayed from the 18th Atlantic weather systems again became the norm. Strong westerly winds on the 21st (gusting up to 60 mph through the Central belt) were accompanied by heavy showers, these being prolonged and of snow in the western hills. A spell of quieter weather with night frosts then followed with high-pressure (1031 mb, 29th) building over Scandinavia from the 28th.

February was milder and much drier than normal. The mean temperature of 3.95°C was 0.85°C above the norm while rainfall of 22.2 mm was only 23 % of the average making it the driest February at this station. There were 12 air-frosts while measurable precipitation was recorded on only 8 days (average = 17), equaling the previous low number in 2003. Average pressure was 1024 mb with a high of 1040 mb and a low of 997 mb. Across Scotland the mean temperature was 1.8°C above the 1971-2000 average making it the warmest February since 1998. The east of Scotland (from the Lothians to Aberdeenshire) received only a third of their normal February rainfall.

The high-pressure system over Scandinavia (1040 mb, 2nd) persisted until the 16th with nightly frosts (–7.0°C, 2nd, –11.8°C Cromdale, Highland, 3rd) and cold, calm, mostly sunny days. An Atlantic frontal system briefly breached the fringes of this high, moving SE across the UK on the 4th/5th. Scotland only received a little rain and sleet at low levels with snow on the hills on a raw southerly force four wind but England, from a line south-east of Newcastle to Manchester, had moderate snowfall (16 cm in Yorkshire) throughout the day and night of the 4th/5th as the warmer occluded front came across the much colder static air mass. The 6th and 7th were days of virtually unbroken sunshine with night frosts (–7.2°C, 7th). A weak weather front pushed in from the Atlantic on the 8th, remaining stationary over Scotland until the 13th. This caused a marked split in the weather between England and Scotland and as the former continued to shiver under clear skies (–15.6°C, Holbeach (Lincs.), 11th; the lowest temperature in the UK since Boxing Day 2010) we endured several days of damp, murky and misty weather – just what the word 'dreich' was coined for. It was virtually calm throughout with a small temperature range of –0.6°C to 4.5°C. The murk started to lift on the 12th with the first glimpse of sun for 6 days. The weather remained 'quiet' up until the 17th with some sunshine and light winds. It was very mild for February with the 12.8°C and 12.9°C recorded at Strathallan on the 15th and 16th being the highest temperatures at a metrological station in the UK. A front crossing Scotland from the north-west during the afternoon and evening of the 17th not only produced the first notable amount of rainfall for the month (5.5 mm, (71.0 mm Achnagart, Highland)) but dragged down Arctic air in its wake which produced blizzard conditions on northern coasts and hills on the 18th. The Stirling area escaped with only occasional snow flurries on a bitterly cold wind. After a sharp frost (–5.6°C) the 19th was a rare sunny, calm day. However, broken cloud drifting in from the west during the late afternoon heralded yet another Atlantic front. The following 4 days were all overcast and damp with varying amounts of rain on fresh to strong south-westerly winds. The 24th was mostly sunny with a brisk west, drying wind before damp, overcast, and dreich weather returned the following day. This damp, dull weather persisted until the month end with only a brief spell of sunshine during the early afternoon of the 29th.

March 2012 was the warmest and driest at this station. The monthly mean temperature of 7.55°C was 2.52°C above the average while the maximum temperature of 18.6°C on the 28th set a new high here (after 17.5°C on 27.03.2003). There were only four air-frosts (mean = 10).Total precipitation of 35.7 mm (all rain) was only 47 % of the norm with measurable amounts on only 8 days – another new low at this station (average 16 days). Mean pressure was 1024.0 mb (average = 1010 mb) with a high of 1037 mb and a low of 1001 mb. Many other locations across Scotland recorded their highest ever March temperatures culminating in a new Scottish March high of 23.6°C at Aboyne, Aberdeenshire on the 27th. The previous Scottish high of 22.2°C was set in March 1957 at Gordon Castle, Moray, and equalled at Strachan, Kincardineshire in 1965. It was the third warmest March on record across the UK.

The weather continued dull and damp until the 4th. An overnight frost (–4.2°C) heralded a cloudless day on the 5th as a brief ridge of high pressure lay over the UK. The clear skies lasted until the afternoon of the following day when an Atlantic front moved in from the west. This deposited 6.0 mm of rain during the night of the 6th/7th with further heavy showers the following day. Pressure built again from the 9th (1037 mb max.) and settled over the UK until the 15th. However, apart from the 11th and 12th which were mostly sunny, a layer of cloud was trapped beneath the high pressure system resulting in dull if calm days. Another Atlantic front produced 12.0 mm of rain during the morning of the 16th but this quickly cleared from the north and the 17th and 18th were days of unbroken sunshine and light winds. After an Atlantic weather front deposited 7.0 mm during the afternoon and night of the 19th/20th pressure began to build (1034 mb, 22nd). Apart from the 22nd, which was a day of unbroken sunshine and light airs, early mist lifted slowly to reveal cloud cover through which a hazy sun attempted to break through in the afternoons. The 26th to 31st were all either cloudless or virtually cloudless days with record high temperatures for March being set at this station with 18.6°C (28th) and successively for Scotland with 22.8°C at Fyvie, Aberdeenshire (25th); 22.9°C, at Fyvie and Aboyne, Aberdeenshire (26th – an all-time UK record high for this date) and 23.6°C at Aboyne, Aberdeenshire (27th). Most of Scotland enjoyed higher temperatures than southern Europe during this spell. There was no precipitation during the final 13 days of the month.

April was wetter and much colder than normal. The mean temperature of 5.98° C was 1.94° C below the average and the coldest April at this station (the previous was 6.32°C in 2000). It was also 1.57°C below the mean for the previous month. The maximum high was 14.8°C (1st) with a night low of –4.6°C (5th, –8.2°C Braemar). There were 10 air frosts (mean = 4.5). Precipitation of 95.0 mm was 51 % above the norm with measurable amounts on 20 days (average = 15) and snow lay on the ground at 09.00 hours on two occasions. Scotland-wide, the mean temperature was 0.8°C below the 1971-2000 average making it the coldest April since 1998. The eastern half of Scotland received over 250 % of the normal precipitation making it the wettest since 1934 with the number of days of recorded rain the highest in 50 years. Across the UK it was the coldest April since 1989 and the wettest on record with much of eastern and southern England recording up to three times the normal amount. Despite all this rain, much of eastern and southern England retained their official drought designations. Sunshine amounts were mostly close to or below normal apart from the west coast of Scotland, the Western Isles and the west of Northern Ireland.

After a calm, cloudless day on the first, a front moving down Scotland from the north deposited 7 cm of snow from the early hours of the 3rd. The driving snow continued on a bitter Arctic NE 3-4 until mid-am but did not lie in Bridge of Allan or Stirling. NE Scotland bore the brunt of this weather with 22 cm at Whitehillocks, Angus with several high level roads being closed. Ten thousand homes in NE England lost their electricity supply as iced lines were brought down by the strong winds. The 4th was mostly sunny on a cold NE 2 as the north-east of England was hit by the Arctic blast. The M62 and A66 roads were closed all day and the heavy, wet snow on gale-force winds brought down many powerlines leaving c. 60,000 homes without electricity. It remained mostly overcast but dry until the 10th with light winds and some patchy rain on the 6th and 8th. Heavy rain in the early hours of the 10th died out by noon having deposited 13.0 mm (28.0 mm Tyndrum). After more rain in the early hours of the 12th a northeasterly airstream depressed temperatures with night frosts from the 13th-16th (–2.9°C, 15th). It was mostly sunny with very clear air and the occasional short shower, some of hail. The maximum temperature of 9.7°C (14th) was just below the seasonal norm. A north-easterly airstream continued to pre-dominate for the rest of the month, depressing temperatures. There was precipitation most days, often in the form of heavy showers but heavy rain/sleet during the night of the 16th/17th deposited 15.0 mm (37.6 mm Lochgilphead). Strong winds (gusts of up to 76 mph in Cumbria) and prolonged heavy rain across most of England from the 28th-30th caused much localised flooding while many trees were blown down which severely disrupted power supplies.

May was slightly cooler and drier than normal. The mean temperature of 10.63°C (0.33°C below the norm) masked some wide variations during the month with a maximum daily high of only 7.2°C (10th) contrasting with 28.2°C (24th), which was a record for May at this station (the previous being 26.0°C on 21 May 2010). There were two air frosts. Precipitation of 68.1 mm was 98 % of the norm with measurable amounts falling on only 12 days. Barometric pressure ranged from 1002 mb to 1031 mb. It was notably sunnier in the north of Scotland where it was the third sunniest in a series dating back to 1929.

The persisting north-easterly airstream continued to depress temperatures in the east of the country but as is often the case with this airflow, the north-west basked in virtually continuous sunshine with temperatures reaching 21.1°C at Kinlochewe (2nd). Closer to home, Tyndrum recorded 20.9°C on the 3rd when the maximum in Dunblane was only 15.7°C. A weak front crossing southwards over Scotland during the early hours of the 4th brought little rain but the Arctic airstream behind it depressed temperatures even further with a night frost of –3.1°C on the 5th nipping the early growth on tender plants (–6.2°C Saughall, E. Ayrshire). Despite clear skies, daytime temperatures struggled to only 12.2°C (5th). Fresh snow on the Trossach Hills on the morning of the 6th was another indicator of below seasonal temperatures. The weather continued changeable with a front crossing Scotland from south-west to north-east the following day being followed by 2 days with long sunny spells. However, another area of low pressure, with its associated front, moving up from the south on the 10th, deposited varying amounts of rain at lower levels across Scotland with enough snow on the hills for skiing to be resumed on Cairngorm. The raw north-easterly wind and maximum temperature of only 7.2°C was reminiscent of winter and caused the central heating to be turned up in this house and doubtless many others. The low-pressure system lingered over Eastern, Central and Southern Scotland throughout the following day before retreating in the face of an advancing high pressure in the Atlantic

(1035 mb, 12th). Rainfall amounts varied with Dunblane receiving only 0.2 mm while Stirling and Clackmannanshire were subject to several downpours from the leaden skies. After an overnight frost, the 12th was a sunny day with a fresh south-westerly drying wind. Rain returned on the 13th with a marked west to east gradient. While Dunblane had a 24 hour total of 7.5 mm, Tyndrum received 63.0 mm and Kinlochewe (Highland) experienced the wettest Scottish May day on record with 101.0 mm. It was also windy with a gust of 67 mph being recorded on Blackford Hill in Edinburgh. A couple of mostly sunny, if cool, days followed (a minimum of –2.5°C Tyndrum, 16th) before a slow moving front settled over Scotland from late on the 16th to the 18th. This time, the eastern half of Scotland fared worst with drenching rain on raw north-easterly winds more reminiscent of winter than May as temperatures struggled to a maximum of 7.8°C. Thereafter, daytime temperatures rose steadily to a May record high of 28.2°C (24th) with largely sunny and warm (or very warm) days until the 29th. The 29.3°C recorded at Achnagart (Highland) on the 25th was a new May record high for Scotland. There was no measurable precipitation from the 18th to the 29th. 'Normal service' resumed during the final 2 days of the month as an Atlantic weather system produced 25.7 mm of rain.

June was notably cooler and wetter than normal. The mean temperature of 12.51°C was 1.4°C below the norm with the maximum daily high of 21.8°C being the lowest ever for June at this station and the daily low of 9.8°C being the coldest since 9.1°C in 2000. Rainfall of 116.9 mm was 52 % above the norm making it the wettest June since 2002. Measurable rain fell on 22 days, seven more than the mean and the most for this month. A minimum temperature of –3.5°C was recorded at Loch Glascarnoch (5th). Across Scotland it was the coolest June since 1998 with southern and eastern areas recording their wettest June ever with 250 % to 300 % of normal rainfall. By marked contrast, it was drier and sunnier than average in north-west Scotland and the Western and Northern Isles. Across the UK it was the coolest June since 1991 with daily maximum temperatures well below normal. It was also the wettest June in England and Wales in a series dating back to 1766.

The first days of the month were largely sunny but a cool easterly airstream depressed temperatures which only reached 13.8°C on the 2nd. The weather remained changeable and cool although Scotland, especially the west, fared much better than England, which received regular drenchings as a conveyor belt of low pressure systems, caused by the Jet-stream being further south than usual, crossed that country from south-west to north-east. The Aberystwyth area of west Wales received double the normal June rainfall in 24 hours on the 8th (186.0 mm in 48 hours) causing the R. Lery to burst its banks flooding two villages and four caravan sites with 1,000 people having to be evacuated. The weather remained changeable and yet another low pressure system, entering the UK in the south-west on the 14th, made its way up into southern Scotland, where it remained for all of the 15th and 16th, depositing 18.0 mm of rain (52.6 mm, Threave, Dumfries and Galloway). The accompanying raw north-east force 3-4 winds made it feel more like November as temperatures struggled to a maximum of only 9.8°C on the 15th. The 18th-20th were mostly sunny, warm days (21.0C, 20th) but these proved to be the lull before yet more storms. Twenty-four hours of non-stop rain beginning at 09.00 hours on the 21st produced 24.2 mm (54.3 mm, Durris (Aberdeenshire). The gusting north-easterly winds depressed temperatures such that the maximum value of 11.9°C on the 21st was only 2.0°C more than the previous night's low. Although the 22nd was largely dry, a further 10.0 mm of rain fell during the following night as a low pressure system and associated encircling fronts remained virtually stationary over Scotland. Most of Great Britain received large amounts of rain during this spell but the worst flooding was reported from the Lancashire/ Yorkshire boundary around where a month's rain fell in just 24 hours flooding roads and swamping houses (93.8 mm at Blencathra, Cumbria). The west-coast main railway line was also cut at Carlisle as floods washed away part of the track. A ridge of high pressure (1019 mb) produced a largely sunny day on the 25th but this respite was all too brief as heavy rain fell again the following afternoon. It remained largely wet to the month end as yet another slow moving low pressure system settled over Scotland. 23.0 mm of rain fell from noon till midnight on Friday 29th ensuring that very little (if any) cricket was played in Scotland for the third weekend running. Despite this miserable weather, Central Scotland escaped relatively lightly as electrical storms on the 28th caused havoc in the midlands and north-east of England with the main line between Newcastle and Edinburgh being blocked by two landslips south of Berwick. Landslips also closed the Glasgow to Fort William line with Tyndrum receiving 34.0 mm on the 28th while only 2.4 mm was recorded in Dunblane.

July was cooler and wetter than normal with the mean temperature of 14.66°C being 1.11°C below the average. This was mostly due to the mean daily high temperature being 2.07°C below the norm. Rainfall of 142.7 mm was 66 % above average making it the 3rd wettest at this station (156.3 mm July 2002). Measurable rainfall fell on 20 days, four below the mean. The average pressure was 1011.0 mb which, considering the frequent low pressure systems during the month, had a narrow range of 1002 mb-1021 mb.

With the Jet-stream still over the south of England the very unsettled weather of June continued. It rained every day during the first 2 weeks of the month. Amounts at this station were never excessive (15.0 mm, 2nd) but the south-east of Scotland and several areas in England fared worse. Torrential rain during the night of the 6th/7th caused flooding in Edinburgh and Midlothian with the Edinburgh southern by-pass closed at one point. Maximum daytime temperatures fluctuated between 14.3°C (2nd) to 22.6°C (6th). From the 3rd to the 6th both the days and nights were quite humid with a minimum night temperature of 15.0°C on the 5th/6th. Another spell of prolonged rain during the 11th/12th added 21.9 mm to already waterlogged ground forcing the cancellation of local weekend cricket matches for the 5th successive weekend. The first dry day of the month occurred on the 16th but this respite was short lived as yet another slow moving weather front produced 54.7 mm in 24 hours from 22.00 hours on the 17th. Falling on already saturated ground, several roads in central Scotland, Fife and Angus quickly became impassable due to flooding. The 19th to the 21st were largely dry with some good sunny periods. It rained all day again on the 23rd (10.6 mm) but this was followed by four rare dry and mostly sunny days. It became quite warm with temperatures peaking at 23.3°C (31.4°C London) on the 25th. The 28th/29th were classic 'sunshine and showers' days. The final 2 days of the month were sunny.

The weather in **August** was very similar to that of July. Although the mean temperature of 15.27°C was virtually identical to the average, the rainfall total of 147.4 mm was 62 % above the average with measurable amounts on 21 days – five more than the norm. The maximum temperature of 11.3°C (31st) was the coldest August day at this station (after 12.1°C on 06/08/2008). Again, despite several low pressure systems and associated fronts during the month, barometric pressure remained within a fairly narrow range of 1000 mb to 1028 mb.

The month started with yet another front which produced 8.0 mm in the 24 hours starting at 22.00 hours on the 31st of July. Thundery downpours caused several flash floods across southern Scotland from the afternoon of the 4th until the 6th. Dunblane received 23.5 mm from noon on the 5th until midnight on the 6th. High pressure then built across the UK (1028 mb, 10th) giving six consecutive dry, mostly sunny, warm days (24.6°C, 10th; 25.9°C Eskdalemuir). The weather became unsettled from the 13th with rain every day, occasionally accompanied by claps of thunder until the 18th when the clouds cleared. It was often humid during this spell with a high of 22.4°C (13th) and a night low of 16.0°C (18th) – the highest of the year so far. The south-east of England experienced a mini-heatwave over the weekend of the 18th/19th with 32.4°C at Cavendish, Suffolk (18th). Unsettled weather returned on the 19th with rain every day until the 30th, often in the form of sharp downpours interspersing spells of sunshine. However, rain all day on the 27th produced 17.0 mm while isolated, torrential, thundery downpours on the 29th resulted in a further 34.5 mm. This station received c.20.0 mm between 16.00-17.30 with hail at times. The night of the 30th/31st was unusually cold (2.2°C; –2.5°C at Cromdale (Highland)).

September was cooler and wetter than normal with the mean temperature of 10.82°C being 1.34°C below the norm. Rainfall of 106.0 mm was 18 % above average with measurable amounts on 20 days. There was one air frost (–0.7°C, 22nd).

Sunny spells and showers typified the first two weeks of the month with winds mostly from a south-westerly direction. It was warm at times during the first week with a maximum temperature of 20.8°C (3rd). Heavy rain during most of the 16th/17th produced 30.3 mm while a further 13.0 mm fell on the 20th when a maximum temperature of only 8.6°C was reached. High pressure

(1021 mb) with a light northerly airstream and clear skies produced the first air-frost of the winter on the 22nd. A deep low pressure system (973 mb – the lowest in September for 30 years), deposited copious amounts of rainfall on strong NE 5-6 winds from the afternoon of the 24th continuing all of the following day. Dunblane received 25.0 mm but NE England fared the worst with virtually continuous rain from the 23rd-25th (124.0 mm) with the A1 road being impassable for three days both north and south of Newcastle from the 24th. In all, there were 92 flood warnings across the UK during this period. Spume, whipped-up by the gales, coated seaside buildings white in Aberdeen. The 26th/27th were the calm after the storms with much sunshine but unsettled weather returned on the 28th with heavy showers – some of hail. A further 11.7 mm of rain fell during the night of the 29th/30th.

October was much colder and a little drier than normal. The mean temperature of 6.3°C was 2.13°C below the mean making it the coldest yet at this station. There were 10 air-frosts (mean = 3.2) and two ground frosts. Total precipitation of 115.4 mm was 86 % of the norm with measurable amounts on 20 days. Barometric pressure ranged from 976 mb to 1029 mb. Across Scotland, the mean temperature of 6.1°C was 1.9°C below average making it the coldest October since 1993, and with regards to minimum temperatures, the coldest since 1981. A minimum temperature of –7.4°C was recorded at Braemar (17th) while 70.4 mm of rain fell at Crombie Country Park, Angus during the 24 hours ending at 09.00 on the 13th.

The south-westerly airstream continued for the first 3 days of the month producing 19.6 mm of rain. A high pressure system building from the 4th led to a succession of sunny, mostly calm days with ground and air frosts in the early mornings (–2.3°C, 10th) and several gloriously sunny, calm autumn days. Very heavy rain during the night of the 11th/12th (31.9 mm) heralded a change to more unsettled weather with rain every day until the 20th. A high pressure system then built over the country (1028 mb, 24th) which resulted in several sunny days, highlighting this year's spectacular autumn colours to maximum effect. Snow showers during the early evening of the 26th were a reminder that winter is almost upon us. Pressure fell rapidly on the 30th/31st with wind and rain on the final 2 days of the month.

November was colder and a little drier than normal. The mean temperature of 3.83°C was 0.85°C below the norm. There were 12 air frosts with a low of –6.7°C (29th). Rainfall of 105.0 mm was 9 % below the average with measurable amounts recorded on 20 days. Monthly rainfall totals across Scotland varied from 130 % above normal in parts of the Borders to only 50 % of normal in the north-east. The north of Scotland was the sunniest area of the UK in November.

More heavy rain fell during the early hours and morning of the 1st (19.0 mm; 34.0 mm Tyndrum) but thereafter the days were mostly sunny. A southwesterly airstream dominated from the 6th-10th providing duller and damper weather although rainfall amounts were low. The 13th was much milder than usual with a high of 11.8°C (16.3°C Kinloss, Moray). A ridge of high pressure (1022 mb) brought calm but damp and dreich days from the 14th-16th. Heavy rain during the night of the 18th/19th (27.0 mm) heralded the start of a spell of wet weather with rain every day until the 25th. The Water of Ruchill burst its banks in Comrie on the 19th causing widespread flooding with many houses inundated. In England, a swathe of the country from Devon to Tyneside endured the wettest seven day period (20th-26th) in 50 years. These downpours and storms caused widespread flooding and structural damage with over 1,000 homes swamped. Holne (Devon) received 88.4 mm in the 24 hour period up to 09.00 on the 25th. High pressure then brought more settled weather with night frosts (–6.7°C, 29th; –7.3°C Braemar) and sunny, calm days until the month end. The temperature remained below freezing all day on the 29th (–1.0°C max) and rain, followed by freezing temperatures during the evening of the 30th, produced lethal black ice.

December was a little colder and much wetter than normal. The mean temperature of 1.48°C was 0.24°C below the norm while precipitation of 196.4 mm was 87 % above average and the most at this station (193.8 mm, December 2006). There were 13 air frosts and snow lay on the ground at 09.00 on 9 occasions. Across the UK rainfall totals were 150 % of the long-term average making it the wettest December since 1999. Aberdeenshire recorded over twice the normal rainfall for this month and across Eastern Scotland it was the wettest December since 1929.

Five-and-a-half centimetres of snow fell during the night of the 2nd/3rd. and successive night frosts until the 9th (–7.3°C, –12.9°C Braemar, 6th) meant that it remained lying until that date. The temperature remained below freezing on both the 2nd and 5th. A front crossing Scotland from the northwest to the southeast on the 6th/7th deposited 6.4 mm of rain in Dunblane rather than the forecast snow although Fettercairn recorded a depth of 20 cm. A high pressure system built over the country from the 9th (1032 mb). This produced several sunny, calm days but also some severe frosts (–8.0°C, 11th) with daytime temperatures remaining below freezing on three consecutive days (11th-13th). A deep depression (975 mb, 15th) moving up from the southwest initially produced a dusting of snow on the 13th but turned to rain the following afternoon with 16.5 mm in 21 hours. The east coast of Scotland from Shetland down to Berwick-upon-Tweed was battered by severe south-easterly gales during the early hours of the 15th. These caused major structural damage at several harbours including Lossiemouth, Peterhead, Fraserburgh, Stonehaven, Eyemouth and Berwick. A weak ridge of high pressure (1017 mb, 19th) brought a brief spell of quieter weather before a very moist front moved up from SW England. This deposited 52.2 mm (101.2 mm Tyndrum) in the 40 hours from 17.00 on the 19th. Another pulse of rain approaching from the same area produced a further 35.3 mm in 35 hours from 09.00 on the 22nd. The whole of the UK suffered these deluges with over 500 flood alerts in place on the 23rd. Devon and Cornwall were worst affected with many properties flooded and road and rail links severed. Locally, the Perth to Gleneagles line was cut by a landslide as was the A85 between St Fillans and Lochearnhead. Some residents in Stonehaven were moved to a community centre as their homes were flooded. The wet and occasionally stormy weather – a gust of 72 mph was recorded at Stornaway (28th) – continued until the month end. The dominant south-westerly airstream ensured that this period remained frost free and relatively mild.

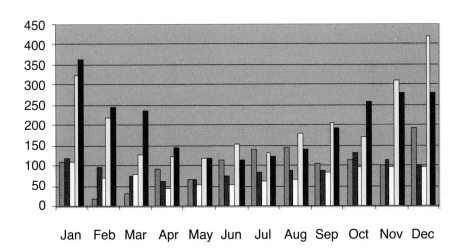

Jan Feb Mar Apr May Jun Jul Aug Sep Oct Nov Dec

Figure 1. Rainfall 2012

Table 1. Temperature and precipitation 2012. Climatological Station Dunblane.

	Temp Mean maxima	Temp Mean minima	Number of air frosts	Total precipitation (mm)	Greatest 24 hour total (mm)	Number of days of measurable precipitation
January	4.8 (4.5)	-0.1 (0.0)	17/11 (15)	111.7/325.5 (120/364)	23.9 (35.0)	21/26 (20)
February	6.9 (5.9)	1.0 (0.3)	12/13 (13)	22.2/220.6 (97/248)	5.5 (38.0)	8/21 (17)
March	11.7 (8.7)	3.4 (1.4)	4/6 (11)	35.7/127.2 (76/240)	9.5 (30.5)	8/17 (16)
April	10.3 (12.4)	1.7 (3.5)	10/9 (5)	95.0/123.7 (63/149)	15.0 (27.8)	20/23 (15)
May	15.7 (16.1)	5.6 (5.8)	2/5 (2)	68.1/119.7 (70/120)	16.9 (27.1)	12/20 (17)
June	16.7 (19.0)	8.3 (8.9)	0/3 (0)	116.9/153.5 (77/118)	24.2 (39.8)	22/21 (15)
July	18.8 (20.9)	10.5 (10.7)	0/0 (0)	142.7/135.6 (86/124.1)	28.0 (33.5)	20/23 (16)
August	19.6 (20.0)	10.9 (10.5)	0/1 (0)	147.4/183.6 (91/143)	34.5 (40.0)	21/24 (16)
September	13.7 (15.9)	8.0 (8.4)	1/2 (<1)	106.0/208.5 (89/196)	15.3 (36.5)	20/27 (16)
October	9.9 (11.7)	2.7 (5.2)	10/11 (3)	115.4/175.0 (134/262)	31.9 (41.9)	20/25 (22)
November	6.7 (7.3)	1.0 (2.0)	12/9 (8)	105.0/313.0 (116/282)	22.0 (39.0)	20/28 (20)
December	3.7 (3.9)	-0.7 (-0.4)	13/16 (16)	196.4/420.7 (105/282)	35.0 (35.0)	22/23 (19)
Year	11.5 (12.2)	4.4 (4.8)	81/86 (71)	1263/2507 (1124/2528)	35.0 (41.9)	214/279 (208)

The climatological means for Dunblane are shown in ( ). Where either two 2012 values or climatological means are given, the first relates to Dunblane and the second to Kirkton. Figure in parenthesis in the 'Greatest 24 hour total (mm)' table refer to the highest ever 24 hour value for that month (09.00 hours to 09.00 hours). Temperatures are given in degrees Celsius.

CLACKMANNANSHIRE OTTERS

Lisa Ford

Introduction

The otter (*Lutra lutra*) was a widespread UK species before it dramatically declined from the mid 1950s to 1970s particularly in the industrial parts of its range. Concern led to it being designated in Schedule 5 of the Wildlife and Countryside Act 1981 and given special protection under Annex II and IV of the EC Habitats Directive.

Figure 1. An adult otter.

The decline was considered to be partly due to the introduction of organochlorine pesticides. These toxic compounds progressively accumulate at each stage of the food chain (i.e. Invertebrates → fish → otters) so they have their greatest impact among the top predators like otters (www.environment-agency.gov.uk). Other factors were also thought to have a role such as a reduction of prey due to both acid rain and watercourse pollution and incidental mortality particularly due to road deaths (Willet, 2001).

During the 1700s and 1800s otters were relatively common in Clackmannanshire. The 1791 and 1845 Statistical Accounts of local parishes (Sinclair, 1791; New Statistical Account 1845) simply lists the otter as present along with all the other common mammals. The Rev. William Osburn of Tillicoultry in 1791 did mention that "the skin of the otter is valuable and fetches a good price". In 1978 concern about their decline led Green and Green (1980) to carry out the first of a series Scottish otter surveys. Of the 146 sites visited in Central Region 49 % were occupied. By 1985 otter numbers had increased so that 66 % were positive. They found that the Clackmannanshire otters were concentrated along a large strip of the Forth estuary and reported that *on the rivers Allan and Devon the local population appears to be holding but these eastern remnants remain isolated and under threat.* In their final survey from 1991-4 a further expansion of range was discovered so that 81 % of the 146 Central Region sites were positive. The vulnerable populations on the Allan, Devon and Black Devon were isolated no longer. A further national survey was carried out by Scottish Natural Heritage in 2004 (Strachan, 2007). Unfortunately it cannot be directly compared with Green and Green's surveys since it used different administrative areas and concentrated on assessing populations in Special Areas of Conservation (SACs), areas of low activity in the 1991-94 surveys and areas of particular risk such as high acidity and high road death mortality. A total of 1376 sites within 574 different 10 km squares were surveyed over the period 2003-04 and of these 1267 sites (92.08 %) were recorded as positive. The author concluded that: *The species can now be considered ubiquitous throughout Scotland, occupying sites in urban areas and in highly disturbed waterways where it seems unaffected by human activity.*

In 2002 a team from the Clackmannanshire Biodiversity Partnership wrote a Species Action Plan (SAP) for the otter which was included in Clackmannanshire Biodiversity Action Plan (Campbell, 2003). The first objective of the SAP was to monitor the distribution on an annual basis and identify population trends. In 2004 the Clackmannanshire Countryside Ranger Service undertook this responsibility and the study's progress is reported below.

Monitoring Otters

Otters are quite difficult to observe being largely nocturnal animals which when not hunting in water favour dense cover for resting and breeding. For the most part the adults are solitary and their social system allows them to partition resources without direct contact between individuals. This is achieved by marking their territories by the deposition of faeces or 'spraints' on prominent features such as rocks. Otters rest in cavities amongst bankside tree roots and rocks and these are known as 'holt' sites. Each otter will use a large number of 'holts' but those used for breeding are secluded and remote (Willet, 2002). Sometimes otters rest in 'couches' or ground level nest-like structures (0.3-1 m in diameter). These are constructed from nearby vegetation often in reed beds and bramble patches. The territory of an otter can be large covering between 5 and 20 km along the side of freshwater rivers and lakes (forestry.gov.uk). Otters are opportunistic feeders, catching mainly fish, but they are also known to take amphibians, crustaceans, small waterfowl and small mammals. Where the otter hunts in salt water like the Forth Estuary and mouth of the Devon it requires a source of fresh water to wash and maintain the condition of its fur.

Owing to the secretive nature of these mammals, their mobility and nocturnal habits, surveys have to be based on finding their ' spraint' or faeces and 'spoor' or tracks (Plate 8) to provide evidence of their presence.

Spraint is recognised:

- firstly by its prominent positioning for territory marking generally in a high place, possibly to prevent it washing away during flooding.
- Secondly by its shiny appearance and the presence of fish bones and scales within it. The scales glitter when the spraint is illuminated with a torch.
- Lastly, for the real enthusiast, taking a sniff. If it smells of jasmine it is otter and if it smells of rotten meat it is likely to be mink.

The 'spoor' or tracks are characteristic and are found commonly in the mud at the water side. Each footprint is about 6 cm wide and has five toes although usually on hard ground, only four show. The webs and claws on the otter's feet are occasionally apparent in their tracks.

The Clackmannanshire Countryside Ranger Service (CCRS) has surveyed for signs of otters every autumn since 2004. A total of 17 annual freshwater sample points were selected. They spanned the length of the Devon from Cambus to the Yetts o' Muckhart including the main feeder burns running down the Ochil Glens. There were also two sampling points on the Black Devon and two not included in Table 1 at Gartmorn North (NS921,944) and Gartmorn Lade (NS928,941). Nearly all the survey stations were near to bridges because a river is canalised at these points and otters tend to spraint in these areas.

The results of these presence or absence determinations are shown for 15 of the sample sites in Table 1. Between 2004 and 2008 otter activity was only found at between 6 and 8 of the 15 sites. Since then they appear to have spread so that by 2012 activity was detected at 13 of the 15 stations. The difficulties surveying when the rivers were in spate accounted for the reduction in 2011. Although otter presence has always been found in the Dollar Burn the increase in occupied sites has been predominately due to spread up the other main burns of the Ochil Glens as well as up the Black Devon from Clackmannan to Forest Mill. The anomalous absence of otters at Marchglen, Glenfoot Bridge in Tillicoultry is most likely due to the lack of suitable sprainting sites since otters were found both up and downstream of this station. The two Gartmorn sites were not tabulated because only one sign of an otter was found in Gartmorn lade in 2005. Their absence may well be due to the drying out of the feeder lade, making travel to the Dam itself less likely but not impossible. The banks of the Forth were not included in the survey though otters have been seen fishing at Cambus, South Alloa and Longcarse and a 'holt' was found in the roots of a bankside tree just upstream of Cambus Pools nature reserve.

Although Scottish otters have shown a remarkable recovery there is no room for complacency. The disappearance of suitable prey species, such as the collapse in the eelpout population, is a real threat. In the Shetlands the increase in eelpout numbers in summer has been found to be closely associated with otter reproductive success (Kruuk, 2008).

Conflicts associated with otter increase

Increase in otter numbers brings with it possible conflicts with fisheries. Research carried out by the Environment Agency suggests that not all fisheries are negatively impacted. In rivers where otters have been established for a while the loss of fish was less noticeable. Otters eat a range of fish species, but generally they take whatever is most abundant. Studies reveal that on average the fish they catch are less than 300 mm length; although very large fish can be taken, their choice of fish prey generally reflects what is available. Still water fisheries are more vulnerable than faster flowing rivers. Most of the anecdotal evidence points to the otters taking older, larger fish – this may be because the taking of larger fish is more noticeable and not because the otters do not take smaller fish.

Acknowledgement

Thanks to the volunteers and past Countryside Rangers who have made the surveys possible.

References

Campbell, L. 2003. *Clackmannanshire Biodiversity Action Plan* Published by Clackmannan-shire Council, Alloa.

Environmental Agency Report http://www.environmentagency.gov.uk/static/documents/Leisure/otters_and_stillwater_fisheriesv4 pdf

Green, J. and Green, R. 1980. *Otter Survey of Scotland 1977-197*. London: The Vincent Wildlife Trust.

Green, J. and Green, R. 1987. *Otter Survey of Scotland 1984-1985*. London: The Vincent Wildlife Trust.

Green, J. and Green, R. 1997. *Otter Survey of Scotland 1991-1994*. London: The Vincent Wildlife Trust.

Sinclair, J. 1791-1799. *Statistical Account* Vol. 15 for Parish of Tillicoultry. Wakefield: EP Publishing.

Kruuk, H. 2008. *Otters, Ecology, Behaviour and Conservation*. Oxford: Oxford University Press.

New Statistical Account of Scotland 1845 Parish of Alloa Volume 8 Edinburgh and London: Blackwood and Sons.

Otter range report www.forestry.gov.uk/forestry/otter

Strachan, R. 2007. National survey of otter Lutra lutra distribution in Scotland 2003-04. Scottish Natural Heritage Commissioned Report No. 211 (ROAME No. F03AC309).

Willet, J. 2002. *Stirling Council Area Biodiversity Action Plan* Published by Stirling Council, Stirling.

Site and map reference		2004	'05	'06	'07	'08	'09	'10	'11	'12	Presence
River Devon											
Cambus Bridge	NS 853 940	+	+	+	+	+	+	+	+	+	100%
B 9096 Road Bridge	NS 846 951	+	+	+	+	+	+	+	+	+	100%
Menstrie South	NS 857 959	+	-	+	+	-	+	+	+	+	77.8%
Sauchie Tower bridge	NS 893 959	+	+	+	-	-	+	+	+	+	77.8%
Marchglen, Glenfoot	NS 910 964	-	-	-	-	-	-	-	-	-	0%
Devonside	NS 920 964	+	-	+	+	-	+	+	+	+	77.8%
Dollarfield	NS 960 969	-	+	-	-	-	+	-	+	-	33.3%
Vicars Bridge	NS 985 979	-	+	-	-	+	+	-	-	+	44.4%
Yetts o'Muckhart	NO 010 018	-	-	+	+	+	-	+	-	+	55.6%
Black Devon											
Forest Mill	NS 952 938	-	-	-	-	+	+	+	+	+	55.6%
Clackmannan	NS 917 923	+	-	+	+	+	-	+	+	+	77.8%
Burns											
Menstrie burn	NS 848 970	-	-	-	-	-	+	+	+	+	44.4%
Alva burn	NS 884 974	-	-	-	-	-	+	+	-	+	33.3%
Mill Glen	NS 914 974	-	-	-	-	+	-	+	-	+	33.3%
Dollar Glen	NS 963 983	+	+	+	+	+	+	+	+	+	100%

Table 1. The results of the CCRS survey (2004-2012) recording the presence (+) or absence (-) of signs of otter activity at 15 sites on the River Devon, the Black Devon and the burns flowing down the Ochil Glens.

DICRANOPALPUS RAMOSUS: A DISTINCTIVE NON-NATIVE HARVESTMAN INVADING SCOTLAND

Michael B. Usher

Dicranopalpus ramosus is a harvestman which has an interesting, albeit short, history in Great Britain. A specimen was collected in Bournemouth in 1957, given the name *Dicranopalpus insignipalpus*, and deposited in the Natural History Museum, London (Sankey and Savory, 1974). A similar harvestman was collected in 1966 in Hove, Sussex, but this time it was allocated to the species *D. caudatus*. Subsequently, further harvestmen were recorded using this name from Essex and Cornwall (Sankey and Savory, 1974).

By 1988 this apparently introduced species had spread northwards through many southern English counties, as well as along the south coast of Wales as far as Cardigan (distribution map 22 in Hillyard and Sankey, 1989). By this time it had been identified as *D. ramosus*, a species originally described in 1909 from Morocco. Subsequently, the species was recorded from Portugal in 1948, from Spain in 1965 and from France in 1969. It is completely unknown how this harvestman reached British shores, or how long it had been present before it was discovered on the south coast of England in 1957.

Hillyard (1999) refered to its spread in Britain as "quite amazing". He mentioned that it had been found that year in Thorpe Arch, Yorkshire, and Forton, Lancashire. A year later, Hillyard (2000) noted that the species had now been found in a garden in Edinburgh as well as in a number of sites in North Wales. However, the distribution map in Hillyard (2005) only shows one 10 km grid square with this species north of Yorkshire and Lancashire, and that is on the Cumbrian coast. *D. ramosus* was by then also widely recorded in the southern half of Ireland.

The species is now spreading into Scotland. Davidson (2010) refered to recent records in Fife and Perth. It is now known to occur in the Stirling District, having been discovered on a church wall in Bridge of Allan (grid reference NS793974). Adults have been found in each of the months September, October and November 2012.

D. ramosus is a very easily recognised species of harvestman. The useful indicators are the way that it rests, with its very long legs and its pedipalps, which almost appear as a fifth pairs of legs in front of the animal. The species tends to rest flat against a wall, face down, with the four legs on each side of its body stretched out at an acute angle (less than 40°). Figure 1, which shows only the proximal part of its very long legs, demonstrates its characteristic resting position. Other species of harvestmen rest with their legs spread out in a much wider, usually obtuse, angle. However, confirmation of the species' identity can be sought from the pedipalps. The patella has an apophysis which is more than half as long as the tibia. The female illustrated in Figure 1 shows this apophysis to be nearly as long as the tibia, making the pedipalp look almost like a 'lop-sided claw'! This is a character which separates *D. ramosus* from any other harvestman in the British Isles. The markings on the body (the prosoma and opisthosoma) are very variable (Hillyard and Sankey, 1989) and hence are not useful in the identification of this species. The area of the raised eyes, the ocularium, is rounded in lateral view and has no ornamentation of spines or spicules, unlike many of the other British harvestmen species.

References

Davidson, M.B. 2010. *The Scottish Invertebrate Species Knowledge Dossier: Opiliones (Harvestmen).* Buglife – The Invertebrate Conservation Trust.

Hillyard, P. 1999. Spread of *Dicranopalpus ramosus. Ocularium,* **2**, 1.

Hillyard, P. 2000. *Dicranopalpus ramosus. Ocularium,* **3**, 2.

Hillyard, P.D. 2005. *Harvestmen, 3rd edition.* Field Studies Council, Shrewsbury.

Hillyard, P.D. and Sankey, J.H.P. 1989. *Harvestmen, 2nd edition.* Linnean Society of London and E.J. Brill, Leiden.

Sankey, J.H.P. and Savory, T.H. 1974. *British Harvestmen.* Linnean Society of London and Academic Press, London.

Figure 1. The characteristic pose of *Dicranopalpus ramosus*, resting face-down on a wall at Bridge of Allan, September 2012.

TAIGA BEAN GEESE IN SCOTLAND

Angus Maciver and John Simpson

Introduction

The Taiga Bean Goose *Anser fabalis fabalis* is a winter visitor to Scotland and is restricted to the Slamannan Plateau in the upper Forth. This is the only known regular wintering ground for this species and it is regarded as a vagrant when appearing elsewhere in Scotland.

During the 19th century, Bean Geese were regarded as the commonest of our wintering grey geese in many parts of Scotland (Berry, 1939). Whilst there is thought to have been confusion between Greylag Goose *A.anser* and Pink footed Goose *A. brachyrhynchus* populations, all the evidence suggests a much more widespread distribution.

For most of the 20th century, the stronghold of the Taiga Bean Goose was around the Dee and Ken Marshes of Castle Douglas, Dumfries and Galloway (Watson, 1986). From a population of about 500 birds, the flock gradually dwindled until this area was abandoned in the 1980s. The reasons for their decline are not entirely clear, but habitat changes and the intensification of former feeding areas are the most likely factors.

As the Castle Douglas flock declined, Bean Geese started to be observed in other areas. In February 1981, a flock of 73 birds was found at Carron Valley Reservoir (Upper Forth) and these returned for several years before dam improvements and the raising of the water level saw the flock forage further afield. During the mid 1980s, the birds were recording more frequently on the Slammanan plateau but still returned to the Carron Valley to roost. Interestingly, anecdotal evidence from the local farming community suggests that the birds may have been present infrequently since the 1930s, exploiting areas rarely visited by bird watchers.

The Slamannan flock has been intensively monitored from 1989 when 112 birds were noted at Garbethill Farm, south east of Cumbernauld. The flock has steadily increased to around 250 birds and has stabilised around that figure in the late 2000s to the early 2010s.

The flock arrives in a number of influxes which can start in early to mid September. However in recent years the first birds have arrived around late September to early October and the flock reaches its peak around mid October. The birds invariably arrive in the western part of their Slammanan range and remain there until the flock is complete. From favoured sites, such as Luckenburn Farm, the flock eventually fragments and exploits the available grazing throughout the Slamannan Plateau.

During the late 1980s and early 1990s, the birds' range extended as far as Loch Elrigg and Shieldhill. The birds would often exploit the grazing of the improved pasture land bordering the muirs of Garbethill and Fannyside which they also use for loafing.

Diurnal behaviour

In the early 1980s, very little was known about the feeding and behavioural ecology of the Bean Geese. Whilst there was a well studied flock in the Yare Valley in Norfolk, the only other flock in the UK, much of the data and direct observation of this species was new for the Scottish conservation community and these were exciting times. It became evident that both populations exhibited different behaviour. They had differing priorities. The Yare Valley flock was, at that time, larger and more tolerant of disturbance, whilst the Slammanan birds were shy and wary. The sward composition of their feeding fields was also different. The Slammanan flock preferred habitats that were of poorer quality and quantity of grazing. The Yare flock benefited from high quality and specifically managed swards.

The Slammanan birds flew off from their feeding fields and utilised muirs to loaf on, allowing them to digest the grass after a 3 hour grazing bout. This was achieved in the comparative safety of an environment that gave them excellent cover from view and reduced their chances of being disturbed. However, the use of muirs to loaf was unusual and had not been documented before, so it was a surprise to find that the birds were also roosting there overnight. The birds favoured Fannyside Muir and settled down in rank heather peppered with small pools, occasionally flighting off in the night to feed in neighbouring fields.

In the early 1980s, when the birds were using the Carron Valley Reservoir, their daily routine was simply one of leaving the centre of the reservoir where roosting had taken place and moving onto the shoreline of one of the bays on the southern side to feed. At this time good feeding was available due to the low level of the water due to work taking place on the dam structure.

On the Slamannan plateau the diurnal routine of the flock has changed little since the late 1980s when regular observations on the distribution of the geese began. The birds leave their roost site on or about the time when dawn is breaking. Often, groups of c.15-40 birds fly out to their preferred feeding field at intervals which vary considerably on different occasions. Sometimes much larger groups of c.80 birds will leave in a clamour of noise. Flying time between roost and preferred feeding site can often be as little as three minutes but more often slightly longer.

Once the birds arrive on their feeding field they immediately graze intensely for several hours. Adult pairs will graze together throughout the day and rarely move from each other's side. It would be unusual to see them separated by more than about 2 metres. Adult pairs with juveniles in attendance stay together in a similar way although it is often the case that juveniles join up with other juveniles but still never stray very far from their parents.

Generally by around 10-11am, birds stop feeding and rest to digest the grass in their crops. This can last for about an hour before feeding resumes. If there is no drinking water available to the birds in the feeding field they will flight to a nearby source to drink before returning. Feeding fields during the winter months often have pools of water so flying off to drink is often not necessary.

During the daylight hours the birds are liable to be disturbed by many different causes. A farmer tending to stock is one of the more common and understandable causes of disturbance. When it occurs the birds will fly off to a nearby refuge area and spend the time away from feeding by merely resting and spending some of the time preening. The norm is for the birds to return to the same field after an absence of approximately 1 hour.

Other forms of disturbance are many and varied but, regardless of the cause, the birds will fly off for a time and generally return to the same field. On occasions however, the flock will fly to another totally different field which may be several kilometres away. The daylight hours are spent feeding and resting as long as the weather permits. The birds will stay out in their feeding areas till after dusk before returning to one of their preferred roosting sites.

Night feeding can and does occur which often coincides with the time of a full moon. It can often be the case too that cold weather with conditions of snow and ice on the ground will see the birds stay out on fields rather than flying to roost on lochs or moors which are frozen over. When snow covers the ground the birds are capable of sitting out the bad weather and appearing not to feed but simply conserving their energy by not moving.

Bean Geese are very wary and will often use the landscape to their advantage by remaining hidden from view. It can be something as simple as a contour line in a field which separates them from being seen. Long grass and *Juncus* in feeding fields will also often hide them from view.

The Bean Goose flock can on occasions be accompanied by small numbers of Pink-footed, Greylag or European White-fronted Geese *A.albifrons albifrons*, however, they rarely mix freely and tend to remain in groups of their own species. The Bean Geese will often feed in fields stocked with sheep and no conflict seems to take place.

Migrations and recent marking

The Slamannan Bean Geese belong to the northern European population which numbers about 60,000 birds and breeds across northern Scandinavia and into western Russia (Fox *et al.* 2010). It is thought that the total population has declined in number during the last 30 years.

In March 1986, seven colour ringed Bean Geese (in a flock of nine birds) were reported from the Beauly Firth, Inverness-shire. The colour ringed birds were part of a re-established population being released by Lambart von Essen and the Swedish Sportsmens' Association with support from WWF-Sweden. Between 1974 and 1988, 324 Bean Goose goslings were released in Sweden. The aim of the re-establishment programme was to repopulate an area in the southern part of the range where geese had formerly bred but were thought to have become extinct.

Sightings revealed that most of the released birds wintered in Scania (southern Sweden) but clearly a very small number had crossed the North Sea to spend at least one winter in Scotland. Subsequently, in February 1987, three colour ringed Bean Geese, amongst a flock of 114 birds, were reported from the Carron Valley Reservoir, although none of the colour combinations could be determined and, in December 1987, six colour ringed Bean Geese, amongst a flock of 56, were also seen there. No colour ringed birds from the Swedish release programme were subsequently reported from Scotland. However, the apparent link between the Slamannan Plateau wintering flock and the Swedish re-established flock became more interesting 25 years later.

In early autumn 2011, cannon-nets were set by the Wildfowl and Wetlands Trust on the Slamannan Plateau and 15 Bean Geese were caught on 12 October. This increased the number ringed in Britain and Ireland to 20 birds. After capture, 13 of the 15 birds fitted with plastic neck collars were then seen many times in the Slamannan Plateau wintering area. On 20 March 2012, seven of the marked Slamannan Bean Geese were seen together near Akershus, south east Norway in a flock of 143 birds, thus identifying a staging area of part of the Slamannan flock prior to moving to their breeding grounds.

Six Bean Geese were also caught on the Slamannan Plateau on 14 October 2012. Three adult males and three first-winter birds were fitted with GPS tracking units (Plate 13). After capture, all six collared birds were seen throughout the winter. The GPS data provided detailed locations several times each day leading to a greater understanding of the distribution of the birds on the plateau, the fields they chose to feed in, their movements and nocturnal activity, including roost locations.

In late February 2013, the six marked geese left the Slamannan Plateau and the birds were recorded in north west Denmark – thus identifying a new staging area of part of the Slamannan flock prior to moving to the breeding grounds. In mid March, the marked birds had moved to Akershus, Norway (as in 2012). By mid April, the tags showed the location of the birds to be 200 km further north in Dalarna county, south west Sweden. Although on the very southern edge of the range of Bean Geese in Sweden, this is an area where the geese could potentially be breeding. This also proved to be one of the areas where re-established Bean Geese had been released in the 1970s/1980s. Location data from these tagged individuals will hopefully continue to shed further insights into the movements of Scotland's Bean Geese.

Conservation

In recognition of the importance of the flock and the conservation pressures the Slamannan Bean Geese faced, in 1991 an initial working group was formed. By 1993, the group was formalised and developed to become the Bean Goose Action Group, a pro active body of conservation bodies and local councils all working to protect and promote the interests of the birds. The group is made up of representatives of Scottish Natural Heritage, the two local councils, the Royal Society for the Protection of Birds and the Wildfowl and Wetlands Trust and oversees conservation.

It was at this time that a study of the flock was commissioned and this was conducted by the Royal Society for the Protection of Birds (Smith *et al.* 1995). The study set out a field numbering system and a standardised methodology which is still used today. The study identified the most important areas for feeding, roosting and the possible factors for site usage by the flock were analysed.

The study was timely, as the Slammanan Plateau faced a number of pressures and landscape changes. One such example was when a wildfowling syndicate tried to obtain the lease of east Fannyside Loch. The RSPB stepped in to purchase the loch and the surrounding land holding to safe guard what was, at that time, the main roost which still gets used on occasion today.

Given the importance of the Slammanan Plateau and the increased national significance of the Bean Goose population, the plateau was declared as a Site of Scientific Importance in September 2007. Further recognition of the importance of this wintering area followed when in October 2008, part of the plateau was classified as a Special Protection Area. Both designations drew heavily on information provided by the monitoring and field use data collected since the 1980s.

Protection has been extended with the acquisition, in 2013, by Forestry Commission Scotland of Fannyside Muir. This extensive area of raised bog and heather moorland is of considerable importance to the birds. It is used as a night time roost as well as a site to loaf through the day and as a refuge when they are disturbed.

The Slammanan Bean Geese face ever increasing pressures from a wide variety of sources. From changes in farming practice to proposed wind farm developments all of which have a potential impact of field usage. Even subtle changes in lifestyle in rural small holdings can deny the flock access to grazing they have exploited over many years. However, with an active multi agency action group dedicated to the protection, monitoring and the promotion of the flock, the future appears bright for our only regular wintering Bean Goose flock.

References

Berry, J. 1939. *The status and distribution of wild geese and wild duck in Scotland. International Wildfowl Inquiry, Vol II*. Cambridge: The University Press.

Fox, A.D., *et al.* 2010. Current estimates of goose population sizes in the western Palearctic, a gap analysis and an assessment of trends. *Ornis Svecica* **20**, 115-127.

Smith, T., Bainbridge, I., and O'Brien, M. 1995. *Distribution and Habitat Use by Bean Geese in the Slamannan Area*. RSPB Report.

Watson, D. 1986. Bean Geese in south west Scotland. *Scottish Birds* **14**, 17-24.

FORTH AREA BIRD REPORT 2012

A.E. Thiel and C.J. Pendlebury

This is the 38th bird report for the Forth Area (or Upper Forth). The area covered by the report comprises the council areas of Falkirk, Clackmannanshire and Stirling but excludes Loch Lomondside and other parts of the Clyde drainage basin as well as the Endrick Water, i.e. Fintry and Balfron, all of which are currently covered by the Clyde bird report.

The report was written by Chris Pendlebury (non-passerines, excluding waders) and Andre Thiel (waders, passerines and escaped/introduced species). Chris Pendlebury, the current SOC recorder, can be contacted by e-mail at chris@upperforthbirds.co.uk, by leaving a message on 07798-711 134 or by mail to 3 Sinclair Street, Dunblane FK15 0AH.

The main part of the report consists of detailed species accounts presented in a systematic list arranged in the latest taxonomic order, as adopted by the BOU, and using the now internationally agreed nomenclature for English names of Gill & Wright (2006), as also adopted by the BOU and recommended by the SOC. This is preceded by a summary of the main bird news from 2012 and a Ringing Report, both compiled by Andre Thiel.

ROUND-UP OF THE YEAR

January
The year began with very mild conditions – overall it was the mildest January since 2008 – but Atlantic depressions resulted in stormy weather. A major storm across Scotland, particularly in the Central Belt on 3rd, resulted in gusts of 160 km/h at Blackford Hill, Edinburgh. Mid-month was settled, followed by more unsettled conditions with westerly winds bringing weather fronts and colder conditions at the end of the month. Birdingwise the year started with several good sightings on 1st. This included a one-day Great Grey Shrike at Cock Hill, Loch Rusky, several Eurasian Nuthatches in Aberfoyle, two Tundra Bean Geese at Blairdrummond Carse and the by now almost traditional New Year's Day Eurasian Blackcap at Alexander Drive, Dunblane. Dunblane also provided the highlight on 2nd in the form of an immature female Northern Goshawk, with a supporting cast of a first-winter Mediterranean Gull at the regular site of Airth on the same day and an adult Mediterranean Gull just upstream at South Alloa on 3rd. A flock of 130 European Greenfinches provided a colourful display at Carse of Lecropt, Bridge of Allan on 5th. The next day provided the first of four sightings this year of White-tailed Eagles, this one at Muir Dam, Thornhill. All are believed to have been birds from the Fife re-introduction programme. An overwintering Ruff at Skinflats on 8th was of note. A Common Blackbird that had been ringed in Norway in October 2011

flew into a building at Brightons, Falkirk on 11th and unfortunately died. The Ring-billed Gull that has been faithful to Kinneil since 2007 returned on 16th and stayed until 21st March. A bird of the Continental *sinensis* race of Great Cormorant at Airthrey Loch, Bridge of Allan on 25th was the first record of this uncommon race in our recording area. Somewhat more common was an overwintering Spotted Redshank at Skinflats on 28th, the same day that saw 31 Snow Buntings fly over Auchtertyre Glen, Strathfillan. January finished with a 2nd winter Iceland Gull at Haugh of Blackgrange on 30th.

February

After a cold, fine start westerly winds brought generally mild weather, especially in the last 10 days of the month. Cloud and rain were most frequent in the west. Sheltered eastern areas were mainly dry and saw unusually high temperatures (e.g. 17°C at Dyce, Aberdeen on 28th). Overall it was the mildest February since 1998. February started with two Golden Eagles at Gleann a'Chlachain. The largest Chaffinch flock recorded this year in the recording area was seen at Greenyards, Dunblane on 5th. A good flock of 26 Red Crossbills graced Kirkton Farm, Tyndrum the following day. Mid-month saw the second Great Grey Shrike of the year at Milton, Kilmahog from 11th onwards. Large wildfowl flocks dominated the remainder of the month, especially 12th, when 122 Northern Pintails were between Kinneil and Bo'ness and year maxima of 12 Grey Plovers were logged at Kincardine Bridge, 2,750 Red Knots at Skinflats as well as 3,936 Dunlins and 1,104 Common Redshanks between Grangepans (Bo'ness) and Grangemouth. A redhead Smew at Gartmorn Dam on 14th was a good sighting as were 33 Common Snipe at Carse of Lecropt, Bridge of Allan the same day. Twenty-four European Greater White-fronted Geese at South Alloa were the largest count in Upper Forth of this uncommon race during its 2011/12 winter influx to Scotland.

March

The start of March was unsettled but thereafter high pressure gave plenty of fine, dry weather and record-breaking temperatures on three successive days in the north (22°C on 25th and 23°C on 27th in Aberdeenshire, with 23°C on 26th in Moray). There was less than a third of the normal rainfall in the east, which had its third driest March since 1910. A Northern Harrier in Alva on 9th was in a very unusual location for this species. Five Jack Snipe each were at Carse of Lecropt, Bridge of Allan and Carnforth, Stirling on 12th. The 16th saw the highest count of Greylag Geese with 926 at Alloa Inch, a species whose numbers have declined in the Central Belt due to the recent phenomenon of short-stopping further north, especially in Grampian and Orkney, thought to be the result of global warming. The next day two Rock Pipits at Kinneil were the only ones seen this year in the recording area. Spring arrived in the form of a Northern Wheatear at Inverlochlarig and a Chiffchaff at King's Park, Stirling on 18th. Not far behind was the first Sand Martin of the year at Lake of Menteith on 23rd and the first Osprey of the year at Loch Venachar on 25th. The same day three Razorbills, an uncommon species in our area, were recorded at Blackness and three to four Eurasian

Nuthatches on the east shore of Lake of Menteith, a suspected breeding location for this spreading species.

April

Low pressure systems dominated the weather in the UK for most of the month, making it the coldest April since 1998. There were lots of showers and some sleet and snow during the first few days. In eastern Scotland, it was the equal-third wettest April on record and the number of days with rain was the highest in over 50 years. Spring migrants followed those arrived in March thick and fast with the first migratory Eurasian Blackcap of the year at Skinflats on 1st, the first Barn Swallow at River Carron, Stenhousemuir on 7th, the first Willow Warbler at Mine Wood, Bridge of Allan on 8th, the first Common House Martin at Newton Crescent, Dunblane on 10th and the first Common Sandpiper at Grangepans, Bo'ness on 11th. Winter hadn't left us completely, though, as witnessed by a high count of 18 Ruddy Turnstones, also at Grangepans, on 11th and four Short-eared Owls at Skinflats on 12th. This didn't stop the next migrants from arriving, though: two Tree Pipits were at Skinflats, a Whinchat at Waterside, Braes of Doune and a Garden Warbler at Kingseat Place, Falkirk, all on 15th and a Common Redstart at Rednock, Lake of Menteith on 16th. A good sighting was a Eurasian Nuthatch on 17th at Dollar Glen. The last third of the month started with a single Common Grasshopper Warbler at Skinflats and two at Blackdevon Wetlands on 21st, the site that also hosted a singing Reed Warbler the same day. This was the first of a remarkable run of four sightings of what looks like another colonising species. The next day saw both leavers with 320 Pink-footed Geese flying over Glen Finglas and 100 over Killin and arrivals with an excellent 25 White Wagtails (race: *alba*) at Skinflats, the first Sedge Warbler at Cambus and the first Common Whitethroats at Cambus and King's Park, Stirling. The first two Cuckoos at Loch Rusky followed on 27th. Another 24 hours and another two species appeared in the form of a Common Swift at Bridge of Allan and a male Garganey at Kinneil. Much more common and yet unusual was a sighting of 15 Goldcrests at Drumloist, Braes of Doune. The last day of the month saw the extended stay of one to two Little Ringed Plovers at a site in Killin.

May

The weather was generally cool and unsettled during the first three weeks of May, with some strong winds at times. The final week was dry, sunny and very warm with some unusually high temperatures, particularly across Highland Scotland where a measurement of 30.9 °C on 25th broke the Scottish temperature record for May. The hot conditions triggered some scattered heavy showers for central areas, with a thunderstorm and 35.8 mm of rainfall in Livingston (West Lothian). Conditions turned cooler and unsettled again at the end of the month. A late Redwing at New Sauchie, Alloa on 1st contrasted with a freshly arrived Wood Warbler at Kilmahog the same day. The latter was the first of an encouraging series of sightings of this severely declining species. A Merlin at Loch Venachar on 5th was one of only a handful of records. The 6th heralded a small spring influx of Whimbrels with two at Kinneil culminating in nine at the Rhind, Alloa on 11th and 12th. The 6th also saw the last four Fieldfares of the year at Blaircessnock, Flanders Moss. Two days later the first flock of 30 Common Terns was sighted at Kinneil. Just as thrilling to see is Marsh Harrier, the first of which was seen on 12th at Tullibody Inch, while nearby in the Ochils the first Spotted Flycatcher was recorded at Tillicoultry Glen. The 14th saw a small influx of Common Ringed Plovers of the *tundrae* race when 30 were at Kennetpans with, later, 88 at Kinneil on 30th. Mid-month our area joined the fascinating satellite-tagging study that is being carried out by the BTO, when five Common Cuckoos were ringed on the shores of Loch Katrine. Four of these made it to Africa, where they staged in Chad, Eastern Gabon, central Congo and the Democratic Republic of Congo. From Africa back to Blackness where the first Sandwich Tern arrived on 20th. A pair of Common Shelducks with 10 goslings at Longcarse, Alloa was of note on 24th. Continuing the same theme, there were two unfledged Long-eared Owls at Skinflats on 27th. Spring Curlew Sandpipers are rather uncommon and sightings of birds at Blackness on 29th and Skinflats on 30th were noteworthy.

June

June was dominated by low pressure over the UK, which brought cool days (the coolest since 1998), strong winds and very high rainfall (250 to 300 % of the normal amount in southern and eastern Scotland), making it the wettest June on record. As the breeding season was in full swing, interesting sightings became scarcer in a month that has thrown up some exciting birds in the past. The 4th saw the second Reed Warbler sighting of the year, at Skinflats, as well as one of only a handful of records of Eurasian Pied Flycatchers in central Glen Lochay. An estimated 35 Red Crossbills flew over Castlebridge Business Park, Forestmill on 7th, the same day that a Golden Eagle that had been ringed 39 years earlier at Loch Fyne was found dead near Dalveich. A Little Ringed Plover was sitting on a nest in Killin between 9th and 14th but not on 17th, thereby rasising doubts about whether the species had bred there or not. An adult and two juvenile Tawny Owls and an adult and a single juvenile Long-eared Owl were seen on 18th at the West Lothian Golf Course in Bo'ness, while a Common Quail was at the reliable site of Thornhill on 27th.

July

As in June, low pressure dominated the weather, resulting in a cool and very unsettled month (the coolest since 1998) with little sunshine. There was over twice the normal amount of rain in eastern and southern Scotland where it was one of the wettest Julys on record, with thunderstorms on 4th in central and southern areas. July kicked off with two male and one female Ring Ouzels at Stob a Choin. Arctic Terns are much scarcer than their cousins, Common Terns, in our area. A bird at Bo'ness on 7th was the first of only a handful of birds. A Hobby at Flanders Moss on 14th was even rarer, being the only record of this species in 2012. It is known that Kinneil is an important staging location for Black-tailed Godwits and this year was no exception. Two Black-tailed Godwits colour-ringed at Montrose Basin in Angus in August 2011 and March 2012, respectively, were seen on 10th, while birds colour-ringed in Portugal in

February 2007 and Iceland in July 2009, respectively, made Kinneil their home on 30th. Coming across six Wood Warblers in Glen Finglas on 16th would have been rather satisfying. Four Ring Ouzels at Crag MacRanaich, Balquhidder on 19th was an excellent sighting, as were 12 Spotted Flycatchers at Edinchip, Lochearnhead. Of note on 26th were Tufted Duck broods of 7 and 9 young, respectively, at Gart Gravel Pits, Callander. 29th saw the start of a short stay of an adult and immature Spoonbill at Kinneil which lasted till 8th August for the adult and 29th August for the immature.

August
 A mainly changeable month with many showery days, sometimes thundery and only one warm settled spell from 8th to 11th. It was wetter than normal across parts of eastern and southern Scotland, with twice the average rainfall in a few locations. Barely into August and return migration was evident with eight Common Sandpipers at Kinneil on 1st. On the topic of returning: the regular Ring-billed Gill returned for its autumn stay to the same location on 2nd, staying there till mid-October. Kinneil continued its good run with two Green Sandpipers on 4th. Two Water Rails at Blackdevon Wetlands on 12th was one of rather few highlights this month. Three adult Little Gulls were at Bo'ness on 15th, the same day a Fieldfare appeared at Kinneil – somewhat puzzling. Skinflats put in appearance on 16th when three Sanderlings staged, as did a Common Whitethroat on its way back south. Another traditionally early leaver is Common Swift, the last two of which were seen in Bridge of Allan on 20th, while the last three Spotted Redshanks were at Kinneil the next day. Six Ruff at Shieldhill roadside pools, Falkirk was the highest count in what was rather a poor passage for this species. The month ended with two Roseate Terns at Blackness and an excellent count of 20 Hooded Crows in Crianlarich on 31st.

September
 The month began generally dry and warmer than late August but became much more unsettled and cooler towards the middle and remained cool and changeable until the end. A storm from 24th to 26th brought heavy rain and strong winds to eastern areas. Two Pale-bellied Brent Geese were at Blackness and the last Spotted Flycatcher at Gartmorn Dam on 1st. Fifteen White Wagtails (race: *alba*) at Tullibody Inch on 3rd were noteworthy, as were two Long-tailed Skuas at Kinneil. The 9th was a good day to be in the Grangemouth area: the first Pink-footed Geese arrived at Blackness, where two Roseate Terns were spotted as well as four Tree Pipits. Twenty-one Parasitic Jaegers were off Bo'ness. Kinneil hosted the last Sand Martin and the last two Tree Pipits of the year as well as overflying Red-throated Loons, while six Common Greenshanks were at neighbouring Skinflats. This was a sign of things to come. Black Terns were off Bo'ness on 10th and 12th. A count of 17 Curlew Sandpipers at Kinneil on 11th stood out of the autumn passage of this species. Six Redwings at Cambus the same day were the first of the autumn. Kinneil scored again on 12th with a massive 215 Guillemots and on 14th with another Black Tern and the last Northern Wheatear. 23rd brought the first flock of 11 Whooper Swans to Skinflats as well as the last Willow Warbler just in time before things really took

off, literally ! Strong east-north-easterlies on 25th produced at least 2 Manx Shearwaters at Kinneil, an excellent count of 67 Great Skuas and three Little Gulls off Bo'ness, the location where a Sabine's Gull, a very rare species in our area, was spotted. Braving the weather was a chattering Ring Ouzel at Auchtertyre, Strathfillan the same day. The next day brought the first of only three sightings of Little Stints, a juvenile at Skinflats. 27th saw an incredible 10,000+ Fieldfares in Glen Lochay, potentially also as a result of the very windy weather. Finally, the last Common House Martins of the year were recorded at Blackness and Kinneil, where else ?, on 29th.

October

Most of the month was unsettled with rain and showers. However, there were some settled spells from 5th to 10th and 21st to 25th. It was the coldest October since 1993, with several frosty nights and snow in the northeast towards the end of the month. Thirt-five Greater Scaup off Blackness on 1st was the highest count of the year. On 4th an adult pale phase and an immature Pomarine Skua were off Bo'ness. The next day a Slavonian Grebe was at Kinneil with the last two Common Chiffchaffs there on 7th. A flock of 10 Sandwich Terns off Blackness on 10th turned out to be the last for 2012. A flock of thirteen Common Pochards, a once common and widespread species, at Kinneil on 12th was, incredibly, the highest count in our area of this declining species. 14th was a rather late date for a Little Stint recorded between Grangepans and Grangemouth, while five Jack Snipe were at Netherton Marsh, Bridge of Allan. Two days on and 6,950 Pink-footed Geese flew in to roost at Skinflats, representing the highest count in 2012. Sixty Twite in Airth on 25th was a good record, while two Bohemian Waxwings in Doune on 27th were the vanguard of a rather modest showing this year compared to the previous invasion years. Four Blackcaps at Holmehill, Dunblane, on 24th were either very late migrants or early overwintering birds. On 28th the regular drake Green-winged Teal returned to Kinneil where it stayed until the end of the year, while over in Bo'ness the only Red-necked Grebe of the year was recorded.

November

The month started with cold nights and autumnal showers then became milder and wetter. The last few days of the month were colder and more settled with widespread frosts and some snow, mainly across higher ground. A Red-rumped Swallow at Blackness on 3rd is believed to be the first one for the recording area. Overwintering Green Sandpipers were spotted at Glensburgh, Grangemouth on 4th and, later, at Gilston on 7th and 20th. Very late Swallows flew past Blackness (2) and Killin on 4th. Two Rock Ptarmigans at Sgiath Chuil, Dochart on 7th was a good sighting, as were 96 Black Scoters off Bo'ness on 16th and a roost gathering of 60 White Wagtails (race: *yarrellii*) at Stirling train station on 17th. Twelve White-throated Dippers on the River Devon at Crook of Devon on 21st was of note, as were eight Eurasian Woodcocks at Argaty, Braes of Doune on 22nd at a time when Scandinavian migrants typically arrive on the east coast of Britain. Probably no longer migrating was a male Blackcap in Coneyhill, Bridge of Allan on 24th. At least 300 Golden Plovers at Kinneil on 23rd were the highest count of the year of this specially protected species. 28th revealed three Common Greenshanks at Skinflats with five Twite there on 29th.

December

The majority of the first half of the month was cold with wintry showers and some snow, especially across the mountains, followed by a brief settled spell before the middle of the month. After the 14th conditions were milder but very unsettled with rain and strong winds, reaching gale force in eastern coastal areas on the 15th. In eastern Scotland it was the wettest December since 1929. A massive 250 Bramblings as well as 450 Common Linnets at Blairdrummond GPs on 1st was an excellent find with another good winter flock of 400 Lesser Redpolls at Gartmorn Dam on 2nd. Of note on 9th were four Long-tailed Ducks at Bo'ness. 13th saw the maximum count of Red Kites at Argaty, Braes of Doune with an impressive 53 birds there as well as another good showing of 100 Bramblings at Greenyards, Dunblane. 211 Mallards at Skinflats on 15th was the highest 2012 count in our area of this declining species. An overwintering Common Greenshank at Kinneil the same day was the latest sighting of this species this year. The by now almost annual occurrence of Little Egret materialized very late this year, with one bird on 15th-16th at Skinflats and on 29th at Skinflats and Kincardine Bridge. Five Whimbrels at Kinneil on 18th was an unusual date for this species, while Blairdrummond GPs was an unusual site for a Common Loon on 23rd. Seven Gadwalls were at Gartmorn Dam on 27th, the day a redhead Smew was on the River Forth at East Frew. Nearing the end of the year an adult Iceland Gull was found at Skinflats on 29th. The year came to a close with seven Eurasian Jays at Blairdrummond GPs on 31st.

RECORD SUBMISSION AND FORMAT

Due to space limitations, details of record submission and report format are no longer presented here but can be found in previous versions of the bird report, e.g. Thiel, A.E. and Pendlebury, C.J. (2011), Forth Area Bird Report 2010. *Forth Naturalist and Historian*, **34**: 69-112.

Following past appeals for more complete information, most records now include the locality a bird was recorded in, the name of the nearest town/village and a 6-figure grid reference. However, some records are still submitted with only a town/village name and/or birds recorded as 'present'. This greatly diminishes the value of a record and the editors will use their discretion in considering whether to include such records.

Vetting of records of species that are locally rare or otherwise notable is now carried out by a panel of six members, which currently consists of Graeme Garner, Cliff Henty, Mark Lewis, Duncan Orr-Ewing, Chris Pendlebury and Andre Thiel. Any species which is a vagrant to the area and some of those which are asterisked (*) in this report fall into this category. A full list is available from Chris Pendlebury.

Finally, good quality photos of rare, uncommon or otherwise noteworthy birds or of interesting behaviour patterns will be considered for inclusion in the report, subject to space limitations.

CONTRIBUTORS

This report has been compiled from records submitted by the contributors listed below. Where initials are given, the contributors are listed in species entries of birds which are rare, uncommon or otherwise noteworthy. The editors are grateful to all the contributors for submitting their records. Thanks also go to Mike Bell and Neil Bielby who made available WeBS and BBS count data, to Alison Hannah who assisted with compiling the report and to Cliff Henty for proof-reading the report. Apologies to anybody who has been inadvertently missed out.

L. Albert (LA), M. Albert, D. Anderson, P. Ashworth (PMA), A. Ayre, K. Ballantyne, M. Beard (MFB), M. Bell (MVB), N. Bielby (NB), C. Bird (CB), Birdguides (BG), A. Blair (AB), A. Baird (ABa), J. Bray (JB), D. Bell (DB), R. Broad (RB), P. Brooks, K. Broomfield, D. Bryant (DMB), J. Burgum, J. Calladine (JRC), A. Carrington-Cotton (ACC), G. Checkley (GCh), F. Clark, C. Convery (CC), G. Cook (GC), J. Cowie, R. Cranston, D. Crosbie, R. Dalziel (RD), B. Darvill (BD), B. Dawson (RJD), R. Devine, A. Dobson, D. Douglas, E. Douglas, L. du Feu (LAF), K. Duffy (KJD), R. Eades, D. Eggerton, R. Elliot (RE), I. Ellis, A. Everingham (AE), R. Ferguson, K. Findlater (KF), J. Finlayson (JFi), D. Flynn, I. Fulton (IF), J. Gallacher, G. Garner (GG), S. Gillies, T. Goater (TG), R. Gooch (RG), H. Gorman (HEG), M. Granger, A. Guthrie, D. Hall, M. Harding (MH), M. Harrison, C. Henty (CJH), D. Hodgson, J. Holland (JPH), S. Holoran (SHo), T. Houslay, A. Inglis, D. Irvine (DI), C. Isherwood, R. Jackson, D. Jarvie, D. Jones (DJ), D. Kerr, G. and E. Leisk (GEL), M. Lewis (ML), B. Lynch, M. MacLean, R. Mann, G. Martin, J. Martin, S. Mathieson, D. Matthews, A. Matthewson, J. McArdle, W. McBay (WMcB), S. McBride (SMcB), S. McDerment, M. McDonnell (MMcD), S. McGeachie (SMcG), E. McGuire, C. McKay, H. McLaren, E. McLoughlin, I. McPherson, E. Mepham, N. Metcalfe, S. Milligan (SPM), B. Minshull, C. Moore (CM), R. Morley, A. Muirhead (AMu), F. and L. Murray (FAM), G. Murray, J. Nadin (JSN), A. Neeson, J. Neil, D. Orr-Ewing (DOE), the late G. Owens (GO), B. Paterson, C. Pendlebury (CJP), F. Poulter, D. Rees (DR), A. Renwick (ARe), C. Renwick, J. Richard, S. Rivers (SRG), J. Robertson, A. Robinson (ARo), T. Rogers, C. Ross, S. Roos and L. Coiffait (SR), G. Scott (GS), L. Scott, R. Shand (RS), K. Shaw (KDS), W. Shearer, R. Smith, C. Spray (CJS), P. Stevens, A. Stewart, R. Stewart, P. Strangeman, R. Strathdee, S. Swinney (SS), C. Tatchley, P. Taylor, A. Thiel (AET), I. Thomson, D. Thorogood (DT), L. Turner (LT), F. Waterworth, C. Wernham (CVW), N. Whyte, Robbie Whytock (RCW), Rory Whytock (RTW), K. Wilkinson, (KW), K. Wilson and M. Wood.

RINGING REPORT

This is the ninth ringing report. The following section lists birds ringed and/or controlled in the recording area during 2012 (as well as some earlier reports that have only recently become available). A large part of these records come from the BTO on-line ringing report. Contributors are encouraged to report all ringed, especially colour-ringed, birds to the relevant organizers and/or the BTO and not to assume that somebody else has already done so. All movements are of interest to the ringers and add to the understanding of bird ecology, migration patterns and demographics. In addition data should also be submitted to the bird recorder for inclusion in the bird report.

There were 40 reports of birds, involving 24 species, ringed or controlled in the recording area. There were movements of birds from Iceland, Norway, the Netherlands and Portugal to the recording area as well as movements of the well publicized five satellite-tagged Cuckoos ringed around L Katrine and which flew via the Netherlands, France, Germany, Austria, Switzerland, Italy, Czech Republic, Italy, Croatia, Montenegro, Albania, Libya, Egypt, Niger, Nigeria, Sudan to their wintering grounds in Chad, Congo, Cameroon, Gabon, Sudan, Central African Republic and Democratic Republic of Congo.

Recoveries are listed in the same order as for the systematic list. After the species heading, data are presented as follows:

Ring number	Date ringed	Location ringed	Observer
	Date recovered	Location recovered	Distance and direction
Additional information			

•MUTE SWAN

W05737	05 Oct 2002	Larbert	BTO
	21 Dec 2012	Forth and Clyde Canal, Falkirk	2 km

Ringed as an adult female. Found freshly dead.

•PINK-FOOTED GOOSE

GBT1408084	16 Dec 2007	L of Lintrathen (Angus)	DOE
Colour ring:	14 Feb 2009	Cavelstone Fm (Perth and Kinross)	
Grey collar	01 Apr 2009	Burnside, Newton (Aberdeenshire)	
TDS	23 Jan 2010	Arlary Fm, Milnathort (Kinross)	
	04 Mar 2012	Blairdrummond Moss	

Ringed as a juv M. Alive (colour-ring read).

•RED KITE

GN37979	10 Jun 2002	Tore, Black Isle (Highland Region)	BTO
	26 Dec 2012	Doune	150 km S

Ringed as a nestling male. Found dead.

GR35117	15 Jun 2011	Doune	BTO
	26 Jul 2011	Kildonan, Arran (Strathclyde)	107 km SW

Ringed as a nestling. Found long dead.

GC66671	10 Jun 2012	Confidential site, near Argaty, BoD	BTO
	12 Oct 2012	Water of Ruchill, Comrie (Tayside)	17 km N

Ringed as a nestling. Found dead.

•EURASIAN SPARROWHAWK

DA87858	13 Jul 2010	Argaty, BoD	BTO
	26 Jul 2012	Dunblane	6 km SE

Ringed as a nestling male. Freshly dead (hit glass).

•COMMON BUZZARD

MA20390	09 Jun 2012	L Ard Forest	BTO
	07 Dec 2012	Kirkdale Scout camp site (Dumfries/Galloway)	147 km S

Ringed as a nestling. Found long dead.

•GOLDEN EAGLE

Z28867	16 Jun 1973	Inverary, Loch Fyne (Strathclyde)	BTO
	06 Jun 2012	Near Sron Nan Searrach, Dalveich	56 km ENE

Ringed as a nestling. Found long dead.

•OSPREY

| 1351745 | 14 Jul 2003 | Achray Forest | BTO |
| | 20 Jun 2012 | Confidential site (Central Region) | 13 km ESE |

Ringed as a nestling male. Alive (ring read in field).

| 1408747 | 11 Jul 2009 | Balnagown (Highland Region) | BTO |
| | 14 Aug 2012 | Flanders Moss | 183 km S |

Ringed as a nestling female. Caught by ringer.

•BLACK-TAILED GODWIT

Yellow over	15 Jul 2011	Langhus, Fljot, SW of Siglufjordur,	GG
Yellow		N ICELAND	
Orange over	25 May 2012	Kinneil	
white flag			

Ringed as a pullus. Alive (colour rings seen).

Left leg:	11 Jul 2009	Siglufjordur, **N ICELAND**	AB
Green/Red	06 Mar 2010	Twellingea, Osterbildt, **NETHERLANDS**	
Right leg:	07 Mar 2010	Twellingea, Osterbildt, **NETHERLANDS**	
White with	20 Apr 2010	Druridge Pools (Northumberland)	
black X	06 Jun 2010	Brumastaðir, Siglufjordur, **N ICELAND**	
	31 Jan 2011	Welney, Ouse Washes (Norfolk)	
	20 Feb 2011	Giganta rice field, Porto Alto, **PORTUGAL**	
	24 Feb 2011	Giganta rice field, Porto Alto, **PORTUGAL**	
	24 Jul 2011	Seaforth Nature Reserve, Liverpool (Merseyside)	
	08 Mar 2012	Skrok, Wommels, Friesland, **NETHERLANDS**	
	30 Jul 2012	Kinneil	
	17 Aug 2012	Kinneil	

Ringed as an adult male. Alive (colour rings seen).

Left leg:	20 Feb 2007	Sarilhos Grandes, Tagus, Setúbal, **PORTUGAL**	AB
Green/Yellow	21 Feb 2007	Esinhosa W, Tagus, Setúbal, **PORTUGAL**	
Right leg:	15 Mar 2007	Samouco Almada, Tagus, Setúbal, **PORTUGAL**	
Yellow/Green	04 Oct 2007	Corroios N, Tagus, Setúbal, **PORTUGAL**	
flag	04 Nov 2007	Seixal Bay, Tagus, Setúbal, **PORTUGAL**	
	03 Dec 2007 -	seen several times at Seixal Bay and Tank,	
	20 Feb 2008	Baixa S, Barreiro S and Samouco Restinga, Tagus, Setúbal, **PORTUGAL**	
	07 Apr 2008	Skrok, Wommels, Friesland, **NETHERLANDS**	
	16 Apr 2008	Skrok, Wommels, Friesland, **NETHERLANDS**	
	08 Sep 2008	Corroios Marsh, Tagus, Setúbal, **PORTUGAL**	
	17 Oct 2008 -	seen several times at Seixal Tank and Barreiro,	
	28 Feb 2009	Tagus, Setúbal, **PORTUGAL**	
	22 Jun 2009	Gaast, Friesland, **NETHERLANDS**	
	19 Oct 2009 -	seen several times at Seixal Bay and Tank,	
	29 Dec 2010	Montijo and Barreiro, Tagus, Setúbal, **PORTUGAL**	
	15 Feb 2011	Alhos Vedros, Tagus, Setúbal, **PORTUGAL**	
	17 Feb 2011	Ze do Pinho, Tagus, Setúbal, **PORTUGAL**	
	19 Mar 2011	Caspar Roblezdijk, Harlingen, **NETHERLANDS**	
	16 Feb 2012 -	seen several times at Montijo, Tagus, Setúbal,	
	23 Feb 2012	**PORTUGAL**	
	30 Jul 2012	Kinneil	

Ringed as an adult male. Alive (colour rings seen).

Left leg: 10 Mar 2012   Wigeon Hide, Montrose Basin (Angus)   DT
Dark   11 Mar 2012   Wigeon Hide, Montrose Basin (Angus)
Blue/Dark   17 Mar 2012 - seen several times Rossie Spit, Montrose Basin
Blue +   13 Apr 2012   (Angus)
metal   10 Jul 2012   Kinneil
Right leg:
Dark Green/
Light Green
EW58511
Ringed as a juvenile. Alive (colour rings seen).

Left leg: 25 Aug 2011   Slunks, Montrose Basin (Angus)   DT
Dark   20 Sep 2011 - seen several times Rossie Spit and Wigeon Hide,
Blue/Dark   13 Apr 2012   Montrose Basin (Angus)
Blue +   10 Jul 2012   Kinneil
Metal
Right leg:
Yellow/
Orange
EL97279
Ringed as a juvenile. Alive (colour rings seen).

•COMMON BLACK-HEADED GULL
NOU80112   20 Jun 1950   Trondheim, **NORWAY**   BTO
                   18 Dec 1950   Grangemouth   1,138 km SW
Ringed as a nestling. Found freshly dead.

•SANDWICH TERN
DE44842   21 Jul 2011   Ythan Estuary, Newburgh, Aberdeen (Grampian) BTO
                   16 Sep 2012   Blackness   174 km SSW
Ringed as an adult. Alive (colour rings seen)

•GUILLEMOT
R61347   26 Jun 2012   Sanda Island, Kintyre (Strathclyde)   BTO
                   20 Sep 2012   Kirkton Fm, Ewich   139 km NNE
Ringed as a nestling. Sick.

•COMMON CUCKOO
DA87026   15 May 2012   G Gyle, L Katrine   BTO
satellite-   16 Jun 2012   Flanders Moss
tagged   18 Jun 2012   North York Moors National Park (N Yorkshire)
'Mungo'   21 Jun 2012   Polaincourt-et-Clairefontaine, **E central FRANCE**
                   23 Jun 2012 - Bourg Saint Pierre, E of Mont Blanc,
                   19 Jul 2012   southernmost tip of **SWITZERLAND**
                   20 Jul 2012   via Piedmont and Liguria to Tuscany, **ITALY**
                   22 Jul 2012   Sicily, **ITALY**
                   26 Jul 2012 - crossed Mediterranean Sea, then via Libya to N
                   2 Aug 2012   of Lake Chad, **CHAD**
Ringed as an adult male. Positions transmitted via satellite-tag. No further information was received
from Mungo. Either his transmitter failed or he died.

DA87027   15 May 2012   near Stronachlachar, L Katrine   BTO
satellite-   11-19 Jun 2012 Flanders Moss
tagged   22 Jun 2012   between Itzehoe and Elmshorn, near Hamburg,
'Chance'   **GERMANY**
                   24 Jun-31 Jul near Gottsdorf, SSW of Berlin, **GERMANY**

2012

05 Aug 2012   N of Graz, **SE AUSTRIA**
10 Aug 2012   Sahara desert, just south of Libya, **N NIGER**
13 Aug 2012   130 km W of Lake Chad, **NE NIGERIA**
14-20 Aug 2012   45 km E of Lake Chad, **CHAD**
22-27 Aug 2012   155 km SE of Lake Chad, **CHAD**
30 Aug 2012   SW of Massakory, near Lake Chad, **CHAD**
01-28 Sep 2012   NE corner of Lake Chad, **CHAD**
16 Oct 2012   edge of Mbang mountain region,
                CAMEROON
07 Nov 2012   SW of Faro Reserve, close to Nigerian border,
                CAMEROON
09 Nov 2012   W edge of Téké Plateau, **E GABON**
29 Dec 2012   25 km W of Congo border, **E GABON**

Ringed as a second-year male. Positions transmitted via satellite-tag. Chance continued transmitting into 2013.

DA87029	15 May 2012 -	S shore, L Katrine	BTO
satellite-	12 Jun 2012		
tagged	14 Jun 2012	E of Stranraer (Dumfries and Galloway)	
'Wallace'	14-18 Jun 2012	between Troon and Irvine (Ayrshire)	
	26 Jun 2012	near Patna (Ayrshire), then Canonbie (Dumfries and Galloway)	
	30 Jun 2012	near Gretna (Dumfries and Galloway)	
	04 Jul 2012	near Harwood Forest (Northumberland)	
	06-18 Jul 2012	near Troon (Ayrshire)	
	20 Jul 2012	E of Keswick (Cumbria)	
	21 Jul 2012	E of Wigan (Greater Manchester)	
	23 Jul 2012	SW of Montdidier, Picardie, **FRANCE**	
	26-28 Jul 2012	S of Tergnier, Picardie, **FRANCE**	
	30 Jul 2012	extreme SW of **GERMANY**	
	15 Aug 2012	Lauterbach, Black Forest, **GERMANY**	
	16-18 Aug 2012	believed to be near Schlüpfheim, **SWITZERLAND**	
	28 Aug 2012	S of Lake Brienz, **SWITZERLAND**	
	03 Sep 2012	S end of Lake Garda, SE of Brescia, **ITALY**	
	06 Sep 2012	W of Lake Garda, **ITALY**	
	17 Sep 2012	believed to be heading SE, E of the Adriatic	

Ringed as an adult male. Positions transmitted via satellite-tag. Wallace's transmitter is thought to have failed but there was no indication that he had died, as the temperature of the tag remained normal.

DA87031	16 May 2012 -	G Gyle, L Katrine with a brief foray	BTO
satellite-	18 June 2012	to Flanders Moss	
tagged	20 Jun 2012 -	SE of Dumfries (Dumfries and Galloway)	
'Roy'	01 Jul 2012		
	03-08 Jul 2012	North York Moors National Park (N Yorkshire)	
	10 Jul 2012	Regensburg, **SW GERMANY**	
	13-15 Jul 2012	Millstätter See, **S AUSTRIA**	
	25 Jul 2012	near Weitental and Margen, **N ITALY**	
	01 Aug 2012	N of Millstätter See, **S AUSTRIA**	
	08 Aug 2012	**CROATIA**	
	10 Aug 2012	Danilovgrad, **MONTENEGRO**	
	26 Aug 2012	Lake Scutari, **N ALBANIA**	

	29 Aug 2012	E LIBYA	
	31 Aug 2012	N Sahel, just W of Sudan border, E CHAD	
	09 Sep 2012	E of Central African Republic border, S SUDAN	
	20 Sep 2012	Basse-Kotto prefecture, CENTRAL AFRICAN REPUBLIC	
	22 Sep 2012	DEMOCRACTIC REPUBLIC OF CONGO	

Ringed as an adult male. Positions transmitted via satellite-tag. Roy's transmitter is thought to have failed but there was no indication that he had died.

DA87032	17 May 2012	S shore, L Katrine	BTO
satelille-	16 Jun 2012	Flanders Moss	
tagged	18 Jun 2012	crossed N Sea somewhere from between	
'BB'		Edinburgh and Berwick-upon-Tweed, heading	
		to Friesland Islands NETHERLANDS	
	26 Jun 2012	Sachsen-Anhalt region, E GERMANY	
	30 Jun 2012	Hranicná, CZECH REPUBLIC	
	02 Jul 2012	AUSTRIA ?	
	05 Jul 2012	Pordenone region, NE ITALY	
	26 Jul 2012	close to border with Libya, EGYPT	
	28 Jul 2012	SW SUDAN	
	30 Jul 2012	E CHAD	
	24 Aug 2012 -	close to border with Sudan, CHAD	
	06 Sep 2012		
	13 Sep 2012	Guera prefecture, S CHAD	
	15 Sep 2012	Tanjile region, S CHAD	
	16 Sep 2012	Chari-Baguirmi region, CHAD	
	18 Sep 2012-	SW of Okoyo, Téké Plateau, **central** CONGO	
	27 Dec 2012		

Ringed as a second-year male. Positions transmitted via satellite-tag. BB continued transmitting into 2013.

•BARN OWL

GF39034	24 Jun 2011	Confidential site, near Blairs	BTO
	24 May 2012	Gallamuir	4 km

Ringed as a nestling. Long dead (hit by train).

•BARN SWALLOW

Y068609	01 Oct 2011	Pett Level (Sussex)	BTO
	02 Aug 2012	Lochearnhead	691 km NNW

Ringed as a first-year. Found freshly dead (taken by cat).

P080770	12 Aug 2011	Argaty, BoD	BTO
	28 Sep 2012	Pett Level (Sussex)	666 km SW

Ringed as a nestling. Caught by ringer.

•WHITE WAGTAIL (PIED WAGTAIL)

L585188	15 Sep 2010	East Kilbride (Strathclyde)	BTO
	20 Apr 2012	Stronachlachar Pier, L Katrine	58 km NNW

Ringed as a first-year male. Alive (colour rings seen).

•COMMON BLACKBIRD

NOS7557565	15 Oct 2011	Sore Merkeskog, Utsira, NORWAY	BTO
	11 Jan 2012	Brightons, Falkirk	632 km NNW

Ringed as an adult female. Found freshly dead (hit building).

•WILLOW WARBLER

DTV708	09 May 2011	Holme bird observatory (Norfolk)	BTO
	16 Jun 2012	Braentrian, Ardeonaig, Killin	495 km NW

Ringed as an adult female. Caught by ringer.

•WESTERN JACKDAW

| EG79661 | 15 May 2011 | Argaty, BoD | BTO |
| | 06 Jul 2012 | Doune | 2 km |

Ringed as a nestling. Found freshly dead.

•EURASIAN PIED FLYCATCHER

| L611351 | 02 Jun 2011 | Inversnaid | BTO |
| | 18 Jun 2012 | Lendrick, Brig o'Turk | 22 km E |

Ringed as a nestling. Caught by ringer.

•BLUE TIT

| X511758 | 15 Jun 2012 | L Katrine | BTO |
| | 05 Oct 2012 | Tarbet, Knoc, Loch Lomond (Strathclyde) | 13 km WSW |

Ringed as a nestling. Caught by ringer.

•GREAT TIT

| TK50407 | 07 Jun 2010 | Aberfoyle Forest | BTO |
| | 11 May 2012 | Cobleland camp site, Aberfoyle | 3 km |

Ringed as a nestling. Freshly dead (predated).

•HOUSE SPARROW

| TL95182 | 08 May 2012 | Argaty, BoD | BTO |
| | 09 Sep 2012 | Deanston, Doune | 3 km |

Ringed as a nestling. Found long dead (natural causes).

•EUROPEAN GOLDFINCH

| Y025975 | 12 Nov 2011 | Norton Sheffield (South Yorkshire) | BTO |
| | 03 May 2012 | Drymen | 360 km NNW |

Ringed as a first-year female. Found freshly dead.

| L611455 | 13 Oct 2011 | Killearn | BTO |
| | 11 Nov 2012 | Anniesland, Glasgow (Strathclyde) | 17 km S |

Ringed as a first-year female. Found freshly dead.

•EURASIAN SISKIN

X088859	15 Mar 2009	The Brackens, Deangarden Wood	BTO
		(Buckinghamshire)	559 km NNW
	14 May 2010	Aberfoyle Forest	

Ringed as a first-year female. Caught by ringer.

| N839988 | 11 Sep 2010 | Aberfoyle Forest | BTO |
| | 27 Feb 2012 | West Tofts (Norfolk) | 526 km SE |

Ringed as a first-year female. Caught by ringer.

L611255	20 Jan 2011	Killearn	BTO
	05 Feb 2012	Torwood Lodge, Lockerbie (Dumfries and	120 km SSE
		Galloway)	

Ringed as an adult male. Caught by ringer.

L611198	05 Jan 2011	Killearn	BTO
	01 May 2012	Torwood Lodge, Lockerbie (Dumfries and	120 km SSE
		Galloway)	

Ringed as a first-year male. Caught by ringer.

SYSTEMATIC LIST

Codes - F, C and S refer to Falkirk, Clackmannanshire and Stirling council areas.

MUTE SWAN *Cygnus olor* (B,W)
Forth Est WeBS: 9 in Jan, 22 in Feb, 22 in Mar, 18 in Sep, 28 in Oct, 36 in Nov and 20 in Dec.
Inland WeBS: 245 in Jan, 270 in Feb, 267 in Mar, 203 in Sep, 195 in Oct, 111 in Nov and 233 in Dec.

F   Breeding: pr and 4 Y Larbert House L 15 Sep; pr and 5 Y Forth/Clyde Canal, Bonnybridge 17 Sep; pr and 5 Y Forth/Clyde Canal, Polmont 18 Sep. Max: 20 Grangemouth 13 Oct; 35 Skinflats 16 Nov; 15 Forth/Clyde Canal, Bonnybridge 12 Jan and 16 Oct.

C   Breeding: F ON Gartmorn Dam 15 Apr; pr and 6 Y Longcarse, Alloa 1 Sep; pr and 4 Y Cambus 1 Sep. Max: 30 R Devon, Alva-Tullibody 21 Jan; 42 Gartmorn 23 Feb; 20 Cambus 19 Dec.

S   Breeding: pr and 6 Y L Tay, Killin in Jun; pr and 2 Y Gart GP, Callander 23 Sep; pr and Y R Teith, Callander 23 Sep; pr and 3 Y Cultenhove Dam 27 Sep; pr and 3 Y Blairdrummond 27 Sep; pr and 3 Y L Dochart 18 Dec. Max: 60 Airthrey L, BoA 13 Jan; 32 L Watston, Doune 11 Mar; 32 Craigforth, Stirling 18 May.

WHOOPER SWAN *Cygnus cygnus* (W)
Autumn arrival: 11 Skinflats 22 Sep (AB).
Forth Est WeBS: 5 in Jan, 0 in Feb, 0 in Mar, 0 in Sep, 48 in Oct, 0 in Nov and 0 in Dec.
Inland WeBS: 44 in Jan, 23 in Feb, 29 in Mar, 0 in Sep, 36 in Oct, 26 in Nov and 42 in Dec.

F   Autumn/winter max: 27 Stenhousemuir 14 Oct; 62 Skinflats 22 Oct.

C   Six Tullibody Inch 12 Jan. 6 Cambus 15 Oct. 3 Tillicoultry 15 Dec.

S   Winter/spring max: 23 N Third Res 28 Jan; 33 Blairdrummond Carse 1 Feb; 26 L Dochart 8 Mar. Autumn/winter max: 21 L Dochart in Oct and Nov; 17 Kersebrock, N of Stenhousemuir 22 Nov.

BEAN GOOSE *Anser fabalis* (W)
There was an influx of Tundra race birds into Scotland in the winter of 2011/2012, with this also being evident in the Forth Area.

F   Regular wintering flock of Taiga race birds in the vicinity of the Slamannan Plateau. Winter/spring max: 160 Slamannan 2 Jan (CJP). Autumn/winter: 158 Slamannan 13 Nov (BG).
1 Tundra race bird S Alloa 3 Jan (CJP).

S   Tundra race birds: Blairdrummond Carse: 2 on 1st Jan, 1 on 5th, 2 on 6th, 3 on 8th; 1 on 28th Feb (CJP, RCW, DOE *et al.*). Flanders Moss: 1 on 14 Jan, 5 on 14 Feb, 1 on 6 Mar (RTW).

PINK-FOOTED GOOSE *Anser brachyrhynchus* (W)
Spring departure: 320>N G Finglas (MVB) and 100 over Killin (JPH) 22 Apr. Autumn arrival: 1 Blackness 9 Sep (CJP).
Forth Est WeBS: 1160 in Jan, 2512 in Feb, 1292 in Mar, 493 in Sep, 182 in Oct, 581 in Nov and 2070 in Dec.

F   Winter/spring max: 2040 High Bonnybridge and 1520 Slamannan 22 Jan; 2420 Skinflats 12 Feb.

C   Winter/spring max: 2000 Blackgrange 12 Feb; 3830 Alloa Inch 9 Mar. Autumn/ winter max: 6950 Skinflats 16 Oct and 6200 Skinflats 11 Nov (both roost counts).

S   Winter/spring max: 2000 Blairdrummond Carse 28 Jan; 3300 Throsk 9 Feb; 3000 Manor Powis, Stirling 12 Feb; 2290 Aberfoyle 23 Mar; 2030 Kinbuck 31 Mar. Autumn/winter max: 600 Blairdrummond Carse 30 Nov.

GREATER WHITE-FRONTED GOOSE *Anser albifrons*
There was an influx of European (*albifrons*) race birds into Scotland in the winter of 2011/2012, with this also being evident in Upper Forth. Greenland (*flavirostris*) race birds were present in normal low numbers in 2012.

F   European race birds: 15 S Alloa 2 and 4 Jan, 3 there on 6 Jan (RJD, CJP); 3 Airth 11 Jan (RTW); 1 Slamannan 12 Jan (KDS); 1 Skinflats 15 Jan (CJP); 3 High Bonnybridge 22 Jan (NB). 13 European and 1 Greenland race birds Airth 24 Feb (JSN). 1 Greenland race bird Airth 2 and 5 Oct (ACC).

C   European race birds at Blackgrange: 1 on 22 Jan, 3 on 29 Jan, 1 on 12 Feb, 2 on 18 Feb (RJD, ACC, GC, DMB). Also 3 European race birds Alva 16 Feb (RE) and 2 Alloa Inch 9 Mar (DMB) 1 Greenland race bird Blackgrange on 18 Dec (DMB).

S   European race birds: up to 7 Blairdrummond Carse on 6 Jan (DOE); up to 25 Lecropt Carse 9 Jan (CJP); up to 24 Blairdrummond Moss 19 Feb (RTW); 3 Manor Powis 12 Feb (NB); 2 Flanders Moss 6 Mar (RTW); 10 Aberfoyle 23 Mar (NB); 2 Ashfield 24 Mar (CJP).
Greenland race birds: 2 Lecropt Carse 7 Jan (CJP); 4 Blairdrummond Carse 28 Jan to 1 Feb (DOE).

GREYLAG GOOSE *Anser anser* (b, W)
Spring departure and autumn arrival are blurred by the presence of resident feral birds.
Forth Est WeBS: 6 in Jan, 6 in Feb, 0 in Mar, 291 in Sep, 28 in Oct, 222 in Nov and 0 in Dec.

F   Winter/spring max: 155 Black L, Limerigg and 357 High Bonnybridge 22 Jan. Summer max (feral): 53 Skinflats 19 Jul. Autumn/winter max: 500 Blackness 5 Oct.

C   Winter/spring max: 500 Alva 9 Mar. 926 Alloa Inch 16 Mar. Autumn/winter max: 700 Cambus 22 Sep.

S   Winter/spring: 523   Blairdrummond   24   Feb.   Autumn/winter: 100 Blairdrummond Carse and 208 L Watston, Doune 10 Nov.

CANADA GOOSE *Branta canadensis* (b W)
Forth Est WeBS: 43 in Jan, 0 in Feb, 0 in Mar, 11 in Sep, 0 in Oct, 1 in Nov and 9 in Dec.
Inland WeBS: 412 in Jan, 304 in Feb, 243 in Mar, 429 in Sep, 345 in Oct, 286 in Nov and 64 in Dec.

F   Max: 35 Black L, Limerigg and 67 St Helen's L, Bonnybridge 22 Jan; 138 Skinflats 26 Sep.

C   Max: 3 Gartmorn Dam 22 Mar; 107 Tullibody Inch 15 Aug.

S   Breeding: 21 ads and 19 Y Gart GPs, Callander 24 June. Max: 107 Blairdrummond GPs 29 Jan, 170 G Finglas 15 Jul, 170 L Venachar 9 Oct and 110 Killin Marshes 25 Nov.

BARNACLE GOOSE *Branta leucopsis* (w)
In our area it is difficult to distinguish between wild migrants and feral birds resident in Britain.

F   One Blackness 9 Sep and 5 Oct. Airth: 9 on 2 Oct, 2 there 5 and 10 Oct and 1 there 25 Oct. 11 Kinneil 8 October. 5 Skinflats 3 Nov with 31 there 11 Nov.

C   Two Haugh of Blackgrange 29 Jan and Alva 14 Feb.

S   Max Jan: 24 Blairdrummond Carse 5 and 8 Jan, 11 Thornhill 7 Jan and 2 Fallin 14 Jan. 8 Aberfoyle 29 Jan. 2 Ashfield 24 Mar. 25 Thornhill 8 Oct. 6 Carse of Lecropt 26 and 27 Nov. 2 Blairdrummond Carse 30 Nov and Carse of Lecropt 28 Dec.

*BRENT GOOSE *Branta bernicla*
F   Ad and juv of pale-bellied race Blackness 1 and 29 Sep (ACC, CJP, DOE).

COMMON SHELDUCK *Tadorna tadorna* (b, W)
    Forth Est WeBS: 673 in Jan, 814 in Feb, 995 in Mar, 2489 in Sep, 1308 in Oct, 754 in Nov and 383 in Dec.
    Inland WeBS: 0 in Jan, 2 in Feb, 6 in Mar, 0 in Sep, 0 in Oct, 0 in Nov and 0 in Dec.
F   Moult flock of 4217 ads and 152 juvs Grangemouth 2 Aug (DMB).
C   Seventy-three Longcarse, Alloa 24 May including pr and 10 Y.

EURASIAN WIGEON *Anas penelope* (b, W)
    Forth Est WeBS: 725 in Jan, 593 in Feb, 188 in Mar, 28 in Sep, 482 in Oct, 467 in Nov and 487 in Dec.
    Inland WeBS: 448 in Jan, 540 in Feb, 180 in Mar, 46 in Sep, 167 in Oct, 143 in Nov and 182 in Dec.
F   Winter/spring max: 133 Skinflats 8 Jan; 444 Kincardine Br 9 Jan. Autumn/winter max: 288 Kincardine Br 14 Oct, 276 Bo'ness 16 Nov and 250 Blackness 17 Nov.
C   Winter/spring max: 1 Blackdevon Wetlands 28 Apr.
S   Winter/spring max: 71 Gart GPs, Callander 9 Jan; 134 L Venachar 17 Jan; 99 L Watston, Doune 13 Feb. Autumn/winter max: 93 L Dochart 22 Dec; 60 Gart GPs, Callander 28 Dec.

GADWALL *Anas strepera* (s, w)
F   Three Skinflats 10 Sep. 2 Kinneil 16 Sep.
C   Two Gartmorn Dam 27 Mar. Blackdevon Wetlands: 4 on 31 Mar; 2 in Apr; max 5 on 14 May. Cambus: max 4 on 1 May. 1 Alva 16 Sep. Gartmorn Dam: max 7 on 28 Dec.
S   Two Cowie 27 Apr.

EURASIAN TEAL *Anas crecca* (b, W)
    Forth Est WeBS: 1983 in Jan, 2269 in Feb, 1153 in Mar, 422 in Sep, 1293 in Oct, 1590 in Nov and 1395 in Dec.
    Inland WeBS: 1064 in Jan, 1351 in Feb, 992 in Mar, 326 in Sep, 756 in Oct, 659 in Nov and 793 in Dec.
F   Winter/spring max: 1083 Kinneil and 427 Skinflats 12 Feb. Autumn/winter max: 540 Skinflats, 474 Kinneil and 251 Kincardine Br 16 Nov.
C   Winter/spring max: 409 Alloa Inches and 106 Cambus 12 Feb. Autumn/winter max: 108 Cambus 22 Aug; 374 Alloa Inches 14 Oct; 258 Kennetpans 14 Oct; 100 Tillicoultry 15 Dec.
S   Winter/spring max: 207 R Forth, Stirling 14 Jan and 12 Feb. Autumn/winter max: 168 L Watston 10 Nov; 221 R Forth, Stirling 16 Dec; 112 Gart GPs, Callander 28 Dec.

*GREEN-WINGED TEAL *Anas carolinensis*
F   M Kinneil from 28 Oct 2011 to 31 Dec (CJP, GO, DT *et al.*). This bird has been recorded annually since December 2006 and may even be the same bird as recorded on the R Forth near Stirling in 2004. This is the 9th record of this species, thought to involve 2-3 individuals.

MALLARD *Anas platyrhynchos* (B,W)
    Forth Est WeBS: 297 in Jan, 314 in Feb, 174 in Mar, 215 in Sep, 262 in Oct, 342 in Nov and 474 in Dec.
    Inland WeBS: 2250 in Jan, 2594 in Feb, 1296 in Mar, 1663 in Sep, 1641 in Oct, 1317 in Nov and 1499 in Dec.
F   Max: 50 Bo'ness 28 Jan; 141 Kincardine Br 14 Oct; 211 Skinflats 15 Dec; 50 Blackness 29 Dec.
C   Max: 46 Cambus 22 Jan.
S   Max: 121 Callander 13 Feb; 135 Airthrey L, BoA 14 Feb; 100 Blairdrummond GPs 16 Aug; 173 L Watston, Doune 16 Sep.

NORTHERN PINTAIL *Anas acuta* (W)
Forth Est WeBS: 97 in Jan, 170 in Feb, 24 in Mar, 0 in Sep, 44 in Oct, 31 in Nov and 51 in Dec.
F   Max: 87 Skinflats 8 Jan; 122 Kinneil - Bo'ness 12 Feb.
C   Two Kennetpans 11 Mar. 1 Tullibody Inch 3 Sep.
S   M Blairdrummond GPs 29 Jan. 1 Frew 26 Feb. M L Watston 11 Mar and 1 there 16 Sep.
GARGANEY *Anas querquedula*
F   M Kinneil 28 Apr (CJP).
NORTHERN SHOVELER *Anas clypeata* (p)
F   Pr S Alloa 29 Feb. 2 Skinflats 17 Mar. 1 Kinneil 21 Apr. 1 Skinflats 4 Jun.
C   One Cambus 31 Mar. 2 Tullibody Inch 15 Aug.
S   Two Cambushinnie, Kinbuck 24 Mar. 1 Killin, L Tay 24 Mar.
COMMON POCHARD *Aythya ferina* (W)
Inland WeBS: 9 in Jan, 13 in Feb, 9 in Mar, 3 in Sep, 18 in Oct, 9 in Nov and 2 in Dec.
F   Three Skinflats 24 May. 2 Kinneil 11 Sep. 5 Blackness 1 Oct. 8 Kinneil 7-10 Oct. 13 Bo'ness and 1 Kinneil 12 Oct. 2 Skinflats 17 Nov.
C   Gartmorn Dam: 1 on 26 Feb with M there 1 Apr and 6 on 28 Oct.
S   One Gart GPs, Callander 6 Jan. 6 CVR 17 Jan. 4 Killin 7 Feb to 4 Mar. 7 Lake of Menteith 26 Feb. 2 L Coulter Res 13 Mar. 2 Lake of Menteith 26 Sep. 2 L Watston, Doune 21 Oct. 1 Killin, L Tay 18 and 24 Nov with 3 there 2 Dec.
TUFTED DUCK *Aythya fuligula* (B, W)
Inland WeBS: 228 in Jan, 390 in Feb, 428 in Mar, 274 in Sep, 570 in Oct, 354 in Nov and 242 in Dec.
F   Twelve Callendar Park, Falkirk 13 Jan. 16 Kinneil 18 Oct. 13 Grangemouth 18 Oct. 14 Larbert 24 Oct. 46 Skinflats 3 Nov.
C   Winter/spring max: 105 Gartmorn Dam 22 Mar. Autumn/winter max: 295 Gartmorn Dam 28 Oct.
S   Winter/spring max: 83 Blairdrummond 27 Mar. Breeding: 140 ads and 2 brs of 7 and 9 Y Gart GPs, Callander 26 Jul. Autumn/winter max: 34 Gart GPs, Callander 23 Sep; 65 Blairdrummond 25 Oct; 10 Killin, L Tay 2 Dec.
GREATER SCAUP *Aythya marina* (s, w)
Forth Est WeBS: 4 in Jan, 7 in Feb, 0 in Mar, 3 in Sep, 7 in Oct, 7 in Nov and 8 in Dec.
F   Kinneil max: 2 in Jan, 6 in Feb, 16 in Mar, 5 in Apr, 1 in Jun, 2 in Jul and Aug, 11 in Sep, 19 in Oct, 8 in Nov, 15 in Dec. Skinflats max: 4 in Jan, 3 in Feb, 2 in Mar, 1 in May, 1 in Aug and Sep, 5 in Oct, 5 in Nov. 35 Blackness 1 Oct.
COMMON EIDER *Somateria mollissima* (w, s)
Forth Est WeBS: 9 in Jan, 40 in Feb, 25 in Mar, 21 in Sep, 7 in Oct, 11 in Nov and 14 in Dec.
F   Blackness max: 19 in Feb, 25 in Mar, 10 in Jun, 20 in Jul, 25 in Sep, 20 in Oct, 22 in Nov, 2 in Dec. Bo'ness max: 6 in Aug, 10 in Sep, 6 in Nov. Kinneil max: 6 in Feb, 5 in Mar, 6 in Apr, 11 in Jul, 11 in Sep, 22 in Oct, 8 in Nov, 17 in Dec. Skinflats max: 33 in Feb, 19 in Mar, 2 in Apr, 6 in May with 4 Y there 30 May.
*LONG-TAILED DUCK *Clangula hyemalis*
F   One Blackness 17 Nov (DOE). 1 Bo'ness 17 to 23 Nov, 4 there 9 Dec and 3 on 15 Dec (DMB, CJP, GG, JRC). 1 Kinneil 23 Nov (DMB).
C   One R Devon, Cambus 18 and 19 Dec (AMu, KW).
*BLACK SCOTER (COMMON SCOTER) *Melanitta nigra*
F   F Kinneil 8 Feb (DT). 21 Blackness 8 Jul (CJP). Bo'ness: 1 on 27 Aug, 2 there 30 Aug, 1 on 12 Sep, 2 on 8-15 Oct, 17 on 27 Oct, 26 on 28-31 Oct; Nov max: 96 on

16th; Dec max: 32 on 9th (GG, DMB, DOE, JRC *et al.*). Blackness: 4 on 9 and 26 Sep (DOE). Kinneil: singles 25 Sep and 7 Oct (DOE, DMB).

S   M L Coulter 29 Nov (NB).

COMMON GOLDENEYE *Bucephala clangula* (W)

Forth Est WeBS: 67 in Jan, 68 in Feb, 44 in Mar, 0 in Sep, 10 in Oct, 13 in Nov and 44 in Dec.

Inland WeBS: 332 in Jan, 426 in Feb, 290 in Mar, 2 in Sep, 37 in Oct, 113 in Nov and 253 in Dec.

F   Max: 18 Skinflats 8 Jan, 44 Kincardine Br 9 Jan and 33 S Alloa 30 Nov.

C   Max: 40 Cambus 29 Feb and 29 Gartmorn Dam 2 Dec.

S   Max: 93 Lake of Menteith 26 Feb and 55 L Tay, Killin 4 Mar.

*SMEW *Mergellus albellus*

C   Redhead Gartmorn Dam 14 Feb (GG, CJP).

S   Redhead R Forth, E Frew 27 Dec (RTW).

RED-BREASTED MERGANSER *Mergus serrator* (B, W)

Forth Est WeBS: 74 in Jan, 78 in Feb, 64 in Mar, 75 in Sep, 45 in Oct, 52 in Nov and 70 in Dec.

Inland WeBS: 2 in Jan, 6 in Feb, 8 in Mar, 7 in Sep, 2 in Oct, 0 in Nov and 3 in Dec.

F   Max: 26 Kincardine Br 9 Jan, 16 Skinflats 11 Mar, 61 Kinneil 16 Sep, 25 Bo'ness 3 Nov and 18 Blackness 17 Nov.

S   Max: 5 Craigforth, Stirling 14 Feb; 2 L Tay, Killin Apr to Jun.

COMMON MERGANSER (GOOSANDER) *Mergus merganser* (B, W)

Forth Est WeBS: 4 in Jan; 1 in Feb, 0 in Mar, 16 in Sep, 8 in Oct, 26 in Nov and 10 in Dec.

Inland WeBS: 144 in Jan, 145 in Feb, 121 in Mar, 47 in Sep, 77 in Oct, 62 in Nov and 88 in Dec.

F   Max: 12 Stenhousemuir 22 Jun; 15 Skinflats 2 Aug; 13 Kinneil 17 Nov; 20 Forth/Clyde canal, Bonnybridge 16 Dec.

C   Max: 29 Cambus Pools 10 Mar.

S   Max: 32 Blairdrummond GPs 24 Feb; 21 R Forth, Stirling 11 Mar.

WILLOW PTARMIGAN (RED GROUSE) *Lagopus lagopus* (B, W)

S   Seven Dumyat 5 Jan with 6 there 2 Apr (CJP, DOE). 2 Sheriffmuir 17 Mar (DOE). 1 Cairnoch, CVR 21 Apr (ACC). Present Ben Our 15 May and Bein Dubhchraig 17 May (JJB). 1 L Arklet Res 18 May (NW). 5 L Maragan 4 Jun (JPH).

ROCK PTARMIGAN *Lagopus muta* (B, W)

S   One Beinn a'Chieibh 27 Mar (CI). 2 Meall ant-Seallaidh 28 Apr (ABa). 1 Bein Dubhchraig (JJB). 2 Sgiath Chuil 11 Nov (GG).

BLACK GROUSE *Tetrao tetrix* (B, W)

C   Afer many years of absence a lek was active again at a former site in Glen Devon, which is now managed by the Woodland Trust, following grazing restriction and native woodland establishment.

S   Records from: Carron Valley, Callander, G Finglas, Tyndrum, Strathfillan (JPH, SHo, DMB, DOE, JB).

RED-LEGGED PARTRIDGE *Alectoris rufa*

S   One Kinbuck 18 Jan (ARe). 1 Dumyat 2 Apr (DOE). 1 Biggins, Dunblane 6 May (CJP). 1 Kelt, Dunblane 8 Jul (DOE).

GREY PARTRIDGE *Perdix perdix* (B, W)

F   Three Airth in Jan (DMB, CJP). Skinflats max: 2 in Feb - Jun (DMB, CJP *et al.*). 4 Kinneil 26 Jul (ADI).

C   One Alva 11 Mar (SMcG). 2 Alloa Rhind 17 Mar (DMB). 1 Tullibody Inch 18 Mar (DMB). 2 Alva 20 May (PMA).

*COMMON QUAIL *Coturnix coturnix*
S   Singles at Thornhill on 27 Jun and 1 Jul (ARo, GG, CJP).
COMMON PHEASANT *Phasianus colchicus* (B, W)
     Very large numbers released on shooting estates, otherwise widespread but in smaller numbers.
S   Max: 45 Lanrick, Doune 21 Dec.
RED-THROATED LOON *Gavia stellata* (b, w)
F   One Blackness 25 Feb (MH). 14 over Kinneil (CJP), 3 over Bo'ness (GG) and 1 over Blackness (DOE) 9 Sep. 1 Bo'ness 14 Sep (DOE). 1 Kinneil 28 Sep (DT). 2 Bo'ness and 1 Kinneil 14 Oct (JRC). 1 Bo'ness 3 Nov (DOE). 2 Blackness and 1 Bo'ness 21 Nov (RTW). 3 Kinneil 23 Nov (DT). 1 Bo'ness 29 Nov (DMB). 1 Kinneil 4 Dec (DT).
S   One at an undisclosed location in the Trossachs 15 Jul (DOE).
*ARCTIC LOON (BLACK-THROATED DIVER) *Gavia arctica*
S   One head of L Tay, Killin 11 Feb (JPH). 1 at an undisclosed location in the Trossachs 18 Mar (NB). Pr at another undisclosed location in the Trossachs in April (RTW, CJP). 1 head of L Tay, Killin 19 May (JPH).
*COMMON LOON (GREAT NORTHERN DIVER) *Gavia immer*
S   1 Blairdrummond GPs 23 Dec (DOE).
LITTLE GREBE *Tachybaptus ruficollis* (B, w)
     Inland WeBS: 36 in Jan, 40 in Feb, 57 Mar, 100 in Sep, 73 in Oct, 35 in Nov and 31 in Dec.
F   Breeding: pr and 2 Y Larbert pond 25 Jul; 2 Y Skinflats 6 Aug. Max: 4 Forth/ Clyde canal, Bonnybridge 15 Jan; 4 ads Larbert Pond Mar to May.
C   Max: 9 Blackdevon Wetlands 12 Apr; 6 R Devon, Alva 18 Nov; 4 R Devon, Tillicoultry 19 Dec.
S   Breeding: pr Cocksburn Res, BoA 12 Mar; pr Lochan Reoidhte, Achray Forest 24 Mar. Max: 9 L Voil 5 Mar; 42 Gart GPs, Callander 23 Sep; 9 L Lubnaig 25 Oct.
GREAT CRESTED GREBE *Podiceps cristatus* (b, W)
     Forth Est WeBS: 4 in Jan, 6 in Feb, 3 in Mar, 8 in Sep, 16 in Oct, 31 in Nov and 14 in Dec.
     Inland WeBS: 22 in Jan, 28 in Feb, 43 in Mar, 20 in Sep, 7 in Oct, 3 in Nov and 1 in Dec.
F   Max: 27 Kinneil 11 Sep; 25 Blackness 7 Oct and 3 Nov.
C   Max: 7 Gartmorn Dam 20 Oct.
S   Breeding: 2 prs and 3 Y Gart GPs, Callander 23 Sep; pr and 2 Y Lake of Menteith 26 Sep. Max: 25 Lake of Menteith 26 Feb.
*RED-NECKED GREBE *Podiceps grisegena*
F   One off Bo'ness 28 Oct (GG).
*SLAVONIAN GREBE *Podiceps auritus*
F   1 Kinneil 5 Oct (DT).
*NORTHERN FULMAR *Fulmaris glacialis*
F   One Bo'ness 12 Aug (CJP). 3 Kinneil 28 Aug (DT). Bo'ness: singles 6 and 10 Sep (GG). 1 Kinneil 11 Sep (DMB). 1 Blackness 14 Sep (DOE). 3 Bo'ness (DMB) and 2 Blackness (CJP) 25 Sep. 2 Skinflats 29 Sep (DMB).
*MANX SHEARWATER *Puffinus puffinus*
F   One Bo'ness 24 Sep (GG). 2+ Kinneil 25 Sep (DT). 1 Kinneil 12 Oct (DT).
NORTHERN GANNET *Morus bassanus* (p)
     The large majority of birds recorded were imms.
F   Blackness max: 150 on 14 Sep (DOE). Bo'ness max: 1 on 12 Aug; 235 on 10 Sep; 1 on 14 Oct (GG, CJP). Kinneil max: 520 on 11 Sep; 6 on 12 Oct (DMB, DT). Skinflats max: 178 on 16 Sep (MVB).

S   40 > W Dunblane (CJP, CJS) and 3 > Stirling 16 Sep (PB). 6 > W BoA 18 Sep (DT). 2 Killin, L Tay 19 Sep (JPH). 2 > SW Stirling 19 Sep (DT). 1 > N Tyndrum 21 Sep (JPH). 3 L Ard Forest 22 Sep (AM). 1 Doune 5 Oct (RCW).

GREAT CORMORANT *Phalacrocorax carbo* (S, W)

     Forth Est WeBS: 49 in Jan, 29 in Feb, 54 in Mar, 137 in Sep, 86 in Oct, 84 in Nov and 71 in Dec.

     Inland WeBS: 68 in Jan, 52 in Feb, 57 in Mar, 75 in Sep, 46 in Oct, 38 in Nov and 59 in Dec.

F   Max: 61 roosting off Bo'ness 12 Aug; 58 Skinflats 16 Sep.

C   Max: Alloa Inch area: 42 on 11 Mar and 53 on 16 Sep.

S   Max: 17 Lake of Menteith 26 Sep; 26 Killin, L Tay 18 Nov; 10 Craigforth, Stirling 16 Dec.

     One Europaean race *sinensis* bird at Airthrey L, BoA 25 Jan (ACC); this is the first record of this race for the recording area, accepted by SBRC.

*SHAG *Phalacrocorax aristotelis*

F   One Blackness 5 Aug (CJP). 1 Kinneil 9 Sep (DOE). 1 Bo'ness 10 Sep (GG). 1 Blackness 26 Sep (DOE).

*LITTLE EGRET *Egretta garzetta*

F   One Skinflats 15-16 Dec and 29 Dec; also at Kincardine Br 29 Dec (MVB, AB, AC). This is the 13th record for the recording area.

GREY HERON *Ardea cinerea* (B,W)

     Forth Est WeBS: 36 in Jan, 7 in Feb, 8 in Mar, 48 in Sep, 50 in Oct, 37 in Nov and 33 in Dec.

     Inland WeBS: 85 in Jan, 69 in Feb, 63 in Mar, 76 in Sep, 70 in Oct, 47 in Nov and 53 in Dec.

F   Breeding: 17 AONs Dunmore, 45 discarded eggs (AB). Max: 8 Kinneil 29 Aug; 30 Skinflats 16 Sep.

C   Max: 5 Cambus 22 Jan; 16 Gartmorn Dam 23 Feb.

S   Breeding: 31 AONs Nyadd, Blairdrummond 2 May, 66 discarded eggs (CC). Max: 12 Craigforth, Stirling 14 Oct.

SPOONBILL *Platalea leucorodia*

F   Ad and imm Kinneil 29 Jul to 8 Aug, with imm until 29 Aug (CJP, RS, DT *et al.*).

RED KITE *Milvus milvus* (b ,W)

S   Breeding: of 27 prs 26 laid eggs, 21 prs successfully fledging 31 Y (DA, MMcD, DOE). Argaty, BoD: max number recorded was 53 on 13 Dec (per MMcD). Away from BoD regular in areas of Stirling, Dunblane, Blairdrummond, and Callander. Also recorded at: CVR area, Kippen, Lake of Menteith, G Finglas, Lochearnhead, G Beich and Ben Our.

*WHITE-TAILED EAGLE *Haliaeetus albicilla*

     All likely to refer to birds from the Fife reintroduction scheme.

S   One Muir Dam, Thornhill 6 Jan (DOE). 1 imm Sheriffmuir 15 Feb (DSK), 1 L Chon 24 Feb and 1 Argaty, BoD 15 Mar (DOE).

MARSH HARRIER *Circus aeruginosus*

F   Imm/F Skinflats 26-27 May (GO, CJP). F Kinneil 26 Aug (AB).

C   Imm/F Tullibody Inch 12 May (NB).

NORTHERN HARRIER (HEN HARRIER) *Circus cyaneus* (b, w)

C   F Alva 9 Mar (RE).

S   Ringtail Lake of Menteith 15 Jan (KF). M Flanders Moss 2 May (ABa). 1 Gargunnock 6 Nov (RTW). 1 Milton, Kilmahog 5 Dec (LA).

*NORTHERN GOSHAWK *Accipiter gentilis*

F   One over Parkhead, Slamannan 7 Feb (GG, RM).

S   Breeding: pairs in the BoD, Aberfoyle and CVR areas (CSRSG). Also: imm F

Dunblane 2 Jan (MVB), imm Lecropt Carse 16 Jan (DT), M Dunblane 11 Mar (CJP) and imm Lake of Menteith 10 Aug (DT).

EURASIAN SPARROWHAWK   *Accipiter nisus*   (B, W)
Recorded in the majority of the recording area. Contributors are encouraged to submit breeding records.

COMMON BUZZARD   *Buteo buteo*   (B,W)
Inland WeBS counts: 57 in Jan, 41 in Feb, 68 in Mar, 46 in Sep, 36 in Oct, 28 in Nov and 29 in Dec.
Breeding: 242 occupied sites; of 102 prs with eggs, 81 prs successfully fledged 102+ Y (DA, MMCD, DOE).

GOLDEN EAGLE   *Aquila chrysaetos*   (b, w)
S   Two Gleann a'Chlachain 2 Feb (JPH). 1 G Ogle 12 Mar (RTW). 1 Beinn Tulaichain 18 Mar (CJS). 1 G Balquhidder 30 Apr (FAM). 1 Stob a Choin 1 Jul (GG). 1 Crianlarich 4 Sep (SS). 1 Ben Ledi 27 Nov (RE). 1 L Earn 29 Dec (ISE).

OSPREY   *Pandion haliaetus*   (B)
First record of the year: singles L Venachar 25 Mar and Doune and Lake of Menteith 27 Mar, 2 L Rusky, 1 Dunblane and 1 Flanders Moss 31 Mar.
Breeding: 15 occupied territories; of 14 prs with eggs, 10 prs successfully fledged 18 Y (DA, MMcD, DOE).
F   One Falkirk 13 Apr. 1 Blackness 8 May. 1 Skinflats 2 Aug.
C   One Alva 28 Apr.
S   Records from BoA, Blairdrummond, Callander, CVR, G Finglas, L Achray, L Katrine and Killin.

COMMON KESTREL   *Falco tinnunculus*   (B,W)
Recorded in most of the recording area. Contributors are encouraged to submit breeding records.

MERLIN   *Falco columbarius*   (b?, w)
F   One Kinneil 29 Feb (CJP). 1 Larbert 10 Mar (CJP). Singles Skinflats 21 Mar (MH) and 16 Oct (DMB). Singles Kinneil 1 Oct (JM), 23 Nov (DMB) and 29 Dec (DOE). 1 Slamannan 3 Dec (RD).
S   One Blairdrummond Carse 5 Feb (DOE). 1 Carse of Lecropt 12 Feb (MVB). 1 Meall Leathan Dhail 24 Mar (GG). 1 Edra, L Katrine 2 Apr (DOE). 1 L Venachar 5 May (DOE). 1 Tyndrum 25 Jun (DOE). 1 Argaty, BoD 1 Dec (DOE).

HOBBY   *Falco subbuteo*
S   One Flanders Moss 14 Jul (DOE, DA).

PEREGRINE FALCON   *Falco peregrinus*   (B, W)
F   Singles throughout year at Kinneil. 2 Blackness 25 Sep hunting Guillemot.
C   Singles Tillicoultry 16 Apr and Strude, Alva 4 Sep.
S   Singles Argaty, BoD 26 Feb, Callander 3 Mar, Kippen 8 Apr, Bucklyvie 16 Jun, Lochearnhead 19 Jul, Strathfillan 26 Oct, Killin 25 Nov and Dunblane 18 Dec.

WATER RAIL   *Rallus aquaticus*   (b, w)
F   Skinflats: singles recorded throughout year (CJP, AB *et al.*). 1 Kinneil pond 17 Mar (CJP). 1 Kinneil 20 Apr (DT).
C   Tullibody Inch: recorded Jan-May, max 2 (DMB, NB). Cambus: singles on 31 Mar and 4 Oct (DOE, DMB). Blackdevon Wetlands: 1 on 15 Apr with 2 there 12 Aug (CJP). 1 R Devon, Alva 18 Nov (CVW).

COMMON MOORHEN   *Gallinula chloropus*   (B,W)
Inland WeBS: 58 in Jan, 68 in Feb, 74 in Mar, 83 in Sep, 88 in Oct, 52 in Nov and 50 in Dec.
F   Max: 11 Forth-Clyde Canal, Bonnybridge 18 Nov; 12 Skinflats 25 Nov; 12 Callendar Park, Falkirk 21 Dec.
C   Max: 6 Cambus 1 Sep.

S   Max: 15 Airthrey L, BoA 14 Feb.
COMMON COOT *Fulica atra* (B, W)
        Inland WeBS: 156 in Jan, 226 in Feb, 187 in Mar, 93 in Sep, 69 in Oct, 75 in Nov
        and 75 in Dec.
F   Max: 29 Callendar Park, Falkirk 14 Sep; 12 Larbert pond 29 Nov.
C   Max: 53 Gartmorn Dam 23 Feb.
S   Max: 56 Airthrey L, BoA 13 Jan; 29 L Watston, Doune 22 Jan and 29 Lake of
        Menteith 26 Feb. 2 L Tay, Killin 11-18 Feb, with singles there 4 Mar and 16 Dec.
EURASIAN OYSTERCATCHER *Haematopus ostralegus* (B, W)
        Forth Est WeBS: 407 in Jan, 598 in Feb, 355 in Mar, 392 in Sep, 218 in Oct, 374 in
        Nov and 260 in Dec.
        Inland WeBS: 16 in Jan, 271 in Feb, 276 in Mar, 0 in Sep, 2 in Oct, 0 in Nov and
        0 in Dec.
F   Bo'ness: 4 on 28 Jan with 110 there 28 Dec. Blackness: 25 on 31 Mar with 40 there
        9 Sep, 50 on 7 Oct, 35 on 17 Nov and 45 on 29 Dec. Kinneil: 50 on 28 Jan with
        200 on 12 Feb, 76 on 10 Mar, 223 on 14 Aug, 40 on 9 Sep, 60 on 7 Oct, 52 on 28
        Nov, 200+ on 17 Dec with Grangepans to Grangemouth counts of 314 on 8 Jan,
        520 on 12 Feb and 216 on 16 Sep. Skinflats: 4 on 19 Feb with 45 on 6 May, 35 on
        9 Jun, 163 on 16 Sep, 137 on 14 Oct.
C   Inland return: 2 Blackdevon Wetlands 12 Jan; 2 R Devon, Alva 19 Feb. Max: 37
        Longcarse, Alloa 16 May.
S   Inland return: 5 Carnforth, Stirling 16 Jan; 5 Carse of Lecropt, BoA 16 Jan with
        57 there 14 Feb; 4 Doune 19 Jan with 110 there 26 Feb and 35 on 15 Apr; 6
        Blairdrummond GPs 26 Jan with 73 there 24 Feb, 148 on 10 Mar and 45 on 31
        Mar; 1 Cocksburn Res, BoA 11 Feb; 2 L Watston 13 Feb; 29 Ashfield 18 Feb; 2
        head of L Tay, Killin 18 Feb with 25 there 22 and 29 Mar; 5 Lake of Menteith 26
        Feb; 2 Argaty, BoD 27 Feb; 50 Allan Water, Kinbuck 31 Mar.
*LITTLE RINGED PLOVER *Charadrius dubius*
S   Singles Killin 30 Apr and 1 May with 1-2 birds on several dates in Jun, including
        a bird on a nest 9 to 14 Jun but not 17 Jun (JPH, DOE, CJP). This is the 20th record
        for the area since modern recording began in 1974.
COMMON RINGED PLOVER *Charadrius hiaticula* (b, W)
        Forth Est WeBS: 0 in Jan, 0 in Feb, 5 in Mar, 8 in Sep, 0 in Oct, 0 in Nov and 0 in
        Dec.
F   Blackness: 10 on 12 Jun with 18 there 1 Sep down to 2 by 14 Sep. Kinneil was
        back to more commonly recorded numbers than the highs of last year: 5 on 3
        Mar with 8 there 12 Mar, then 2-3 AoTs 27 Jun (DMB), 12 on 29 Jul, 9 on 30 Jul
        and 1 Aug, 5 on 6 Aug, 6 on 15 Aug and 10 on 30 Aug. Skinflats: 1 on 5 Apr, 88
        on 30 May were migrants of the *tundrae* race (DMB) with 15 there 29 Aug and 1
        on 14 Sep. Elsewhere: 6 Shieldhill, Falkirk on roadside pools 30 Aug.
C   Thirty Kennetpans 14 May, 26 there on 23 May and 27 on 30 May were mostly
        of the *tundrae* race.
S   One Gart GPs, Callander 25 Mar with 2 there 14 Apr and 6 May and singles 24
        Jun and 25 Jul. 2 prs on territory at undisclosed site, Stirling 28 Mar with 1 pr
        there with chicks and 2nd pr apparently incubating 15 Jun (DT). Singles Killin 22
        Apr and 2 May with 3 there 1 Jun. Two Earlsburn Res 22 May. 3 Lecropt Carse
        11 Jul with 4 there 24 Jul.
EUROPEAN GOLDEN PLOVER *Pluvialis apricaria* (B, W)
        Forth Est WeBS: 0 in Jan, 2 in Feb, 0 in Mar, 19 in Sep, 250 in Oct, 153 in Nov and
        65 in Dec.
F   Blackness: 33 on 26 Aug with 38 there 1 Sep, 4 on 9 Sep, 15 on shore 1 Oct, 10
        on 7 Oct, 100 on 20 Oct and 5 on 3 Nov. Kinneil: 1 on 12 Feb, 2 on 15 Aug, 7 on

29 Aug, 65 on 30 Sep, 98 on 1 Oct, 238 on 14 Oct, 195 on 29 Oct, 140 on 18 Nov and 300+ on 23 Nov. Skinflats: 2 on 22 Aug, 17 on 16 Sep, 70 on 29 Sep, 12 on 14 Oct, 180 on 25 Oct and 50 on 29 Dec. Elsewhere: 20 Kersebrock, N of Stenhousemuir 2 Oct, 1 on roadside pool Shieldhill, Falkirk 30 Aug and 3 Carronshore, Stenhousemuir 4 Nov.

S　　One Lecropt Carse, BoA 23 Apr.

GREY PLOVER *Pluvialis squatarola* (W)

Forth Est WeBS: 0 in Jan, 12 in Feb, 0 in Mar, 0 in Sep, 0 in Oct, 0 in Nov and 14 in Dec.

F　　Blackness: 9 on 27 Feb with singles there 15 Sep, 1 Oct and 1+ on 3 Nov. Kinneil: singles 28 Sep and 27 Oct with 2 between Grangepans and Grangemouth 15 Dec. Skinflats: single 7 Jan with 2 there 27 May, 1 on 20 and 22 Aug and 5 on 25 Oct. Elsewhere: 4 Bo'ness shore east 22 Jan; 2 Muirdyke Burn, Powfoulis 28 Jan; 12 Kincardine Br 12 Feb and 15 Dec.

NORTHERN LAPWING *Vanellus vanellus* (B, W)

Forth Est WeBS: 613 in Jan, 408 in Feb, 7 in Mar, 735 in Sep, 1049 in Oct, 835 in Nov and 138 in Dec.

Inland WeBS: 412 in Jan, 642 in Feb, 128 in Mar, 180 in Sep, 279 in Oct, 104 in Nov and 49 in Dec.

F　　Blackness: 70 on 9 Sep with 150 there 14 Sep, 50 on 29 Sep and 60 on 7 Oct. Kinneil: 250 on 8 Jan, with 150 there 12 Feb, 50 on 4 Aug, 159 on 15 Aug, 200 on 27 Aug, ca. 375 on 30 Aug, 445 on 8 Sep, ca. 370 on 12 Sep, 250 on 23 Sep, 170 on 30 Sep, 300 on 7 Oct, 100 on 3 Nov, 443 (Grangepans to Grangemouth) 16 Nov, 250 on 17 Nov, 150 on 29 Dec. Skinflats: 115 on 12 Feb with 290 there 1 Aug, 100 on 22 and 24 Aug, 245 on 16 Sep, 250 on 29 Sep, 268 on 14 Oct. Elsewhere: 100 NE Airth 2 Oct.

C　　Alloa Inches area: 363 on 6 Jan with 71 there 20 Jul, 553 on 14 Oct and 374 on 17 Nov. Cambus: 50 on 12 Feb with 56 there 1 Sep. Haugh of Blackgrange: 320 on 14 Jan, with 21 AoTs there 15 Apr. 1 AoT Blackdevon Wetlands 12 Apr (8 AoTs in 2008).

S　　Stirling: 1300 Manor Powis 8 Jan with 113 R Forth there 14 Jan. Carse of Lecropt, BoA: 110 on 12 Feb with 15 AoTs there 12 Apr, 17-18 AoTs 23 Apr, 60 on 22 Jul, 146 on 24 Jul. 4 AoTs Cowie 27 Apr. 64 Blairdummond Quarry 19 Aug.

RED KNOT *Calidris canutus* (W)

Forth Est WeBS: 1115 in Jan, 3393 in Feb, 51 in Mar, 26 in Sep, 192 in Oct, 206 in Nov and 1469 in Dec.

F　　Kinneil: 658 Grangepans to Grangemouth 8 Jan, 300 on 12 Feb, 3 early birds on 10 Jul were followed by 96+ not until 7 Sep, 129 on 11 Sep, 60 on 23 Sep and 7 Oct, ca. 800 on 14 Dec, 1420 Grangepans to Grangemouth 15 Dec and 200 on 29 Dec. Skinflats: 325 on 8 Jan and 2750 on 12 Feb. Elsewhere: 1500 Muirdyke Burn, Powfoulis 28 Jan.

C　　Two hundred and fifteen Kennetpans 12 Feb.

SANDERLING *Calidris alba*

Forth Est WeBS: none recorded.

F　　Kinneil: singles 15 Aug and 12 Sep. Skinflats: 3 on 16 Aug and 1 on 24 Aug.

*LITTLE STINT *Calidris minuta*

Forth Est WeBS: 1 in Oct was the only count.

F　　Juv Skinflats 26 Sep and between 29 Sep and 1 Oct (DMB, DOE, CJP). 1 Grangepans to Grangemouth 14 Oct (JRC).

C　　Juv Kennetpans 30 Sep (DMB)

CURLEW SANDPIPER *Calidris ferruginea* (p)

Forth Est WeBS: 4 in Sep was the only count.

F　　Blackness: 1 on 29 May (BG). Kinneil: 1 on 18 Aug, 17 on 11 Sep stood out from subsequent counts of 3 on 12 Sep, 1 on 23 Sep, 3 on 1 Oct and 3 on 5 Oct (ACC, DMB, RTW, JRC, CJP). Skinflats: singles on 30 May (moulting), 16 Sep, 25 Sep, 29 Sep with 2 there 1 Oct (DMB, TG, DOE, BG).

C   Two Kennetpans 30 Sep (DMB)

Autumn passage, area summary (minimum number/half month)							
Jul		Aug		Sep		Oct	
0	0	0	1	17	6	5	0

DUNLIN *Calidris alpina* (b?, W)

Forth Est WeBS: 4746 in Jan, 6885 in Feb, 532 in Mar, 76 in Sep, 329 in Oct, 1870 in Nov and 1975 in Dec.

F   Kinneil: 50 on 8 Jan with ca. 600 there 23 Jan, ca. 1000 on 30 Jan, 3936 Grangepans to Grangemouth 12 Feb, 127 on 10 Mar, 16 on 21 Mar and 1 on 8 May. Autumn return there: 12 on 26 Jul, with 100+ on 30 Jul, 162 on 1 Aug, 100 on 4 Aug, 13 on 15 Aug, 50 on 24 Aug, 25 on 29 Aug and on 14 Sep, 150 on 29 Sep, 250+ on 1 Oct, 600 on 3 Nov, 1000 on 17 Nov, ca. 2000 on 14 Dec, 2200+ on 17 Dec and 2000 on 29 Dec. Skinflats: 3290 on 8 Jan, 2860 on 12 Feb, 3 on 8 May and a max spring passage count of 43 on 30 May with lower numbers thereafter. Autumn return there was rather poor: 84 on 1 Aug, 50 on 22 Aug, 40 on 29 Aug, 40 on 29 Sep, 560 on 16 Nov and 15 on 17 Dec. Elsewhere: 1500 Muirdyke Burn, Powfoulis 28 Jan.

C   Twelve in summer plumage Kennetpans 14 May.

S   Head of L Tay, Killin: 2 on 14, 15 and 23 May, 5 on 1 Jun and 1 on 2 Jun.

RUFF *Philomachus pugnax* (w, p)

Forth Est WeBS: 1 in Jan, 0 in Feb, 0 in Mar, 3 in Sep, 0 in Oct, 0 in Nov and 0 in Dec.

F   A poor year for this species. Kinneil: M 16 Aug with 2 there 11 Sep and 16 Sep (DMB, JRC). Skinflats: an overwintering bird on 8 Jan, with singles 21 Aug, 16 Sep and 29 Sep to 1 Oct (DMB, CJP, MVB, DOE). Elsewhere: 6 Shieldhill roadside pools, Falkirk 24 Aug (GG).

Autumn passage, area summary (minimum number/half month)							
Jul		Aug		Sep		Oct	
0	0	0	8	2	3	1	0

JACK SNIPE *Lymnocryptes minimus* (w)

Forth Est WeBS: none recorded.

Inland WeBS: 2 in Jan, 2 in Feb, 6 in Mar, 0 in Sep, 6 in Oct, 5 in Nov and 2 in Dec.

F   Single St. Helen's Loch, Bonnybridge 19 Feb (NB). Single Skinflats 10 Nov (CJP).

C   Singles Blackdevon Wetlands 15 Jan, 14 Oct and 18 Nov (RG). Single Kennetpans 1 Oct (DMB).

S   BoA: 1 Carse of Lecropt 16 Jan with 2 there 26 Jan, 1 on 14 Feb, 5 on 12 Mar and on 14 Oct, 4 on 18 Nov, 1 on 7 Dec and 2 on 16 Dec (DT); singles Netherton Marsh 16 Jan and 14 Feb, with 5 there 14 Oct, 2 on 18 Nov and on 16 Dec (DT). 5 Carnforth, Stirling 12 Mar and 2 there 18 Nov (DT). Single R Forth, Br of Frew-E Frew 22 Mar (RTW).

COMMON SNIPE *Gallinago gallinago* (B,W)

Forth Est WeBS: 0 in Jan, 0 in Feb, 0 in Mar, 2 in Sep, 0 in Oct, 4 in Nov and 2 in Dec.

Inland WeBS: 45 in Jan, 57 in Feb, 39 in Mar, 3 in Sep, 75 in Oct, 67 in Nov and 38 in Dec.

F   Kinneil: 12 on 24 Aug with 11 there 4 Nov. Skinflats: 7+ on 22 Aug with 35 there 6 Nov and 7 on 10 Nov.

S   Carse of Lecropt, BoA: 17 on 16 Jan with 33 on 14 Feb, 8 on 12 Mar, 27 on 14 Oct, 40 on 18 Nov, 29 on 16 Dec (DT). Breeding season: singles Bows, BoD and Sheriffmuir 1 Apr and Glen Finglas 20 Apr; 2 Bracklinn, Callander 30 Apr and 5 Jun; 2 Manse Rd, Aberfoyle 2 May; 1 L Rusky 6 May; 1 several dates at head of L Tay, Killin where heard drumming on 19 May; 1 Tigh na Blair 21 May; 1 Buckieburn Res, Carron Valley 22 May.

EURASIAN WOODCOCK *Scolopax rusticola* (B, W)
        Grossly under-recorded during the breeding season.
        Inland WeBS: 0 in Jan, 1 in Feb, 0 in Mar, 0 in Sep, 0 in Oct, 1 in Nov and 3 in Dec.

F   One flushed from former refuse tip, Kinneil 30 Jan. 3 Torwod, Larbert 3 Mar.

S   First winter season: singles Auchtertyre Glen Gorge woodland, Strathfillan 6 Jan; Kippenross House Lodge, Dunblane 12 Jan; Wester Moss, Fallin 14 Jan, central Dunblane 23 Jan; Kirkton, Tyndrum 6 Feb; Lanrick, Doune 12 Feb; 5 roding Polmaise Woods, Stirling 18 Mar; 1 E shore Lake of Menteith 28 Mar.
        Breeding season: roding Killin Marshes 30 Mar and 1 May and at head of L Tay, Killin 14 Apr; calling Manse Rd, Aberfoyle 21 Apr; Holme Hill, Dunblane 29 Apr and 1 Glen Finglas 16 Jul.
        Second winter season: 3 Torrie 13 Nov; 1 Carnforth, Stirling 17 Nov; 8 Argaty, BoD 22 Nov with singles there 1 Dec and 28 Dec. Singles Blairdrummond GPs 1 Dec; Lecropt Church, BoA 3 Dec; Lanrick, Doune 15 Dec; Loch Watston 15 Dec; Kirkton Fm, Tyndrum 21 Dec and Landrick, Dunblane 23 Dec.

BLACK-TAILED GODWIT *Limosa limosa* (W)
        Forth Est WeBS: 43 in Jan, 137 in Feb, 136 in Mar, 495 in Sep, 484 in Oct, 117 in Nov and 90 in Dec.
        Several birds at Kinneil carry colour rings, with birds ringed in France and Iceland using this site as a stop-over. Please scrutinize flocks carefully and submit details to the BTO and the recorder.

F   Recorded all year, apart from Jun, in the Grangemouth area. Monthly peaks at Kinneil: ca. 170 on 23 Jan, 132 Grangepans to Grangemouth 12 Feb, 190 on 12 Mar, 150 on 27 Apr, 52 on 29 May, 225 on 30 Jul, 375 on 20 Aug, 490 on 11 Sep, 481 Grangepans to Grangemouth 14 Oct, 300 on 17 Nov and 250 on 29 Dec. Monthly peaks at Skinflats: 210 on 8 Apr, 93 on 8 May, 118 on 1 Aug and 83 on 16 Sep. Elsewhere: 195 Blackness 8 Nov.

C   Low numbers: 7 Alloa Inch 9 Mar. 1 Cambus 7 Apr.

BAR-TAILED GODWIT *Limosa lapponica* (W)
        Forth Est WeBS: 104 in Jan, 375 in Feb, 100 in Mar, 60 in Sep, 133 in Oct, 83 in Nov and 327 in Dec.

F   Blackness: 230 on 8 Nov. Kinneil: ca. 200 on 30 Jan, 291 Grangepans to Grangemouth 12 Feb, 100 on 27 Oct, 115 on 18 Nov and 295 Grangepans to Grangemouth 15 Dec. Skinflats: 33 on 16 Sep and 30 on 14 Oct.

C   Kennetpans: 6 on 5 Jan with 59 there 12 Feb.

S   One head of L Tay, Killin 22 Apr.

WHIMBREL *Numenius phaeopus* (p)
        Forth Est WeBS: none recorded.

F   Kinneil: 2 on 6 May with 1 there 25 and 29 Jul and 2 on 2 Aug (CJP, DT, BG, DMB), singles on 12 Aug, 26 Aug, 8 Sep, 14 Sep, 7 Oct and, unusually, 5 on 18 Dec (DOE, RS, AB, DT, BG). Skinflats: singles 8 and 30 May, 2 on 20 Aug and singles 22 and 24 Aug (DMB, AB, DOE). Elsewhere: singles Blackness 31 May, Higgin's Neuk 21 Sep and > W Carron, Stenhousemuir 24 Aug (BG, ACC, AB).

C   Nine The Rhind, Alloa 11 and 12 May (DMB, NB). 5 Kennetpans 14 and 30 May and 1 there 18 Jun (DMB).

S   One Gart GPs, Callander 8 May (DOE).

Autumn passage, area summary (minimum number/half month)							
Jul		Aug		Sep		Oct	
0	1	2	4	1	1	1	0

EURASIAN CURLEW *Numenius arquata* (B, W)
Forth Est WeBS: 1100 in Jan, 1103 in Feb, 626 in Mar, 530 in Sep, 943 in Oct, 820 in Nov and 448 in Dec.
Inland WeBS: 9 in Jan, 193 in Feb, 296 in Mar, 25 in Sep, 3 in Oct, 1 in Nov and 21 in Dec.

F   Blackness: 40 on 9 and 14 Sep and on 5 Oct with 50 there 7 Oct and 45 on 27 Dec. Kinneil: 65 on 7 Jan with 60 there 12 Feb, 40 on 7 Apr, ca. 290 on 2 Aug, 55 on 17 Aug, 70 on 24 Aug, 327 on 29 Aug, 50 on 14, 16 and 29 Sep, 100 on 7 Oct, 40 on 13 Oct, 60 on 17 Nov, ca. 250 on 23 Nov and 40 on 29 Dec. Skinflats: 404 on 8 Jan with 225 on 22 Jan, 40 on 19 Feb, 75 on 9 Mar, 70 on 22 Aug, 70 on 23 Sep, 80 on 6 Oct, 405 on 14 Oct and 50 on 29 Dec. Elsewhere: 100 Muirdyke Burn, Powfoulis 28 Jan with 40 there 11 Nov; 177 Kincardine Br to S Alloa 16 Nov.

C   Alloa Inches: 272 on 6 Jan with 300 there 12 Jan, 166 on 20 Jul and 184 on 14 Oct. Kennetpans: 268 on 8 Jan with 150 there 30 Jan, 249 on 12 Feb and 171 on 16 Nov. 55 Haugh of Blackgrange 12 Feb. Cambus: 50 on 10 Aug with 81 there 22 Aug and 192 on 10 Mar.

S   One hundred and seven Carnforth, Stirling and 35 Allan Water, Kinbuck 31 Mar. 47 head of L Tay, Killin 11 Apr.

COMMON SANDPIPER *Tringa hypoleucos* (B)
Forth Est WeBS: none recorded.
Inland WeBS: none recorded.

F   Spring passage: 1 Grangepans, Bo'ness 11 Apr. Autumn passage: Kinneil: 8 on 1 Aug with 6 there 20 Aug, 2 on 21 and 24 Aug and 1 on 26 Aug; Skinflats: 5 Skinflats on 1 and 2 Aug; 1 Carriden, Bo'ness 28 Aug.

C   Breeding season: 1 Longcarse, Alloa 9 May and R Devon, Alva 20 May. Autumn passage: 3 Longcarse, Alloa 20 Jul and 2 Tullibody Inch 2 Aug.

S   Breeding season: 1 CVR 21 Apr; recorded at head of L Tay, Killin on many dates between 22 Apr and 9 Jul with 4 there 6 Jun; 4 Kirkton Fm, Tyndrum 25 Apr; 2 Carse of Lecropt, BoA and 1 Dunblane 29 Apr; present Tigh Mor, L Achray 2 May with 2 there 4 May; 1 L Lubnaig 5 May; 2 Lanrick, Doune 5 and 16 May; 2 Earlsburn Res 5 May with 1 there 22 May; 2 Gart GPs, Callander 6 and 8 May, 5 Blairdrummond GPs 13 May; 2 Bows, BoD 14 May; present Ben Our 15 May; 2 L Watston 16 May; Glen Lochay: present 20 May with 3 in centre and 4 at Kenknock 4 Jun; 4+ L Katrine 20 May; singles Buckieburn Res, Carron Valley 22 May; 1 Edinample, Lochearnhead 4 Jun; 4 Killin 4 Jun with 2 there at Ardeonaig 20 Jun; present Auchlyne Rd, Glen Dochart 9 Jun.

Autumn passage, area summary (minimum number/half month)							
Jul		Aug		Sep		Oct	
1	3	15	7	0	0	0	0

*GREEN SANDPIPER *Tringa ochropus* (w, p)
This species occurs as a passage migrant and, more recently, also as a wintering bird in small numbers.
Forth Est WeBS: 1 in Sep was the only count.

F   Two Kinneil 4 Aug with 1 between Grangepans and Grangemouth 16 Sep and 1 heard 21 Sep (ACC, JRC, DT). 1 Bethankie Br, Polmont 14, 21 and 30 Sep (DB,

RS, CJP, GG). 1 Gilston 21 and 30 Sep, 16 Oct, 7 and 20 Nov (RS). 1 Glensburgh, Grangemouth 4 Nov (AE).

*SPOTTED REDSHANK   *Tringa erythropus* (p)

Forth Est WeBS: 0 in Jan, 0 in Feb, 0 in Mar, 1 in Sep, 1 in Oct, 0 in Nov and 0 in Dec.

F   An overwintering bird at Skinflats 28 Jan (GO). Kinneil: juv 20 Aug, with 3 there 21 Aug, 1 on 23 Aug, juv on 7 Sep, ad on 11 Sep and 2 on 16 Sep (DOE, RS, DT, DMB, JM). Singles 1, 2, 4, 5 and 7 Oct (CJP, DMB, BG, DT, DOE). 1 Blackness 9 Sep (DOE).

COMMON GREENSHANK   *Tringa nebularia* (w, p)

Forth Est WeBS: 4 in Jan, 3 in Feb, 4 in Mar, 4 in Sep, 3 in Oct, 4 in Nov and 2 in Dec.

F   Present at Skinflats in all months, except Apr to Jun. Monthly max: 3 on 8 Jan, 1 on several dates in Feb, 2 on 1, 2 and 17 Mar (CJP, AB, GC, DT, DD, AE, RTW, SMcB, BG, DMB). Autumn passage: 5 on 29 Jul, 2 on 30 Jul, 3 on 1 Aug, 2 on 2 and 4 Aug, 4 on 12 Aug, 3 on 15 and 18 Aug, 2 on 20 Aug, 4 to 5 on 21, 24 and 26 to 30 Aug (AB, RS, MVB, DMB, CJP, NB, ACC, DOE, SG, DT); 2 on 7 Sep, 1 on 8 Sep, 6 on 9 Sep, 2-3 on 11, 16, 23, 25 and 29 Sep, with 5 on 21 Sep and 1 on 30 Sep (CJP, AB, DOE, RS); 4 on 1 Oct, 2-3 on 5, 7, 8 and 11 Oct and 1 on 27 Oct (DT, CJP, DMB, DOE, GG, AB). Second winter period: 1-2 on 13, 17, 18 and 20 Nov, 17, 18, 26 and 29 Dec, with 3 on 28 Nov (RS, DOE, AB, DT, BG, DOE, ARe). Present at Kinneil in all months, except May to Jul. Monthly maxima: 2 on 8, 22 and 29 Jan, 2 on 12 Feb, 2 on 9, 11 and 12 Mar and 1 on 1 and 5 Apr (MVB, AB, CJP, DMB, GG, ACC). Autumn passage: 1 on 8 Aug, 4 on 20 Aug, 2 on 21 and 29 Aug and 1 Sep, singles on 16, 22 and 23 Sep, 2 on 12 Oct, singles on 14 and 19 Oct (RD, DMB, CJP, DOE, GG, MVB, AB, ACC). Winter: 1 on 16 Nov, 2 on 25 Nov and 1 on 15 Dec (MVB, AB). Elsewhere: 1 S Alloa 10 Apr and 1 Blackness 14 Jul (DMB, CJP).

C   Two Cambus 10 Aug with 1 Tullibody Inch 15 Aug (NB, DMB).

S   One head of L Tay, Killin 15 Apr. 2 L Dochart 15 and 16 Apr (JPH).

Autumn passage, area summary (minimum number/half month)							
Jul		Aug		Sep		Oct	
1	5	8	9	8	6	6	2

COMMON REDSHANK   *Tringa totanus* (B, W)

Forth Est WeBS: 1442 in Jan, 1821 in Feb, 1132 in Mar, 1304 in Sep, 1549 in Oct, 1562 in Nov and 1313 in Dec.

Inland WeBS: 0 in Jan, 2 in Feb, 10 in Mar, 0 in Sep, 2 in Oct, 2 in Nov and 0 in Dec.

F   Kinneil: 723 on 8 Jan and 1104 on 12 Feb (both Grangepans to Grangemouth), 343 on 10 Mar and 300 on 31 Mar, 1050 on 1 Aug, 602 on 15 Aug, 200 on 21 Aug, 300 on 24 Aug, 250 on 29 Aug, 300 on 9 and 14 Sep, 250 on 23 Sep, 400 on 29 Sep, 250 on 7 Oct, 883 on 14 Oct (Grangepans to Grangemouth), 150 on 3 Nov, 400 on 17 Nov and 200 on 29 Dec. Again much lower numbers at Skinflats than in previous years: 708 on 8 Jan, 580 on 1 Aug, 50 on 29 Sep, 20 on 7 Oct, 670 on 16 Nov and 100 on 29 Dec. Blackness: 100 on 9 Sep; 150 on 14, 29 Sep and 7 Oct; 200 on 3 Nov and 100 on 17 Nov and 29 Dec. Elsewhere: 100 Bo'ness 17 Nov.

S   One head of L Tay, Killin 18 Mar with 9 there 30 Apr. 1 Buckieburn Res, Carron Valley 2 May.

RUDDY TURNSTONE   *Arenaria interpres* (W)

Forth Est WeBS: 0 in Jan, 0 in Feb, 0 in Mar, 2 in Sep, 0 in Oct, 10 in Nov and 3 in Dec.

F   Blackness: 6 on 26 Feb; 2 on 26 Aug, 1 and 9 Sep; 3 on 15 Sep; 2 on 1 and 5 Oct; 4 on 3 Nov and 7 on 8 Nov (CJP, DOE, DMB). Bo'ness: 10 on 22 Jan, 18 on 11 Apr (Grangepans), 11 on 30 Aug, 6 on 27 Oct, 7 on 3 Nov, 11 on 17 Nov, 5 on 29 Nov (GG, DMB, DOE, MVB). Kinneil: 1 on 15 Aug, 2 on 17 Aug and at Grangepans to Grangemouth 2 on 16 Sep, 6 on 16 Nov and 3 on 15 Dec (DT, AB, JRC).

S   One head of L Tay, Killin 30 Apr (JPH).

*POMARINE SKUA *Stercorarius pomarinus*

F   Off Bo'ness: singles on 10 (ad pale phase) and 12 Sep, with 2 (ad pale phase and imm) on 4 Oct (GG, DOE, DMB). Off Kinneil (all imms): 1 on 11 and 2 on 13 Sep, singles on 23 and 29 Sep (DMB, RS, CJP, DOE). 1 pale phase ad Skinflats 26 Sep (DMB).

*PARASITIC JAEGER (ARCTIC SKUA) *Stercorarius parasiticus* (p)

F   Majority of birds records were dark phase. Blackness: in Sep 1 on 4th, 1 on 9th, 2 on 14th, 1 on 15th, 2 on 26th; in Oct 1 on 7th, 3 on 20th (DMB, CJP, DOE). Bo'ness: in Aug 2 on 12th, 6 on 25th, 4 on 26th, 3 on 29th; in Sep 2 on 6th, 21 on 9th, 18 on 10th, 2 on 12th, 1 on 14th, 1 on 24th, 3 on 25th, 4 on 26th; in Oct 3 on 4th, 1 on 14th, 1 on 28th (GG, CJP, DOE, DMB). Kinneil: singles on 17th, 26th to 28th and 30th Aug; in Sep 9 on 7th, 2 on 8th, 6 on 9th, 1 on 11th, 2 on 12th, 1 on 13th, 1 on 14th, 1 on 16th, 1 on 25th, 6 on 26th, 6 on 28th and 1 on 7th Oct (DT, CJP, DOE *et al*). Skinflats: 1 on 25th Sep and 4 on 26th Sep (DOE, DMB).

*LONG-TAILED SKUA *Stercorarius longicaudus*

F   Bo'ness: imms 29 Aug, 24-26 Sep, 4 and 15 Oct (GG, DMB). Blackness: imms 31 Aug, 29 Sep and 7 Oct (CJP, DOE). Kinneil: 2 ads 7 Sep, 1 imm 9 Sep and 2 imms 11 Sep (DT, DOE, DMB).

*GREAT SKUA *Stercorarius skua*

F   Bo'ness: in Sep 1 on 9th, 1 on 12th, 3 on 24th, 67 on 25th, 3 on 26th and 2 on 4th Oct (GG, DMB, DOE). Kinneil: in Sep 1 on 9th, 1 on 11th, 1 on 19th, 4 on 25th and 1 on 26th (DT, CJP, DMB). Blackness: 1 on 14th Sep, 4 on 25th Sep, singles 26th Sep, 1st and 20th Oct (DOE, CJP, DMB). Skinflats: singles on 25th and 30th Sep (DOE, DMB).

S   One Earlsburn Res 14th Sep (DOE).

*SABINE'S GULL *Xema sabini*

F   > W Blackness and then > W Bo'ness 25 Sep (CJP, GG).

*BLACK-LEGGED KITTIWAKE *Rissa tridactyla* (P, w)

F   Bo'ness: 19 on 12 Aug; in Sep 75 on 9th, 1 on 10th, 153 on 24th, 314 on 25th, 28 on 26th; 29 on 14th Oct, 1 on 26th Oct and 4 on 4th Nov (GG, DMB). Kinneil: 8 on 15th Aug, 4 on 7th Aug; in Sep 52 on 21st, 30 on 25th, 35 on 26th and 3 on 28th (DT). Blackness: 30 on 25th Sep, 9 on 26th Sep (CJP, DOE). Skinflats: 30 on 25th Sep (DOE).

COMMON BLACK-HEADED GULL *Larus ridibundus* (B,W)

    Inland WeBS: 1024 in Jan, 1245 in Feb, 1622 in Mar, 594 in Sep, 624 in Oct, 527 in Nov and 632 in Dec.

    Forth Est WeBS: 862 in Jan, 2526 in Feb, 347 in Mar, 693 in Sep, 405 in Oct, 1478 in Nov and 700 in Dec.

F   Max: 450 Kinneil 29 Sep; 1090 Skinflats 16 Nov.

C   Max: 134 Blackdevon Wetlands 12 Jan; 321 Alloa Inch and 71 Cambus 20 Jul; 205 Tullibody Inch 10 Aug.

S   Max: 207 Ashfield Pools 29 Mar; 300 Kinbuck 31 Mar; 350 Blairdrummond GPs 21 Apr; 300 W Gogar, Stirling 22 Dec.

*LITTLE GULL *Larus minutus*

F   Three ads Bo'ness 15 Aug (GG). Imm Kinneil 9 Sep (CJP). 2 ads and 1 imm Bo'ness and imm Blackness 25 Sep (DMB, CJP). 2 imms Kinneil and 1 Blackness 26 Sep (DT, DOE).

*MEDITERRANEAN GULL *Larus melanocephalus*
F   First-winter Airth 2 Jan (RJD). Ad S Alloa 3 Jan (CJP). Ad Skinflats 5 Feb (DD). 1
        Kinneil 29 Sep and 1 Oct (DOE, DMB). 2w Airth 30 Sep (DMB). Ad Blackness 2-
        7 Oct (DOE). Ad Skinflats 7 Nov (DOE). Ad Airth 18 Nov (GG).
C   Ad Menstrie 10 Mar (GEL).
MEW GULL (COMMON GULL) *Larus canus* (B,W)
        Inland WeBS: 733 in Jan, 784 in Feb, 882 in Mar, 77 in Sep, 127 in Oct, 71 in Nov
        and 65 in Dec.
        Forth Est WeBS: 307 in Jan, 1023 in Feb, 148 in Mar, 107 in Sep, 167 in Oct, 471
        in Nov and 754 in Dec.
F   Max: 150 Kinneil 29 Sep; 653 Skinflats 22 Oct; 200 Blackness 3 Nov.
S   Max count: 150 Blairdrummond GPs 1 Feb; 149 Lake of Menteith 26 Feb; 200
        Kinbuck 31 Mar; 100 Lecropt Carse 26 Dec.
*RING-BILLED GULL *Larus delawarensis*
F   Ad Kinneil from 16 Jan to 21 Mar (CJP, GG, MH) and 2 Aug to 16 Oct (DT, CJP,
        DMB *et al.*). This is the same bird that has returned to this site since 2007.
LESSER BLACK-BACKED GULL *Larus fuscus* (b, S)
        Inland WeBS: 2 in Jan, 128 in Feb, 462 in Mar, 126 in Sep, 24 in Oct, 14 in Nov
        and 2 in Dec.
        Forth Est WeBS: 3 in Jan, 11 in Feb, 32 in Mar, 174 in Sep, 71 in Oct, 7 in Nov and
        0 in Dec.
F   Max: 40 Skinflats 25 Sep; 84 Gardrum Moss, Shieldhill 20 Oct.
C   Max: 73 Tullibody Inch 22 Aug.
S   Max: 20 Lake of Menteith 26 Feb; 356 Gartartan, Aberfoyle 23 Mar; 50 Kinbuck
        31 Mar.
HERRING GULL *Larus argentatus* (b, W)
        Inland WeBS: 112 in Jan, 92 in Feb, 40 in Mar, 46 in Sep, 22 in Oct, 151 in Nov
        and 111 in Dec.
        Forth Est WeBS: 565 in Jan, 267 in Feb, 151 in Mar, 1363 in Sep, 272 in Oct, 359
        in Nov and 320 in Dec.
F   Max: 509 Kinneil 8 Jan and 549 Kinneil 16 Sep.
C   Max: 50 Cambus 12 Feb.
*ICELAND GULL *Larus glaucoides*
F   One Airth 17 Feb (ACa). 1 over Falkirk 1 Mar (ML). Ad Skinflats 5 and 19 Jun and
        29 Dec (DMB, DOE).
C   Second-winter Haugh of Blackgrange 30 Jan and 4 Feb (GG, CJP, AET).
GREAT BLACK-BACKED GULL *Larus marinus* (S,W)
        Forth Est WeBS: 26 in Jan, 5 in Feb, 2 in Mar, 16 in Sep, 10 in Oct, 9 in Nov and
        3 in Dec.
        Inland WeBS: 16 in Jan, 13 in Feb, 8 in Mar, 4 in Sep, 1 in Oct, 0 in Nov and 7 in Dec.
F   Max: 22 Kinneil 8 Jan and 16 Sep; 22 Gardrum Moss, Shieldhill 20 Oct.
C   Max: 4 Cambus 12 Feb.
S   Max: 5 Fallin 14 Jan; 4 Craigforth, Stirling 16 Jan; 4 Gart GPs, Callander 6 May.
*BLACK TERN *Chlidonias niger*
F   Imms Bo'ness 10 Sep (GG) and 12 Sep (DOE) and Kinneil 14 Sep (CJP).
SANDWICH TERN *Sterna sandvicensis* (P)
F   First of year: 1 Blackness 20 May (GG). Max: 315 Bo'ness 28 Aug; 100 Kinneil 9
        Sep; 150 Blackness 9 Sep. Last of year: 10 Blackness 7 Oct (DOE).
C   Max: 6 Blackdevon Wetlands 8 Jul.
COMMON TERN *Sterna hirundo* (B)
F   First of year: 30 Kinneil 8 May (DMB). Max: 115 Grangemouth 16 Aug, 280
        Skinflats 28 Aug and 150 Kinneil 11 Sep.

*ROSEATE TERN Sterna dougallii
F   Ad and imm Blackness 31 Aug, 1 Sep and 9 Sep (CJP, DOE *et al*.). Ad Kinneil 11-12 Sep (DMB, RTW).

*ARCTIC TERN Sterna paradisaea
F   Bo'ness: 1 on 7 Jul, 2 on 27 Aug and 2 on 25 Sep (GG, DMB). Blackness: 1 on 8 Jul, 3 on 29 Jul, 1 on 26 Aug and 1 on 14 Sep (CJP, GG, DOE). Kinneil: 1 on 30 Jul, 1 on 24 Aug, 2 on 11 Sep and 1 on 12 Sep (RS, DOE, DMB, DT).

*GUILLEMOT Uria aalge
    Forth Est WeBS: 0 in Jan, 0 in Feb, 0 in Mar, 56 in Sep, 19 in Oct, 14 in Nov and 0 in Dec.
F   Blackness: singles in Jan on 15th and 29th; Mar max of 6 on 25th; Sep max of 50 on 26th; 1 on 7th Oct; Nov max of 5 on 4th (CJP, DOE, LAF). Bo'ness: 1 on 4th Feb; 1 on 23rd Apr; Aug max of 4 on 30th; Sep max of 50 on 26th; Nov max of 4 on 29th (GG, DMB, CJP). Kinneil: 1 on 23rd Jan; 1 on 8th Feb; 2 on 7th Apr; Aug max of 3 on 28th; Sep max of 215 on 12th; Oct max of 8 on 5th; 1 on 3rd Nov (DT, ACC, DOE). Skinflats: 2 on 5th Feb; Sep max of 9 on 12th and 3 on 11th Nov (AB, MVB).
C   Three Tullibody Inch 3 Sep (DMB). 10 Alloa Inch 16 Sep (LO). 6 Cambus 22 Sep (ACC). Gartmorn Dam: 1 on 23 Sep and 2 there 30 Sep (SR, LC).
S   R Forth, Stirling: 1 on 5 Sep, 1 on 11 Sep, 4 on 18 Sep, 3 on 28 Sep (CB, JB, DJ, DI). 1 L Tay, Killin 19 Sep (JPH). 1 Tyndrum 20 Sep (JPH). 2 Gart GPs, Callander 23 Sep (NB). 2 > Doune and 1 Lake of Menteith 23 Sep (RCW, RTW). 1 dead L Lochart 23 Sep (JPH). 1 Doune 25 Sep (DOE). 22 Lake of Menteith 26 Sep (NB). 6 Blairdrummond GPs (NB) and 2 R Forth, E Frew 27 Sep (RTW). 1 Callander 28 Sep (HEG). 1 > N Tyndrum 2 Oct (JPH).

*RAZORBILL Alca torda
F   Blackness: 1 on 15 Jan, 3 on 25 Mar, 2 on 30 Mar, 1 on 9 Sep and 1 on 12 Sep (DOE, CJP). Bo'ness: 1 on 22 Jan, 1 on 1 Apr, 1 on 9 Sep and 2 on 19 Sep (GG, JRC). Kinneil: 2 on 30 Aug, 1 on 7 Sep and 1 on 29 Oct (DT, DMB).

COMMON PIGEON (FERAL PIGEON) Columba livia (B,W)
    BBS[1]: recorded at 1.1 b/lkm.
F   Thirty Blackness 30 Mar. 40 Kinneil 25 Sep and 29 Dec.
C   Forty-two Alloa 12 Feb. 50 Allaleckie, Forestmill 16 May.
S   Ca. 100 Westleys, Carse of Lecropt 21 Jan.

STOCK DOVE Columba oenas (B, W)
    BBS: recorded at 0.1 b/lkm.
F   Kinneil: 1-2 on 9 Jun, on 4, 6, 12 and 29 Aug and on 29 Dec. Skinflats: 1 on 5 Apr; 3 on 21 Apr; 1-2 on 24 Apr and 24 Jun, 18, 24 and 29 Aug, 23 and 25 Sep and 12 Oct. Elsewhere: 9 Powfoulis 11 Mar.
C   Kennetpans: 7 on 30 Jan, with 9 there 9 May and 4 on 12 Jun. Tullibody Inch: 1-2 on 18 Mar and 10 and 22 Aug. Alva, Woodland Park and Drove Rd: singles on 22 Apr and on 5 and 24 Jun. Alloa: 3 New Sauchie 1 May; up to 3 Longcarse on several dates 9 May to 20 Jul. Blackdevon Wetlands: 2 on 25 Jun.
S   Dunblane: recorded all months Holmehill with max of 6 on 14 Jan and 10 Mar, 8 on 9 Feb and 13 May and 10 on 11 Apr; 6 Keir 28 Mar with 2 there 8 Jul and 4 on 28 Dec; 6 Hill of Row 3 Apr and 2 there 28 Dec; 1 Craigarnhall 5 May. BoA: 1-3 Carse of Lecropt 28 Jan, 28 Mar, 16 May, 5 and 28 Dec; singles Airthrey 29

---

[1] Due to the small and varying number of squares (43 in 2012), turn-over of surveyors and different percentages of habitats covered each year, inter-annual comparisons are unlikely to be valid. Breakdown into habitat categories is not valid due to the unrepresentativeness of the squares surveyed and the varying percentage of each habitat category covered each year. Figures should therefore be seen as reflecting the situation in any one year for those squares covered.

Feb, 12 Apr, 14 Jun and 17 Jul. Blairdrummond GPs: 2 on 5 Feb (Carse), 4 and 10 Mar; 4 on 2 Apr (Carse) and 21 Apr; 2 on 13 May, 8 Jul and 23 Dec; 3 on 26 Dec; 6 on 28 Dec and 1 on 31 Dec. Doune: 1 Loch Watston 11 Mar with 2 there 15 Dec. 4 Lanrick on 10 Mar with singles there 5 and 16 May and 2 on 8 Jul. Stirling: 2 Brucefields 29 Mar. BoD: 2 Bows 1 Apr; 1 Rosehall 15 Apr; 1 Argaty 23 Apr with 4 there 25 Jun and 3 on 1 Dec; 2 Drumloist 6 May. Callander: 1 Gart GPs 6 May. Lake of Menteith: 2 on 14 Jul.

COMMON WOOD PIGEON *Columba palumbus* (B, W)
   BBS: recorded at 3.7 b/lkm
F   Six hundred and fifty Skinflats 16 Nov with 300 there 17 Nov.
S   Dunblane: 3000 Landrick on unharvested barley 2 Jan with 4200 there 1 Feb and 2800 on 1 Mar; 1250 Stockbridge to Glenhead 12 Jan with 700 there 13 Nov and 1100 at Glenhead; 300 Hill of Row 23 Jan, 29 Oct, 25 Nov and 28 Dec. Carse of Lecropt, BoA: 360 on 23 Jan with 200 there 18 Jan, 1300 on 12 Feb and 200 on 28 Dec. Blairdrummond: 1500 at Carse on 28 Jan and 5 Feb with 250 there 19 Feb, 300 on 25 Feb, 200 on 4 Mar and 200 at the Quarry 10 Nov. 200 Brae of Boquhapple Farm, Thornhill 8 Feb. BoD, Argaty: 200 on 24 Nov and 1 Dec.

EURASIAN COLLARED DOVE *Streptopelia decaocto* (B, W)
   Greatly under-reported, especially breeding records. BBS: recorded at 0.3 b/lkm.
F   Breeding season: 2 Carronshore, Stenhousemuir; 1-2 Kingseat Place, Falkirk on several dates 18 Apr to 3 May. Non-breeding season: 12 Blackness 3 Mar with 4 there 31 Mar, 4 on 12 Sep, 7 on 14 Sep and 3 on 4 Nov. 4 Skinflats 14 Sep with 3 there 6 and 7 Oct.
C   Breeding season: 2 Tullibody 6 Apr, 3 Kennet 14 May with 6 there 18 Jun.
S   Breeding season: 1-2 Brae of Boquhapple Farm, Thornhill 5 Apr; Doune 15 Apr; Cromlix 30 Apr and 17 Jun; Lanrick, Doune 5 and 16 May; central Dunblane 15 May; Daldorn, Doune 16 May and 23 Jun; Keir Dunblane 16 and 26 May and 8 Jul; Killin 4 Jun; Holmehill, Dunblane 9 Jun; Argaty, BoD 21 Jul; Hill of Row, Dunblane 26 Jul. Non-breeding season: 1 singing Coneyhill, BoA 23 Jan. 7 Doune 29 Jan and 24 Nov, 3 on 1 Dec. 6 Craigforth, Stirling 5 Feb. 4 Blairdrummond Carse 25 Feb. 4 Doune 4 and 11 Mar.

COMMON CUCKOO *Cuculus canorus* (B)
   Five birds were fitted with satellite tags around L Katrine in May 2012. Their migration to their African wintering grounds is summarized in the Ringing Report. Further details are provided on the BTO web site (http://www.bto.org/science/migration/tracking-studies/cuckoo-tracking). BBS: recorded at 0.1 b/lkm.
   Arrival[2] in Apr: 2 L Rusky 27th was later than during the past 5 years (range: 15th to 25th April), This was followed by a pair L Chon 28th; singles High Corries, L Ard Forest and Kirkton Fm, Tyndrum 29th.
F   One Bo'ness 15 May. 1 Darnrig Moss 5 Jun was mobbed by Lesser Black-backed Gulls.
S   May: 1 Argaty, BoD and 4 singing Tyndrum 1st; single Malling, Lake of Menteith and 3 Glen Finglas 2nd; singles head of L Tay, Killin 2nd, 15th, 16th, 19th and 23rd; 1 Auchtertyre Glen Gorge woodland, Strathfillan 2nd and 16th; 2 Glen Ample 3rd; 1 Aberfoyle 4th and 5th; 1 Brig o'Turk 5th; single Blaircessnock, Flanders Moss 6th; 2

---

[2] Spring arrival and autumn departure dates are not recorded systematically at the same locations with the same effort and coverage across years. Changes between years should therefore be seen as indicative only and not be interpreted as reflecting true phenological variation.

Flanders Moss W 6th and 2 there 26th; singles Drumloist, BoD 6th and 26th; 1 Braeleny, BoD and Callander Crags 9th; 1 BoD, Bows 14th and 21st with 2 there 27th; pair Ben Our 15th; 2 L Arklet Res 18th; 1 Bracklinn, Callander and 2 Drumloist, BoD 19th; 4 L Katrine 20th; 1 Tigh na Blair 21st; singles Buckieburn Res, Carron Valley, Easter Polder, Thornhill and 2 Earlsburn Res 22nd; 2 AoTs Touch 27th; 1 G Beich 28th. June: 1 at Gathering Stone, Sheriffmuir 1st; 1 Drumloist, BoD 3rd; singles Kenknock, G Lochay and central G Lochay, Ardenoig, Killin and Edinample, Lochearnhead 4th; 1 Cairnoch, CVR 5th; singles head of L Tay, Killin and Tigh na Blair 9th; 1 Glen Finglas 10th; 1 Drumloist, BoD 12th and 1 Kilbryde, Dunblane 17th. Aug: juv Flanders Moss 4th.

BARN OWL *Tyto alba* (b, w)
As in 2011, few birds were reported in what looks like another poor breeding season after the harsh winters of 2009 and 2010. The previous apparent spread of the species in the recording area thus seems to have been at least temporarily halted.

F One Nether Kinneil 12 May (GG).
S One Cambusbeg, Callander 28 Jan. 1 Flanders Moss E 5 Feb. 1 Strathyre 14 May. 1 Auchtertyre, Strathfillan 13 Jun. 1 Hill of Row, Dunblane 21 Sep. 1 between Mossneuk and Rosshill 2 Oct (KF, DOE, JPH, SRG).

TAWNY OWL *Strix aluco* (B, W)
F Ad and 2 juvs West Lothian Golf Course, Bo'ness 18 Jun.
C One Clackmannan 6 Apr. 1 calling Castlebridge Business Park, Forestmill 7 May.
S Doune: singles 9 Feb with 1 at Lanrick 20 Jun. Dunblane: 1 Kippenross 25 Feb with 2 at Holmehill 1 Mar and singles there 15 and 26 Aug. Aberfoyle: 1 in E 26 Feb and 1 calling L Ard Forest 29 Feb. Singles Killin Marshes 24 and 30 Mar. BoD: singles Drumloist 13 Apr and 3 Jun; singles Argaty 22 May, 25 Jun, 11 Jul, 23 Oct (Gallowhill) and 2 Nov (Mill). 1 Blairdrummond Carse 2 May. 1 calling Coneyhill, BoA 5 May. Singles head of L Tay, Killin 20 May; L Watston 26 May; Gart GPs, Callander 20 Jun and Glen Finglas 15 Jul.

LONG-EARED OWL *Asio otus* (b, w)
F Skinflats: 2 Y not fledged yet 27 May and 1 there 9 Jun. Ad and juv West Lothian Golf Course, Bo'ness and 1 Glensburgh, Grangemouth 18 Jun (CJP, AB, TG, AE).
S Pr calling L Mahaick, BoD 23 Apr (KJD).

SHORT-EARED OWL *Asio flammeus* (b, W)
For this rather local breeder, a more systematic survey of known breeding areas and potential breeding sites would be of value.

F One in stubble Blackdevon Wetlands 12 Apr (CJH). Kinneil: 1 on 10 Jan with 2 there 14 Jan and singles 31 Jan, 10 Feb, 9 Sep, 15 Nov and hunting around lagoon 18 Nov (DT, GC, GG, SMcB, CJP, RD, AB). Skinflats: 2 on 26 Jan with 1 there 28 Jan, 4 on 12 Apr, 3 on 10 Nov and 1 on 29 Dec (RD, GO, CJP, DOE). Elsewhere: singles on saltmarsh Muirdyke Burn, Powfoulis 28 Jan and S Alloa 10 Apr (AB, DMB).
S Two Wester Moss, Fallin 14 Jan. 2 Sheriffmuir 31 Mar and 2 Apr (RJD, DI, GC)

COMMON SWIFT *Apus apus* (B)
BBS: recorded at 0.5 b/lkm. Spring arrival: 1 BoA 28 Apr was within the narrow range of the past 7 years (27th April to 4th May). This was followed by 1 Skinflats 29 Apr. In May: 1 Doune on 3rd; 4 Stirling and 12 Callander 9th; 2 Doune 11th; present Glensburgh, Grangemouth and 25 Blairdrummond GPs 13th; 1 Blackdevon Wetlands, 3 central Dunblane, present head of L Tay, Killin and 2 Coneyhill, BoA 14th. Autumn departure: Aug: 1 Hydro, Dunblane 7th; 2 Coneyhill, BoA 9th; 1 Skinflats 18th and 2 BoA 20th. This was in the range of the years 2006-2010 (6th to 30th August), with the last departure being later in 2011 (11th Sep).

F   Six Bo'ness 17 May with 12 there 22 May.
C   One to two reported in May from Blackdevon Wetlands on 14th and 22nd and Allaleckie, Forestmill and Devonvale, Tillicoultry on 16th.
S   Four Daldorn and 6 Lanrick, Doune 16 May. 4 L Watston 16 May. 5 Craigforth, Stirling 18 May. 4 Bracklinn, Callander 19 May. 5 at Kingseat Place, Falkirk 27 May. 6 L Ard Forest, Aberfoyle 30 May. 10 BoA 10 Jun with 8 there 25 Jun and 6 Coneyhill 31 Jul. 1-3 also reported in May from Keir and Kilbryde, Dunblane; Carse of Lecropt, BoA; Drumloist and Argaty, BoD; Blairdrummond GPs.

COMMON KINGFISHER *Alcedo atthis* (b, w)
F   Kinneil: singles 24 and 26 Aug, 21 Sep, 8 and 29 Oct, 17, 20 and 23 Nov, 1 and 29 Dec. R Carron: 2 Larbert 27 Jan with 1 on 7 and 24 Feb and 14 Oct with 2 there 16 Oct; 1 Carronshore 28 Jan and 27 Sep, and 1 Skinflats 12 Aug. 1 Kingseat Place, Falkirk 15 Oct. 3 Bonny Water (Underwood, Bonnybridge) 9 May with 2 there 14 Jun.
C   R Devon: singles at Dollar 24 Feb, Alva 13 Apr (singing) and 20 May and Tillicoultry 15 May. 2 Gartmorn 23 Sep with 1 there 20 Oct.
S   Single Lanrick, Doune 12 Feb. Single Howietoun fish hatchery 21 Feb. 1 Carnforth, Stirling 12 Mar and 18 Nov. Singles Carse of Lecropt, BoA 12 Mar, 11 and 12 Apr. 1 Dunblane 15 Mar. Singles Blairdrummond GPs 14 Apr, 28 and 31 Dec. 1 Airthrey, BoA 26 Jul. Singles Aberfoyle at Leamaharnish near sewage outlet 25 Aug and on R Forth 2 and 18 Nov and 16 Dec. One Ashfield, Dunblane 16 Sep and 7 Oct. 1 L Daira, Blairdrummond 27 Sep. 1 Cromlix Br 7 Oct. Singles Callander at Gart GPs 9 Jan and on R Teith 3 Dec.

EUROPEAN GREEN WOODPECKER *Picus viridis* (B, W)
    Mainly concentrated in SE of recording area but a few records from further afield again this year.
F   Present Torwood, Larbert 24 Jun.
C   Single Blackdevon Wetlands 15 Apr. Alva: singles Woodland Park and Drove Rd 22 Apr, R Devon 20 May and in the Glen 27 May. Dollar: singles in the Glen 26 Apr and at Castle Campbell 30 Jul. One Tillicoultry 9 Sep.
S   Two Cocksburn Res, BoA 12 Mar. Present Killin Marshes 1 Apr and Airthrey, BoA 12 Apr. Singles Glen Finglas 22 Apr and High Corries, L Ard Forest 29 Apr and 30 May. 2 Pass of Leny 9 and 22 May. 1 Argaty, BoD 10 May with 2 there 22 May and 1 on 23 Oct. 1 Kilbryde 10 Jun. 1 Lake of Menteith 14 Jul.

GREAT SPOTTED WOODPECKER *Dendrocopos major* (B, W)
    BBS: recorded at 0.1 b/lkm.
F   One drumming Larbert Pond 29 Mar and 1 there 24 Oct. 2 Bo'ness 7 Apr. Singles Skinflats 6 Aug (juv) and 14 Sep. 1 Dunipace, Denny 14 Oct. 1 Strathavon Fm, Slamannan 3 Dec.
C   Forestmill: 1 in unspecified locality there 5 Jan; singles Castlebridge Business Park 11, 17, 20 and 27 Jan and 3 and 4 Jul. 1 R Devon, Alva 19 Feb. 2 Tullibody 6 Apr. 1 Fishcross 15 Apr. 1 New Sauchie, Alloa 1 May.
S   Dunblane: singles Holmehill 14 Jan, 28 Aug, 29 Nov and 2 on 21 Dec; 1 Craigarnhall 5 May; 1 Hill of Row 15 Jun; 1 Keir 19 Jun with 2 there 8 Jul; 1 in centre 28 Aug. Singles Blairdrummond Carse: 1 Feb, 4 Mar, 2 Apr and 30 Nov; singles Quarry 31 Mar, 21 Apr, 8 Jul, 19 Aug, 8 Sep, 10 Nov with 2 there 1 Dec. Aberfoyle: singles Manse Rd 4 Feb and in E on 31 Aug. Doune: 2 Lanrick 12 Feb and 5 May with 1 there 11 Mar, 16 May, 8 Jul, 21 Oct, 11 Nov and 15 Dec; 2 in unspecified locality 19 Feb, 4 Mar and 15 Apr with 1 there 10 Mar, 25 Nov and 26 Dec; singles L Watston 11 Mar, 16 May and 15 Dec; 1 Daldorn 16 May. Callander: 1 Gart GPs 25 Mar; 2 Bracklinn 30 Apr with singles there 19 May and 5 Jun. 2 G Beich 25 Mar. BoD: 2 Drumloist 17 Apr with 1 there 19 May, 3 Jun, 12

Jun; 1 Bows 21 May; 1 Rosehall 21 May and 12 Jun; Argaty: 3 on 22 May and 1 Dec with 1 there 3 Jun, 25 Jun and 24 Nov. Flanders Moss: singles Polder Moss 2 May and in W 14 Jul. Cromlix: 2 on 5 May and singles there 21 May and 17 Jun. L Rusky: 1 on 8 May. Kilbryde: singles 21 May and 17 Jun. Tigh na Blair: singles 21 May and 9 Jun. 2 central G Lochay 14 Jun. 2 Ardeonaig, Killin 4 Jun. 1 Milton, Kilmahog 6 Jun. 2 Lake of Menteith 14 Jul. 2 G Finglas 15 Jul. 3 juv Plean CP 20 Jul. 1 Crianlarich 24 Jul.

SKY LARK *Alauda arvensis* (B, W)

BBS: recorded at 1.7 b/lkm.

F   Ten Glensburgh, Grangemouth 28 Jan. 10 Kinneil 7 Oct. 15 Skinflats 7 Oct with 45 there 14 Oct.

S   Ten L Watston 22 Jan and 11 Mar. 11 Carse of Lecropt, BoA 28 Jan with 9 singing there 29 Jan and ca. 30 on 7 Dec. 10 Allan Water, Kinbuck 31 Mar. 10 Dumyat 2 Apr.

SAND MARTIN *Riparia riparia* (B)

BBS: recorded at 0.6 b/lkm. Very slow apparent arrival again in Mar: 1 Lake of Menteith 23rd was in the latter part of the arrival window of the past 7 years (range: 4th to 30th). The next birds were 3 Keltie Water, Callander 31st, followed by a gap until the next arrival of 15 Skinflats 11th Apr, 2 Blairdrummond GPs 14th, 8 R Devon, Tillicoultry 20th with the main arrival on 21st when 100 Blairdrummond GPs followed by 100 Gartmorn 23rd. Autumn departure: the only record received was 1 Kinneil 9 Sep, which is in the middle of the departure range for the past 7 years (17th Aug to 8th Oct).

S   Callander: 45 on 9 May with 60 Gart GPs 9 May and 50 there 25 Jul. 50 Blairdrummond GPs 13 May. 80 Stuc Mhor 19 Jun.

*RED-RUMPED SWALLOW *Cecropis daurica*

F   One Blackness 3 Nov (BD, RS, CJP, KDS).

This is believed to be the first record for the recording area.

BARN SWALLOW *Hirundo rustica* (B)

BBS: recorded at 2.4 b/lkm.

Late spring arrival in Apr: 1 R Carron, Stenhousemuir 7th was 1 day later than the latest arrival date since 2005 (range: 6th Mar to 6th Apr). This was followed by 1 Skinflats 11th; 1 head of L Tay, Killin 13th; 3 Blairdrummond GPs and 4 Alva 14th; singles Arnprior and Doune 16th; 1 Falkirk Wheel 17th, 2 Corrie Holdings, Callander 19th; 1 Argaty, BoD 21st; 1 Hill of Row, Dunblane 22nd; 2 Kilbryde 23rd; singles Cromlix and G Balquhidder 30th.

Autumn departure: Sep: 1 Blairdrummond GPs 22nd; present Menteith, Carron, Stenhousemuir in and Doune 26th; 3 Kinneil 29th. Oct: 1 Skinflats 6th; 1 Ashfield 7th; 3 Airthrey, BoA 9th followed by very late stragglers at Killin and Blackness (2) on 4th Nov. This was 2 days later than the latest departure since 2005 (range: 3rd Oct to 2nd Nov).

C   Thirty R Devon, Alva 20 May.

S   Twenty Callander 9 May. 250 Blairdrummond GPs 13 May. 25 Inverlochlarig and Edinchip, Lochearnhead 19 Jul. 20 Bannockburn 12 Aug. 50 Carse of Lecropt, BoA 4 Sep.

COMMON HOUSE MARTIN *Delichon urbica* (B)

BBS: recorded at 0.8 b/lkm. Arrival in Apr: 1 Newton Crescent, Dunblane 10th was well within the arrival window since 2005 (range: 6th to 16th). This was followed by 1 Alva 14th; 2 Blairdrummond Quarry 21st; 1 head of L Tay, Killin 22nd; 1 Callander 29th and 1 Doune and 2 Callander 30th.

Autumn departure in Sep: 10 Coneyhill, BoA 15th; present Skinflats village 22nd; 5 Grangepans, Bo'ness 24th; 2 Doune 26th; present Carron, Stenhousemuir and singles Blackness and Kinneil 29th. This was within the departure range since

2005 (range: 11th Sep to 12th Oct), except for 2011 when 2 birds were still in Doune on 24th Oct.

F   Ten Skinflats 8 May.

C   Twenty-one Alloa 10 Jun.

S   Nest visits started at Coneyhill, BoA on 2 May, the day after birds arrived, with 7 there 26 May. 50 Lanrick, Doune 5 May. 15 Callander 9 May and 25 there 26 Aug. 10 BoA 11 May. 20 Blairdrummond GPs 13 May. 10 L Watston 16 May. 12 Ardeonaig, Killin 4 Jun. 10 Braentrian, L Tay 20 Jun. 12 L Mahaick 24 Jun. 35 G Finglas 16 Jul. 20 Inverlochlarig and Edinchip, Lochearnhead 20 Jul. 150 Carse of Lecropt, BoA 4 Sep. 2 still visiting nest Coneyhill, BoA and 10 Skinflats both on 14 Sep.

TREE PIPIT *Anthus trivialis* (B)

    BBS: recorded at 0.1 b/lkm. Arrival in Apr: 2 Skinflats 15th was within the arrival window since 2005 (range: 12th to 27th). This was followed by 2 Balquhidder Station 16th; 1 G Finglas 20th where 4 singing 22nd; 1 Kinneil, 4 David Marshall Lodge, Aberfoyle, and at head of L Tay, Killin 21st; 2 singing L Venachar 22nd; present Tyndrum community woodland 28th; 2 Drumloist, BoD 29th; singles Cromlix and Bracklinn, Callander 30th. Autumn departure dates are rarely received. This year the latest birds were 2 Gartmorn Wood 1 Sep and 2 Kinneil and 4 Blackness 9 Sep.

C   Four Allaleckie, Forestmill 16 May with 2 there 14 Jun.

S   Flanders Moss: 1 Polder Moss 2 May, 2 in W 6 May and 1 there 26 May. 3 G Finglas 2 May. Lake of Menteith: 3 Malling Forest Estate 2 May with 1 in unspecified locality there 6 May. 1 Aberfoyle 4 May. Singles Cromlix, L Ard Forest and 2 Brig o'Turk, 5 May. BoD: 10 Lanrick 5 May; 1 Drumoist 6, 19 and 26 May with 2 on 21 May; 2 Braeleny 9 May; 1 Bows 21 May; 1 Rosehall 21 May; 2 Argaty 22 May. 2 L Rusky 6 May. Callander: singles at the Crags 9 May and 5 Jun; 1 Bracklinn 5 Jun with 3 there 19 May. 18 AoTs Tyndrum 12 May (17 in 2011). Present Ben Our 15 May. 4 Daldorn, Doune 16 May. 3 Cromlix 21 May. 2 Kilbryde 21 May and 1 there 17 Jun. 2 Tigh na Blair 21 May with 1 there 9 Jun. 2 Pass of Leny 22 May. 1 Touch 27 May. 1 G Beich 28 May. G Lochay: 10 in centre and 10 Kenknock 4 Jun. 2 Ardeonaig, Killin 4 Jun. Dunblane: 3 fledged Y Keir 19 Jun. 5 L Mahaick 24 Jun. 5 Edinample, Lochearnhead 19 Jul.

MEADOW PIPIT *Anthus pratensis* (B, W)

    BBS: recorded at 4.5 b/lkm. Scarce mid-winter.

F   Skinflats: 15 on 25 Mar and 23 Sep with 10 there 14 and 29 Sep, 7 Oct and 29 Dec.

S   Twelve L Watston 22 Jan and 16 Sep with 12 there 15 Dec. 25 Dumyat 2 Apr. BoD: 10 Drumloist 17 Apr and 10 Bows 23 Jun. 20 High Corries, L Ard Forest 29 Apr. 25 Ardeonaig, Killin 4 Jun. 10 Bracklinn, Callander 5 Jun. 20 Creag MacRanaich 19 Jul. 40 Sheriffmuir 2 Aug. 10 Hill of Row, Dunblane 26 Aug.

*EURASIAN ROCK PIPIT *Anthus petrosus* (w)

F   Two Kinneil 17 Mar (CJP).

GREY WAGTAIL *Motacilla cinerea* (B, w)

    BBS: recorded at 0.1 b/lkm.

F   R Carron: 1 Carronshore 15 Jan and 1 Larbert 18 Nov. One Carron Den, Fankerston, Denny 30 Apr. Singles Blackness 14 and 26 Sep, 7 and 17 Oct. 1 Kinneil 14 Sep, with 2 there 23 Sep and singles 26 Sep and 7 Oct. 1 Skinflats 14 Sep. 1 Bo'ness 29 Dec.

C   Two R Devon, Tillicoultry 16 Feb. Pr Cambus 15 Apr with 1 at the R Devon there 29 Nov.

S   Breeding season: BoD: singles Bows 1 Apr and 14 May with 2 there 21 Jul, 4

Drumloist 3 Jun. Singles Kirkton Fm, Tyndrum 2, 25 and 30 Apr. Callander: 1 Gart GPs 14 Apr with 2 Bracklinn 30 Apr and 6 May. 1 Blairdrummond GPs 15 Apr. 1 David Marshall Lodge, Aberfoyle 21 Apr. Doune: 1 Lanrick 5 and 16 May. Strathfillan: 2 Auchtertyre Glen Gorge woodland 16 May and 1 in unspecified location there 21 May. 1 Kenknock, G Lochay 4 Jun. 1 Ardeonaig, Killin 4 Jun. 1 Kilbryde 16 Jun. 5 BoA 25 Jun. 2 Edinchip, Lochearnhead 19 Jul. Non-breeding season: singles Carnforth, Stirling 15 Jan and 14 Feb. BoA: singles Airthrey 29 Feb and Netherton Marsh 16 Dec. Doune: singles 26 Aug and 21 Oct. Singles central Dunblane 28 Aug, 27 Sep, 21 Oct and 27 Nov. 1 Auchlyne Rd, G Dochart 20 Oct. Singles Killin 4 and 6 Nov and at head of L Tay 1 Dec. 1 Argaty, BoD 24 Nov.

WHITE WAGTAIL (PIED WAGTAIL) *Motacilla alba yarrellii* (B, w)
  BBS: recorded at 0.5 b/lkm. Scarce in winter (Jan-Feb and Nov-Dec).
F Fifty-two Grahamstone train station, Falkirk 9 Feb. Skinflats: 25+ on 26 Feb. Birds of the Continental European race *M.a.alba*: 25 Skinflats 22 Apr with 2 there 8 May, 1 on 26 Sep, 2 on 29 Sep, 3 on 1 Oct and 1 on 6 Oct.
C Tullibody Inch: 66 on 16 Jul with 5 there 3 Sep in mixed flock with *M.a.alba* birds and 20 at Longcarse 30 Jul. Birds of the Continental European race *M.a.alba*: 1 Tullibody Inch 16 Jul with 15 there 3 Sep and 1 on Tullibody Inch 30 Nov.
S Roost of 50+ Stirling train station 23 Jan with 60 there 17 Nov. 12 L Mahaick 24 Jun. 18 Doune 23 Sep. Birds of the Continental European race *M.a.alba*: singles Pass of Aberfoyle 19 Apr and Kippen 24 Apr. 2 Cowie 27 Apr. Singles head of L Tay, Killin 28 and 29 Apr and 19 May. 1 Gart GPs, Callander 6 May. 2 Carse of Lecropt, BoA 9 May. 1 Bandeath, Fallin 14 May.

BOHEMIAN WAXWING *Bombycilla garrulus* (w)
F Eight Blackness 5 Nov. Falkirk: 20 St. Mungo 7 Nov with 60 in unspecified locality there 9 Nov, 40 Laurieston 13 Nov and 15 there in unspecified locality 19 Nov, 12 near Grahamstone train station 12 Dec and 18 Gartcows Drive 12 Dec. 6 Harbour Rd, Bo'ness 9 Nov. 30 Carron, Stenhousemuir 11 Nov with 2 Carronshore 1 Dec. 2 Polmont 12 Nov. 64 > W over Kincardine Br 16 Nov. 30 Airth 17 Nov. 20 Grangemouth 17 Nov. 18 Liddle Drive, Bo'ness 19 Nov. 15 Skinflats 25 Nov. 2 Larbert 2 Dec.
C Dollar: 35 on 18 Nov with 30 there 21 Nov, 50 on 22 Nov, 91 on 25 Nov and 6 on 10 Dec. 30 Devon Way, Tillicoultry 23 Nov.
S Two Doune 27 Oct with 6 there 9 Nov. Dunblane: 2 Laighhills 29 Oct with 2 in the centre 2 Nov, 80 in unspecified locality 10 Nov, 34 on 12 Nov, 100 Ochiltree and High Street 14 Nov, 12 Newton Crescent 18 Nov, 5 Ochiltree 9 Dec and 11 there 13 Dec. 20 Kilmahog 29 Oct. Stirling: 20 Cornton 30 Oct with 20 Princess St/Barnston St 5 to 8 Nov, 53 near railway station 7 Nov, 200 in unspecified locality 8 Nov with 220 on 10 Nov, 100 on 11 Nov, 150 on 13 Nov and 40 on 16 Nov, 3 over Broomride 22 Nov and 40 Springkerse 13 Dec. 8 Lochearnhead 1 Nov. Killin: 17 on 4 Nov with 38 on 18 Nov. BoA; 30 on 6 Nov with 35 there on 8 Nov, 15 on 11 Nov, 30 Airthrey 14 Nov and 20 on 28 Nov and 8 Dec, 8 Coneyhill 12 Dec and 5 on 25 Dec. 40 Buchany 11 Nov. 30 Aberfoyle E 14 Nov. 150 Gart GPs, Callander 14 Nov. 30 Plean 29 Nov.

WHITE-THROATED DIPPER *Cinclus cinclus* (B, W)
F Carronshore, Stenhousemuir: singles 3 Jan and 5 Feb, 1 on Chapel Burn 14 Jul and 1 on R Carron 8 Sep. Larbert: 1 R Carron 7 Feb and juv near Viaduct 7 Jul with 6 there 14 Oct. 1 Carron Glen, Frankerton, Denny 1 Mar and 30 Apr. 1 Strathavon Fm, Slamannan 29 May. 1 Bonny Water, Underwood-Bonnybridge 9 May.
C R Devon: at Dollar: 5 on 15 Jan with 9 there 31 Jan, 6 on 15 and 24 Feb and on 11

　　　　Mar, 9 on 17 Nov; at Crook of Devon: 5 on 19 Feb, 12 on 21 Nov and 10 on 18 Dec.
S　　　Killin: 2 on 15 Jan, 2 at Marshes 5 and 18 Mar, 1 on 21 Apr, 1 at Falls of Dochart
　　　　9 Jul, 3 at Marshes 23 Sep. Doune: 3 Lanrick 12 Feb, 11 Mar, 21 Oct and 11 Nov
　　　　with 6 there 15 Dec. 2 prs fighting over territory Achray Water 3 Feb. Kilmahog:
　　　　singles 12 Feb and 30 May with 2 Milton 6 Jun. Tyndrum: 2 Kirkton 28 Feb with
　　　　1 at the Fm 26 Apr and 2 at Dail Righ 2 May. Blairdrummond GPs: singles 15
　　　　Apr and 18 Aug, with 2 there 26 Dec. Callander: 1 Eas Gobhain 13 Feb with 2
　　　　carrying food Bochastle, Callander 29 Apr. 1 L Watston 12 May. 2 Strathfillan 21
　　　　May. 1 Kenknock, G Lochay 4 Jun. 1 Bows, BoD 21 Jul. 2 Dunblane 21 and 24
　　　　Oct. 2 Leamahamish, Aberfoyle 2 Dec.

WINTER WREN　*Troglodytes troglodytes*　(B, W)
　　　　Widespread and common but under-recorded. BBS: recorded at 2.0 b/1km.
F　　　Seven Carron Glen, Frankerton, Denny 1 Mar.
C　　　Seven Alva Woodland Park and Drove Rd 11 Mar with 8 there 22 Apr. 13 New
　　　　Sauchie, Alloa 1 May. 10 Cambus 13 Oct.
S　　　Holmehill, Dunblane: 7 on 13 May with 6 there 9 Jun, 10 on 27 Oct, 8 on 29 Nov
　　　　and 6 on 21 Dec. Several roosting in House Martin nests Coneyhill, BoA 29 Oct.
　　　　7 Blairdrummond GPs 1 Dec.

DUNNOCK　*Prunella modularis*　(B, W)
　　　　Widespread and common but under-recorded. BBS: recorded at 0.5 b/1km.
C　　　Kennetpans: 6 on 30 Jan with 13 there 9 May. 4 Blackdevon Wetlands 22 May.
S　　　Dunblane: Holmehill: 8 on 19 Feb with 6 there 10 Mar, 4 on 21 Apr and 7 on 15
　　　　May; Keir: 4 on 8 Jul. BoD, Argaty: 5 on 24 Nov and 1 Dec with 4 there 23 Dec.
　　　　4 Blairdrummond GPs 1 Dec.

EUROPEAN ROBIN　*Erithacus rubecula*　(B,W)
　　　　Widespread and common but under-recorded. BBS: recorded at 1.2 b/1km.
F　　　Pr with 2 juvs Liddle Dr, Bo'ness 12 Apr.
C　　　Ten New Sauchie, Alloa 1 May.
S　　　Holmehill, Dunblane: 7-9 recorded in Jan to Jun and Sep-Dec with 11 on 26
　　　　Aug. 8 Braeval, Aberfoyle 2 May. 7 Airthrey L, BoA 26 Sep. 7 Blairdrummond
　　　　GPs and Argaty, BoD 1 Dec.

COMMON REDSTART　*Phoenicurus phoenicurus*　(B)
　　　　Arrival in Apr: 1 singing Rednock, Lake of Menteith 16th (DT, RB) was 1 day
　　　　earlier than during 2005-2010 and 6 days later than in 2011. This was followed
　　　　by singles at the head of L Tay, Killin 21st and at 1 Coillie Coire Chuilc, Tyndrum
　　　　on 28th (JPH).
F　　　One Glensburgh, Grangemouth 22 Jun (AE).
S　　　Tyndrum: 7 AoTs 1 May, 13 AoTs 12 May and 9 AoTs 4 Jun (DMB). Flanders
　　　　Moss: pr Polder Moss 2 May, 2 on W Moss and 2 Blaircessnock 6 May (ABa).
　　　　Doune: 8 Lanrick 5 May, M there 6 May and 1 on 16 May; 3 Daldorn 16 May and
　　　　23 Jun and 2 Buchany 21 May. BoD: 2 Drumloist 6, 21 and 27 May with 1 on 12
　　　　Jun; 1 Rosehall 21 May; singles Bows 23 and 26 Jun. 4 Lake of Menteith 6 May
　　　　with 1 there 17 Jul. Loch Rusky: 1 on 6 May with 2 there 8 May (DOE). Pass of
　　　　Leny: 3 on 9 May and present 22 May (IF, ACC). Killin: present head of L Tay 14,
　　　　15, 20 and 23 May, 1, 3 and 9 Jun with 4 there 19 May; 1 Ardeonaig 4 Jun (JPH,
　　　　DOE). Ben Our: present 15 May and 12 Jun. Present Auchtertyre Glen Gorge
　　　　woodland, Strathfillan 16 May (JJB, JPH). Tigh na Blair: 2 on 16 and 21 May and
　　　　on 9 Jun. Callander: 2 Bracklinn 19 May with 1 there 5 Jun. 1 Cromlix 21 May.
　　　　Kilbryde: 4 on 21 May with 2 there 17 Jun. G Lochay: 4 in centre and 2 at
　　　　Kenknock 4 Jun (DOE). Present Auchlyne Rd, G Dochart 2 and 9 Jun (DMB,
　　　　JPH). 1 Edinample, Lochearnhead 4 Jun with 3 there 19 Jul (DOE). Chicks
　　　　ringed G Finglas 10 Jun. 2 Crianlarich 24 Jul (DOE, SMcG, AE).

WHINCHAT *Saxicola rubetra* (B)

    BBS: recorded at 0.1 b/lkm. Spring arrival in Apr: an early bird singing at Waterside, BoD 15th was 10 days earlier than the narrow arrival window of 2005-2011 (range: 24th April to 2nd May). The next arrivals were not until May: 1 Aberfoyle and 2 Tigh Mor, L Achray 4th, singles Ben Ledi 5th, Drumloist, BoD and Flanders Moss 6th and Braeleny, BoD 9th. No autumn departure dates were received this year.

F   One Strathavon Fm, Slamannan 29 May. 2 Skinflats 19 Jul and 6 Aug.

C   Blackdevon Wetlands: 1 on 13 May with M and F alarm-calling on AoT 27 May, 2 ads and 2 juvs 8 Jul. 2 Allaleckie, Forestmill 16 May.

S   Three L Arklet Res 18 May. 1 Drumloist, BoD 21 May. Singles Flanders Moss W 26 May and 14 Jul. 2 Kenknock, G Lochay 4 Jun. 2 Bracklinn, Callander 5 Jun. 6 G Finglas 16 Jul. 6 Edinchip, Lochearnhead 19 Jul. BoA: singles Sheriffmuir 10 and 21 Aug with family party (M, F and 4 locally fledged juvs) Cocksburn Res 11 Aug.

EURASIAN STONECHAT *Saxicola torquata* (b, w)

    Few records again; the species does not seem to have recovered (yet) from the cold winters of 2009 and 2010. BBS: recorded at 0.1 b/lkm.

S   Sheriffmuir: pr 16 Jan at Inn with 2 on 1 Apr and 1 on 20 May. CVR: 2 Cairnoch 7 Apr. 1 Ballochleam, Kippen 8 Apr. 2 Milton, Kilmahog 11 Apr. BoD: 2 F Ardoch Burn 15 Apr; 4 Bows 23 Jun. Present Ben Our 12 Jun. F and 3 fledged Y Cocksburn Res, BoA 19 Jul.

NORTHERN WHEATEAR *Oenanthe oenanthe* (B)

    BBS: recorded at 0.2 b/lkm. Spring arrival in Mar: 1 Inverlochlarig 18th was 3 days earlier than the 2005-2010 range (21st Mar to 6th Apr) but 4 days later than in 2011. This was followed by singles Alva 21st, Uamh Mhor, BoD and Meall Leathan Dhail 24th (M), Kinneil 25th, then in Apr: 1 Bows, BoD 1st and 2 Dumyat 2nd. Autumn departure: 1 Sheriffmuir 23rd Aug, then in Sep: 1 Kinneil 7th and 12th; 1 Ashfield, Dunblane and 2 King' Seat Hill 9th; 1 Bo'ness 14th, which falls within the early part of the extended departure window since 2005 (range: 5th Sep to 18th Oct).

C   Blackdevon Wetlands: 2 on 1 and 14 May. Longcarse, Alloa: 4 on 9 May. Present Alva woodland 5 Jun.

S   Two Fallin, Bandeath 10 Apr. 2 Cromlix Br 21 Apr. 9 Blaircessnock, Flanders Moss 6 May. Recorded Ben Our 15 May; An Caisteal 16 May and 13 Jun and Bein Dubhchraig, Alt Coire Dubhachraig 17 May. 2 Bracklinn, Callander 19 May. 4 Ardeonaig, Killin 4 Jun. Present Cairnoch, CVR 5 Jun. 2 Edinchip, Lochearnhead 19 Jul.

*RING OUZEL *Turdus torquatus* (b)

S   M Dumyat 1 May. 1 Auchtertyre G, Strathfillan 2 May. 1 Ben Our 15 May (JG, JPH, JJB). 1 An Caisteal 16 May with M there 13 Jun. 2 singing Ms and an alarm-calling F Stob a Choin 1 Jul (GG). 4 Crag MacRanaich 19 Jul. 1 chattering Auchtertyre, Stratfillan 25 Sep (JJB, GG, JPH).

COMMON BLACKBIRD *Turdus merula* (B, W)

    BBS: recorded at 2.4 b/lkm.

F   Skinflats: 10 on 7 Oct with 15 there 17 Nov and 29 Dec.

C   Ten Blackdevon Wetlands 10 Jan.

S   Eleven King's Park, Stirling 16 Feb. Dunblane: 1 collecting nest material in a garden 8 Mar with 12 Holmehill 13 May and 9 Jun with 14 there 29 Nov. 10 Argaty, BoD 24 Nov and 1 Dec.

FIELDFARE *Turdus pilaris* (W)

    Spring departure: 150 Drumloist, BoD 17 Mar dropped to 8 by 29 Apr. 40 Allan

Water, Kinbuck 31 Mar. Ca. 30 Plean CP 6 Apr. 180 Naggyfold, Cromlix Br 21 Apr. 35 Bracklinn, Callander 30 Apr. 4 Blaircessnock, Flanders Moss 6 May fall within the latter part of the 2005-2011 window (range: 25th Mar to 14th May). The large differences are no doubt a reflection of observer coverage rather than true variation.

Autumn arrival started very early with singles Kinneil 15 Aug and 3 Sep, the former being 53 days earlier than the 2005-2011 window (range: 7th to 22nd Oct). More seasonal were Oct arrivals: 20 Laighhills, Dunblane 13th; 4 Milton, Kilmahog 14th; present Kirkton Fm, Tyndrum 15th; 50 Keir, Dunblane, 150 Braeleny, BoD and an incredible 10,000+ G Lochay 27th.

F   Seventy Dunipace, Denny 22 Jan.

C   R Devon: 47 Menstrie 21 Jan with 360 there 12 Feb and 50 at Alva 9 Dec.

S   Ca. 100 Carse of Lecropt, BoA 16 Jan with 140 there 12 Feb. 150 Brae of Boquhapple Fm, Thornhill 27 Jan. 76 Stockbridge, Dunblane 5 Feb. 62 M. Ghaordaidh and 700 Tullich, G Lochay 11 Nov.

SONG THRUSH *Turdus philomelos* (B, W)

Under-recorded. BBS: recorded at 1.8 b/lkm. 3 Doune 19th Feb; BoA: 1 singing Coneyhill, BoA 25th Feb and 2 at Airthrey, BoA 29th Feb were the only winter records received.

F   Five Skinflats 7 Oct.

C   Three New Sauchie, Alloa 1 May. 4 Fishcross 24 May.

S   Three Doune 4 Mar. 1 singing Coneyhill, BoA 8 May. BoD: 3 Argaty 22 May and 3 Drumloist 26 May. 3 central G Lochay 4 Jun. 3 Ardeonaig, Killin 4 Jun. 3 Lake of Menteith 14 Jul.

REDWING *Turdus iliacus* (W)

Spring departure: 35 Blairdrummond GPs 10 Mar; 3 Dunipace, Denny and 4 Hill of Row, Dunblane 11 Mar; 50 Drumloist, BoD 17 Mar; 1 Eas Gobhain, Callander 18 Mar; 10 Allan Water, Kinbuck 31 Mar; 2 Bows, BoD 1 Apr; 2 Doune 15 Apr and a very late bird at New Sauchie, Alloa 1 May. This is 18 days later than the latest date of the 2005-2011 window (range: 7th Mar to 13th Apr). The large differences are no doubt a reflection of observer coverage rather than true variation.

Autumn arrival in Oct: 6 Cambus 11th was towards the latter end of the 2005-2011 arrival window (27th Sep to 12th Oct). This was followed by 300 there and 50 Laighhills, Dunblane 13th; 13 Larbert, 40 Milton, Kilmahog, 40 Carse of Lecropt, BoA, 50 Dunipace, Denny and 50 Coilhallan Wood, Callander 14th; 2 L Watston 21st; 5 Doune 26th; 5 Keir, Dunblane, 8 Holmehill, Dunblane and 25 Braeleny, BoD 27th; 5 R Devon, Alva 28th.

F   A hundred and thirty Dunmore 13 Jan. 130 Powfoulis 12 Feb.

S   Seventy-five Doune railway track 1 Feb. 50 Frew 18 Feb. 60+ Lake of Menteith 30 Nov.

MISTLE THRUSH *Turdus viscivorus* (B, W)

Under-recorded. Few noteworthy records received again this year. BBS: recorded at 0.2 b/lkm.

F   Four Blackness 4 and 17 Nov.

S   One singing Coneyhill, BoA 23 Jan. 6 L Mahaick 24 Jun. 4 Keir, Dunblane 8 Jul. 6 Braeleny, BoD 27 Oct. 10 Lanrick, Doune 11 Nov. 4 Blairdrummond GPs and 4 Argaty, BoD 1 Dec.

COMMON GRASSHOPPER WARBLER *Locustella naevia* (b)

Spring arrival in Apr: 1 Skinflats and 2 singing Blackdevon Wetlands 21st were within the remarkably stable arrival window of 2005-2011 (range: 17th to 27th). The Blackdevon count increased to 3 on 28th when singing males were also recorded at the head of L Tay and at the Marshes, Killin.

F   Two Skinflats 27 May with birds present there 24 and 30 Jun and 1 singing in the village 19 Jul. 1 Darnrig Moss 5 Jun. Present Kinneil 9 Jun.

C   One Blackdevon Wetlands 22 May.

S   Killin: singles singing on several dates 30 Apr to 1 Jun with 1 also singing at the Marshes 1 May. Singles L Ard Forest 3 May; Strathfillan 21 May; singing Dalrigh, Tyndrum 22 May; Kilbryde 17 Jun; Blairdrummond GPs 8 Jul; Lake of Menteith 14 Jul and Inverlochlarig 19 Jul.

SEDGE WARBLER *Acrocephalus schoenobaenus* (B)

BBS: recorded at 0.1 b/lkm. Spring arrival in Apr was slow: 1 Cambus 22nd was within the remarkably stable arrival window of 2005-2011 (range: 21st to 30th). This was followed by 1 Carse of Lecropt, BoA 29th, then singles Kinneil and Skinflats village not until 6th May. No autumn departure dates were received this year.

F   One Glensburgh, Grangemouth 13 May. Skinflats: 6 on 22 May with 2 in the village 24 May and at least 6 singing there 21 Jul.

C   One Cambus and 7 Kennetpans 9 May. 1 singing Longcarse, Alloa 12 May and also present there 16 and 24 May. Blackdevon Wetlands: singles 12 to 14 May with 11 there 22 May. 1 R Devon, Alva 20 May.

S   Carse of Lecropt, BoA: 2 on 9 May with 4 there 16 May. Blairdrummond GPs: 5 on 13 May with 4 there 27 May; 1 at Carse 26 May. Recorded head of L Tay, Killin on several dates 15 May to 17 Jun. Singles Cromlix, Strathfillan and Tigh na Blair 21 May. Dunblane: singles Hill of Row 22 and 27 May; 1 Keir, 1 Flanders Moss W and 5 L Watston, all on 26 May.

*REED WARBLER *Acrocephalus scirpaceus*

Following the first four records, including confirmed breeding, of the species in 2011, there were another four records, indicating that the species may be colonising the Upper Forth area.

F   One singing Skinflats 27 May (CJP, RS, AB) with 2 there 4 Jun (ACC). 1 Kinneil 9 Sep. These are the 6th to 8th records of the species in the recording area.

C   One singing Blackdevon Wetlands 21 April (CJP). This is the 5th record of the species in the recording area.

EURASIAN BLACKCAP *Sylvia atricapilla* (B)

BBS: recorded at 0.2 b/lkm. Winter records: BoA: as since 2009, recorded Alexander Drive where M and F 1 and 29 Jan. 3 Craigknowe, Alva 28 Jan. M Doune 30 Jan. 1 Blackness 4 Nov. 1 Doune 11 Nov and M Coneyhill, BoA 24 Nov. Spring arrival in Apr: 1 Skinflats 1st was 4 days earlier than the 2005-2011 arrival window (range: 5th to 13th). This was followed by 1 singing Larbert Pond 11th; 1 Airthrey, BoA 12th; 1 King's Park, Stirling and 2 Falkirk 14th; singles Doune and Dunblane allotments and 3 Fishcross 15th; M Lake of Menteith 16th; pr Plean CP 17th; 1 Ledcameroch, Dunblane 18th.

Autumn departure: 1 Hill of Row, Dunblane 2 Sep; M Liddle Drive, Bo'ness 21 Sep; 1 Blairdrummond GPs 22 Sep; M Cromlix Br 7 Oct and 4 Holmehill, Dunblane 27 Oct. The latter is 33 days later than the latest available date since 2005 (24 Sep 2008) but may have been an overwintering bird.

F   One Skinflats 21 Apr with 2 there 16 Aug. 2 Larbert Pond 23 Apr.

C   Three singing Devon Way, Tillicoultry 20 Apr. 3 Kennet 14 May. 3 Woodland Park and Drove Road, Alva 24 Jun. 3 (2 juvs) Cambus 20 Jul. Also recorded during the breeding season from Tullibody, Fishcross and Alloa.

S   Dunblane: 2 Holmehill 21 Apr with 3 there 13 May and 9 Jun and 4 on 27 Oct; 4 at Keir 8 Jul. Doune: 2 in unspecified locality there 29 Apr with 4 Lanrick 5 May. 2 Callander Crags 30 Apr. Cromnlix: 1 on 30 Apr with 4 there 5 and 21 May.

Blairdrummond GPs: 4 on 13 May with 3 there 19 and 26 Aug. 3 L Watston 26 May. 4 Drumloist, BoD 26 May with 3 there 3 Jun.

GARDEN WARBLER *Sylvia borin* (B)

Spring arrival in Apr: 1 Kingseat Place, Falkirk 15th was 4 days earlier than the 2005-2010 arrival window (range: 19th Apr to 2nd May) but 10 days later than in 2011. 1 singing Rednock, Lake of Menteith and 1 King's Park, Stirling 16th; 1 Larbert Pond 23rd. No autumn departure dates were received this year.

F   Seen several dates Kingseat Place, Falkirk 17 Apr to 1 Jul with 2 there 17 Jun. Singles Carronshore, Stenhousemuir 19 May, Bo'ness shore E 20 May and Torwood, Larbert 24 Jun.

C   Singles Tullibody 19 May; R Devon, Alva 20 May and Fishcros 24 May. 2 Alva Glen 27 May.

S   Doune: singles Lanrick 5 May; Daldorn 16 May and 23 Jun. Dunblane: 1 in unspecified locality there 6 May and 2 Baxter's Loan 19 May. 1 Carse of Lecropt, BoA 9 May. Present Plean CP 12 May. Blairdrummond GPs: 2 on 13 May with 1 there 8 Jul. Killin: recorded head of L Tay 19 May; 1 Ardeonaig 4 Jun. 1 Cromlix 21 May. 1 Logie Kirk, BoA 23 May. Singles Drumloist, BoD 26 May and 3 Jun. 1 L Watston 26 May. 2 Tigh na Blair 9 Jun. 2 singing at the youth hostel, Crianlarich 13 Jun. 2 Kilbryde 17 Jun. 1 Gart GPs, Callander 20 Jun. 3 Braentrian, L Tay 20 Jun. 1 Buchany 24 and 25 Jun.

COMMON WHITETHROAT *Sylvia communis* (B)

BBS: recorded at 0.2 b/lkm. Spring arrival in Apr: singles Cambus and King's Park, Stirling 22nd was just outside the 2005-2010 window (range: 23rd Apr to 2nd May) and 2 days later than in 2011. This was followed by singles Skinflats 29th, Kinneil, Skinflats village and Flanders Moss W 6th, Blackdevon Wetlands, Kennetpans and Lecropt Carse, BoA 9th.

Autumn departure: 4 Kinneil 6th Aug and 1 Skinflats 16th was within the 2005-2011 window (range: 2nd Aug to 24th Sep).

F   Three singing Kinneil 8 May. 1 Glensburgh, Grangemouth 13 May. 4 Skinflats 22 May. 5 S Alloa 9 Jun.

C   One Longcarse, Alloa 12 May. 1 Blackdevon Wetlands 12 to 14 May with 5 there 22 May. 6 Fishcross 24 May.

S   One Carse of Lecropt, BoA 9 May. 1 Craigforth, Stirling 12 May. 3 Blairdrummond GPs 13 May. 1 Argaty, BoD 14 May. 1 central Dunblane 15 May with 4 Keir 26 May and 8 Jul. 4 Blairdrummond Carse 26 May. 1 Auchlyne Rd, G Dochart 2 Jun.

WOOD WARBLER *Phylloscopus sibilatrix* (B)

A high number of records again. Arrival in May: 1 Kilmahog 1st (WMcB) was within the standard arrival window of 2005-2010 (range: 17th Apr to 5th May). This was followed by singles Tigh Mor, L Achray and 2 G Finglas 2nd; 2 Aberfoyle 4th; 1 L Ard Forest and 2 Brig o'Turk 5th; 1 Callander Crags and 6 Pass of Leny 9th (RE, FAM, CJP, KF, DOE, IF).

S   Killin: present head of L Tay 14, 15 and 19 May; at Marshes 19 and 23 May and 2 Jun, 1 Baxter's Loan, Dunblane 19 May. 1 singing L Katrine 20 May. 5 Pass of Leny 22 May (JPH, CJP, GS, ACC). 1 Auchlyne Rd. G Dochart 2 Jun; 1 Camusurich, L Tay, 2 AoTs Tyndrum and 3 central G Lochay 4 Jun; 1 heard G Finglas 10 Jun; 3 AoTs Callander Crags 13 Jun; 6 G Finglas 16 Jul (JPH, DOE, DMB, SMcG).

COMMON CHIFFCHAFF *Phylloscopus collybita* (B)

BBS: recorded at 0.1 b/lkm. Spring arrival in Mar: 1 King's Park, Stirling 18th was a typical date within the 2005-2011 arrival window (range: 13th to 31st Mar). This was followed by 1 singing Larbert Pond 21st; 1 singing Holme Hill, Dunblane

24th after which widespread with birds reported from Grangepans, Bo'ness; Forth/Clyde Canal, Bonnybridge; Skinflats; Kinneil (2); Woodland Park, Alva; Tillicoultry; Callander; Lake of Menteith and G Finglas on 25th.
Autumn departure: Sep: singles Blairdrummond GPs, Larbert Pond and Carron, Stenhousemuir 8th; Kinneil 21st; Dunblane 22nd; Airthrey, BoA 26th. Oct: 1 singing Ashfield 6th and 2 Skinflats 7th. The latter was a day later than the 2005-2011 departure window (range: 17th Sep to 6th Oct).

F   Two Larbert Pond 27 Mar and 1 there 11 Apr. 2 Skinflats 13 Apr. 2 Carronshore, Stenhousemuir and 3 Glensburgh, Grangemouth 14 Apr. 1 Lionthorn, Falkirk 26 Apr.

C   One singing Gartmorn Dam 29 Mar. 1 Cambus 31 Mar. 3 Fishcross 15 Apr. 2 Woodland Park, Alva 22 Apr.

S   Blairdrummond GPs: 1 singing 27 Mar with 2 there 31 Mar, 7 on 15 Apr, 3 on 13 May and 8 Jun. Dunblane: 1 singing Holmehill 27 Mar with 3 there 11 Apr, 4 on 21 Apr and on 6 May, 3 on 13 May and on 9 Jun, 5 on 22 Jul and 3 on 26 Aug; 1 Keir 28 Mar; 3 singing Laighhills 14 Apr. 4 Murrayshall, Stirling 29 Mar. 4 Doune in unspecified locality 15 Apr. BoA: 2 singing Mine Wood 8 Apr, 1 Airthrey 12 Apr, 1 singing Coneyhill 13 and 17 Apr. Callander: 2 at Crags and 2 Gart GPs 14 Apr, 1 Bracklinn 30 Apr. BoD: 2 Rosehall 15 Apr, 1 Drumloist 17 and 29 Apr, 4 Argaty 22 May. Aberfoyle: singles at Pass 19 Apr and at David Marshall Lodge 21 Apr. 1 G Finglas 21 Apr.

WILLOW WARBLER *Phylloscopus trochilus* (B)
BBS: recorded at 1.7 b/lkm. Spring arrival in Apr: 1 Mine Wood, BoA 8th was within the 2005-2011 arrival window (range: 3rd to 14th Apr). This was followed by 1 Skinflats and 2 Carse of Lecropt, BoA 11th; 1 Cambus 12th; 1 Alva 13th; singles Laighhills, Dunblane and Gart GPs, Callander and 2 Glensburgh, Grangemouth 14th.
Autumn departure in Sep: 3 Kinneil 21st and 1 Skinflats 23rd, which was well within the 2005-2011 departure window (range: 14th Sep to 6th Oct).

F   Skinflats: 5 on 13 and 15 Apr, with at least 5 singing in the village 15 Apr and 10 on 29 Aug. In the breeding season recorded at Lionheart and Wholeflats, Falkirk; Larbert Pond and Carron G, Frankerton, Denny.

C   Twenty-seven New Sauchie, Alloa 1 May. 14 Allaleckie, Forestmill 16 May with 15 there 14 Jun. 16 Fishcross 24 May. Present Cambus and Tullibody Inch 26 Aug.

S   Ten Blairdrummond GPs 15 Apr and 19 Aug. 5 Manse Rd, Aberfoyle and 5 Flanders Moss E 21 Apr. 40 High Corries 29 Apr. L Ard Forest: 5 on 29 Apr with 15 there 5 May and 13 on 14 May. 15 Lanrick, Doune 15 May. BoD: 12 Drumloist 6 May and 12 Argaty 22 May. 9 L Rusky 8 May. 26 AoTs Touch 27 May. 10 Edinchip, Lochearnhead 19 Jul. In breeding season smaller numbers also recorded at CVR; King's Park, Stirling; Ledcameroch, Dunblane; Cromlix; Doune; Kilbryde, Drumloist and Argaty, BoD; Bracklinn and Callander Crags; G Finglas; G Balquhidder; Tigh Mor, L Achray; Pass of Aberfoyle; head of L Tay, Killin and Tyndrum.

GOLDCREST *Regulus regulus* (B, W)
Under-recorded. BBS: recorded at 1.7 b/lkm.

F   Seven Skinflats 7 Oct.

S   Doune: 8 in unspecified locality there 29 Jan and 15 Apr with 7 Lanrick 11 Mar, 10 there 21 Oct and 6 on 11 Nov. 6 Blairdrummond GPs 15 Apr and 19 Aug and 7 on 31 Dec. 15 Drumloist, BoD 29 Apr with 6 there 6 May. 6 Cromlix 30 Apr.

SPOTTED FLYCATCHER *Muscicapa striata* (B)
Spring arrival in May: 1 Tillicoultry G 12th was a typical date compared to 2005-2011 (range: 9th to 20th May). This was followed by 1 Blairdrummond GPs 13th, 1

G Lochay 20th, 1 Strathfillan, 2 Cromlix and 2 Kilbryde all on 21st; singles Kirkton Fm, Tyndrum and Pass of Leny 22nd; 1 head of L Tay, Killin 23rd; 2 Doune and 3 Blairdrummond GPs 27th; 2 G Beich 28th; 1 Airthrey, BoA 30th. Autumn departure: 1 Blairdrummond GPs 19th Aug and 1 Gartmorn Dam 1st Sep, which was within the 2005-2010 window (range: 25th Aug to 15th Sep) with a likely later departure in 2011 (b/3 still present 10th Sep).

S   G Lochay: 8 Kenknock and 12 in centre 4 Jun. Killin: 4 Ardeonaig 4 Jun with 2 there 20 Jun; 1 head of L Tay 6 and 9 Jun. Lochearnhead: 2 Edinample 4 Jun and 12 Edinchip 19 Jul. 2 Tigh na Blair 19 Jun. BoD: 2 Argaty 15 Jun and 2 there 19 Jul; singles Bows 25 Jun and 21 Jul. 1 G Beich 15 Jun. 3 Cromlix and 3 Kilbryde 17 Jun. 2 Braentrian, L Tay 20 Jun. 2 Buchany 24 Jun. 2 Blairdrummond GPs 8 Jul. Doune: 2 Lanrick 8 and 13 Jul with 4 in unspecified locality there 26 Jul. 2 Keir, Dunblane 8 Jul. 2 Flanders Moss W and 2 Lake of Menteith 14 Jul. 7 G Finglas 16 Jul. 5 Inverlochlarig 19 Jul. 1 Crianlarich 24 Jul.

EURASIAN PIED FLYCATCHER *Ficedula hypoleuca* (b)
S   Two Pass of Leny 9 May. 1 singing G Lochay 20 May with 2 in centre of glen 4 Jun (IF, JPH, DOE). F sitting on young chicks Glen Finglas 10 Jun (SMcG).

LONG-TAILED BUSHTIT (LONG-TAILED TIT) *Aegithalos caudatus* (B, W)
   BBS: recorded at 0.2 b/lkm.
F   Fourteen Skinflats 19 Feb. 10 Liddle Drive, Bo'ness 3 Dec.
C   R Devon: 18 Alva 28 Oct and 12 Cambus 18 Nov.
S   Dunblane: 19 Greenyards 12 Jan with 15 Keir 9 Nov. 18 in unspecified locality, Doune 29 Jan. 15 Airthrey, BoA 26 Sep. 12 Braeleny, BoD 27 Oct. 12 Blairdrummond GPs 26 Dec. 15 Flanders Moss E 26 Dec.

BLUE TIT *Cyanistes caeruleus* (B, W)
   Widespread but under-recorded. BBS: recorded at 1.8 b/lkm.
C   Twelve Woodland Park and Drove Rd, Alva 1 Jan. 10 Forestmill 30 Jan. 10 Kennetpans 30 Jan with 12 there 9 May. 15 R Devon, Alva 19 Feb. 10 New Sauchie, Alloa 1 May.
S   Holmehill, Dunblane: 17 on 14 Jan with 15 there 19 Feb, 17 on 10 Mar, 13 on 11 Apr, 10 on 21 Apr, 10 on 29 Nov and 11 on 21 Dec. 34 Logie Kirk, BoA 23 May. Argaty, BoD: 10 on 24 Nov, 13 on 1 Dec and 10 on 23 Dec. 10 Blairdrummond GPs 26 Dec.

GREAT TIT *Parus major* (B, W)
   Widespread but under-recorded. BBS: recorded at 0.9 b/lkm.
C   Ten Woodland Park and Drove Rd, Alva 1 Jan. Holmehill, Dunblane: 14 on 14 Jan, 20 on 19 Feb, 10 on 11 Apr and 12 on 21 Apr. 46 Logie Kirk, BoA 23 May.

COAL TIT *Periparus ater* (B, W)
   Widespread but under-recorded. BBS: recorded at 0.5 b/lkm.
S   Doune: 10 in unspecified locality there 29 Jan with 12 on 10 Mar and 6 on 1 Dec; 7 Lanrick 12 Feb with 9 there 11 Mar and 10 on 11 Nov. 8 Manse Rd, Aberfoyle 4 Feb. Dunblane: 6 Hill of Row 26 Feb and 9 Holmehill 21 Dec. BoD: 8 Drumloist 17 Mar with 12 there 29 Apr, 8 on 6 May; 6 Bows 21 Jul; 16 Argaty 24 Nov with 12 there 1 Dec, 14 on 23 Dec and 10 on 28 Dec. Callander: 8 Gart GPs 14 Apr with 6 Bracklinn 30 Apr. 7 Blairdrummond GPs 15 Apr with 8 there 19 Aug, 12 on 26 Aug and 1 Dec, 8 on 26 and 31 Dec. 7 Kilbryde 21 May. 8 Lake of Menteith 14 Jul. 10 Flanders Moss E 26 Dec.

EURASIAN NUTHATCH *Sitta europaea*
   Following its first appearance in 1999 and the first breeding record in 2009, the species is consolidating its spread in the recording area.
C   Singles Dollar Glen 17 and 26 Apr (MFB, GCh).
S   Aberfoyle: 1 on feeders in E during 1 Jan to 19 Feb with 2 there 26 Feb and 1 on

31 Aug; singles Leamahamish 19 Feb, Manse Road 26 Aug and 2 Dec on feeder (DOE, KF). BoA: singles Airthrey 13 and 15 Jan, 29 Feb, 12 Apr, 2 May, 24 Aug and 18 Oct; 4 Mine Wood 8 Apr; 1 Lecropt Nursery 24 Nov (DMB, CJP, ACC, BD, RJD, JN). Dunblane: singles Ledcameroch 28 Jan, 17 Mar, 18 Apr and on feeder there 21 Jul; 2 Kippenross 5 Feb; singles Holmehill 31 Mar and 11 Nov with 2 there 29 Nov and 1 on 21 Dec; 2 Craigarnhall 5 May; 1 Keir 8 Jul (CJS, DOE, CJP). 1 Lanrick, Doune 11 Mar. Lake of Menteith: 3 to 4 on E shore 25 Mar and 5 Apr, 1 calling Rednock 16 Apr, 3 on E shore 27 Apr with 1 there 28 May and 1+ on 30 Nov (DOE, DT, RB). 1 singing Callander 25 Mar. Singles Blairdrummond GPs 31 Mar and 1 Dec (LT, DOE). Singles Plean CP 5 Apr and 12 May with a pr there 17 Apr. 1 on nut basket Kirkton Fm, Tyndrum 5 Apr. 1 Brig o'Turk 6 May. 1 Strathyre 14 May (DT, AB, JPH, JB, DOE).

EURASIAN TREECREEPER *Certhia familiaris* (B, W)
Under-recorded. BBS: recorded at 0.1 b/lkm.
S   Three Keir, Dunblane 8 Jul. 4 Lake of Menteith 14 Jul. 4 G Finglas 15 and 16 Jul. 5 Edinchip, Lochearnhead 19 Jul. 3 Bows, BoD 21 Jul. 3 Gart GPs, Callander 25 Jul. 6 Blairdrummond GPs 19 Aug with 4 there 1, 26 and 31 Dec. 3 Holmehill, Dunblane 29 Nov.

*GREAT GREY SHRIKE *Lanius excubitor*
S   One Cock Hill, L Rusky 1 Jan (DR). 1 Milton, Kilmahog 11 to 16 and 19 Feb (LA, DOE, BG, CJP).

EURASIAN JAY *Garrulus glandarius* (B, W)
F   One Kinneil 21 Sep.
C   One Meeks Park, Aberdona 21 Sep. Singles calling Castlebridge Business Park, Forestmill: 2, 5, 8 and 12 Oct.
S   Five Manse Rd, Aberfoyle 4 Feb. 5 Stockbridge to Greenyards, Dunblane 5 Feb. 3 Blairdrummond GPs 5 Feb with 5 there 19 Aug, 3 on 8 Sep and 7 on 31 Dec. 5 High Corries, L Ard Forest 29 Apr. 4 Lanrick, Doune 5 May. 4 Keir, Dunblane 8 Jul.

EURASIAN MAGPIE *Pica pica* (B, W)
Continues to be very scarce NW of Dunblane. Abundant around Stirling but is not usually as frequent in the west; large groups now widespread in Falkirk District. Again only small groups recorded this year. BBS: recorded at 0.5 b/lkm.
C   Ten Blackdevon Wetlands 12 Jan. 12 R Devon, Alva 19 Feb.
S   Dunblane: 19 Stockbridge in Apr; 12 Holmehill 29 Sep. 14 gathering to roost Bo'ness to Kinneil 12 Oct.

WESTERN JACKDAW *Corvus monedula* (B, W)
Widespread but under-recorded. BBS: recorded at 2.6 b/lkm.
F   Fifty Kinneil and 100 Skinflats 27 Dec.
S   One hundred Allan Water, Kinbuck 31 Mar. Blairdrummond: 50 at the Quarry 31 Mar, 26 Aug, 10 and 30 Nov, 1 and 28 Dec with 60 there 31 Dec; 100 on Carse 10 Nov. Doune: 50 Lanrick 5 May and 60 Daldorn 23 Jun; 100 L Watston 10 Nov. BoA: pre-roost gathering of 50 in unspecified locality there 30 Nov; 400 Carse of Lecropt 28 Dec.

ROOK *Corvus frugilegus* (B, W)
Systematic counts of known rookeries (e.g. BoA, Gartmorn, Forth and Clyde Canal, Lake of Menteith, etc.) are welcomed. BBS: recorded at 3.7 b/lkm.
F   One hundred Skinflats village 7 Jan and 100 Skinflats 29 Dec.
S   Dunblane rookeries in Apr had ca. 280 nests compared to 229 in 2010 and 200 in 2011: 13 nests Victoria Hall, 7 nests Strathmore Avenue, 74 nests Holmehill, 90 nests Kippendavie Rd, 43 nests Duthieston House, 21 nests Queen Victoria School, 10 nests Dunblane Hydro, 14 nests Doune Rd/Grant Drive junction and

8 nests Perth Rd (new site) (MVB, CJS). 120 birds Carse of Lecropt, BoA 28 Jan and 150 there 28 Dec. 150 Blairdrummond Carse 5 Feb. 110 Holmehill, Dunblane 10 Mar with 120 on 11 Apr and 100 on 21 Apr. 200 Allan Water, Kinbuck 31 Mar.

CARRION CROW   *Corvus corone* (B, W)

BBS: recorded at 3.5 b/lkm.

C   Breeding season: 40 Woodland Park and Drove Rd, Alva 22 Apr. 36 New Sauchie, Alloa 1 May. 18 R Devon, Alva 20 May. 14 Allaleckie, Forestmill 14 Jun.

S   Breeding season: 10 Daldorn, Doune 23 Jun; 25 Buchany 24 Jun; 10 Blairdrummond GPs 26 Aug.

HOODED CROW   *Corvus cornix* (b, w)

F   Singles Blackness 29 Jan and 25 Feb.

S   One L Doine, Balquhidder 18 Jan. G Dochart: 2 hybrids Bovain and 2 pure birds and 2 hybrids Ledcharrie all 7 Feb. Singles Tigh Mor, L Achray 29 and 30 Apr. 1 Ben Our 15 May. 1 Strathfillan 21 May. G Lochay: 2 Kenknock 4 Jun with 1 Tullich 1 Nov. 1 An Caisteal 6 Jun. 1 Stob a Choin 1 Jul. 20 Crianlarich 31 Aug. Singles Laighhills, Dunblane 13 Oct and 8 Nov. 1 M. Ghaordaidh 1 Nov.

NORTHERN RAVEN   *Corvus corax* (B, W)

Again several reports from NW Stirlingshire but the large roost in the Doune Lodge area seems to have been abandoned since 2010. The slow colonization of Clackmannanshire seems to continue. BBS: recorded at 0.1 b/lkm.

F   One St. Helen's Loch, Bonnybridge 22 Jan. Falkirk: 2 in unspecified locality there 8 Feb and 2 Lionthorn 7 Oct. 2 on electricity pylon Langlees, Carron, Stenhousemuir.

C   Forestmill: 1-2 seen on several dates 27 Jan to 8 Oct Castlebridge Business Park with AoT there 7 Jun; 1 Allaleckie 3 Feb. Alloa Rhind: 2 feeding on sheep carcass 29 Feb with ad pr and Y there 11 May (thought to have possibly bred on nearby electricity pylon) and 1 on 14 Oct. Dollar: 1 Saddle Hill, Craiginnan 18 Mar; 1 Sheardale Woods 15 May. Singles Cambus 12 Apr, 1 May and 13 Oct. 2 Alva 21 Apr.

S   Strathfillan: 6 close to sheep carcass Auchtertyre 6 Jan; 2 Gleann a' Chlachain woodland 28 Jan and 2 Feb. 4 Brae of Boquhapple Fm, Thornhill 11 Jan. BoA: 3 Carse of Lecropt 28 Jan with 2 there 24 Jul and 21 Sep; 5 Airthrey 21 Sep with 4 there 11 Oct. Flanders Moss: 2 in E section 5 Feb and 19 Feb with 1 there 6 May; 1 in W section 6 May with 3 there 26 May. BoD: 1 Argaty 13 and 17 Feb with 2 there 1 Apr, 1 on 24 Nov and 2 on 1 and 23 Dec; 1 Bows 17 Mar with 2 there 1 Apr and 21 May, 1 on 23 and 24 Jun; 1 Drumloist 14 Apr with 2 there 17 Apr, 3 on 6 May, 1 on 26 May, 4 on 12 Jun; 1 Rosehall 15 Apr with 3 there 21 May. Dunblane: 2 Hill of Row 19 Feb; 1 Laighhills 13 Oct. Aberfoyle: 1 L Ard Forest 29 Feb with 2 there 5 May; 7 in village 26 Aug. Doune: 2 Lanrick 11 Mar, 14 Apr and 5 May with 1 on 16 May, 1 on 8 and 13 Jul, 2 on 11 Nov and 1 on 15 Dec; 2 Daldorn 16 May with 5 there 23 Jun; 1 Ashfield 21 Oct. 2 Sheriffmuir 17 Mar. 2 Meall Leathan Dhail 24 Mar. L Mahaick: 1 on 27 Mar and 2 on 24 Jun. 4 Allan Water, Kinbuck 31 Mar. 1 L Rusky 2 Apr. CVR: 2 Cairnoch 21 Apr with 3 there 5 Jun. Callander: 1 Bracklinn 30 Apr with 2 there 6 May, 1 on 19 May; 2 ads and 1 recent fledgling Corrie Holdings 5 Jun; 1 at Crags 29 Dec. 1 G Balquhidder 30 Apr. 1 Tigh Mor, L Achray 30 Apr. 2 prs in aerial display Malling Forest Estate, Lake of Menteith 2 May. Singles An Caisteal 16 May and 13 Jun. Killin: 1 Ardeonaig 4 Jun and 2 head of L Tay 10 Nov. Singles Buchany 24 and 25 Jun. 1 M. Ghaordaidh 1 Nov. 2 Kirkton Fm, Tyndrum 13 Dec.

COMMON STARLING   *Sturnus vulgaris* (B, W)

Greatly under-recorded. BBS: recorded at 5.4 b/lkm.

F   One hundred Kinneil 25 Sep. 200 Skinflats 17 Nov and 29 Dec.

C   One hundred Kennetpans 30 Jan.

S   One hundred and twenty in unspecified locality in Doune 15 Feb. 300 Drumloist, BoD 3 Mar. 150 Blairdrummond Carse 10 Nov.

HOUSE SPARROW *Passer domesticus* (B, W)

Under-recorded. BBS: recorded at 1.8 b/lkm.

F   Ten Forth and Clyde Canal, Falkirk 11 Feb. Breeding season: recorded from Gartcows Drive, Falkirk; Skinflats; Bo'ness and S Alloa (20). Skinflats: 10 on 14 and 23 Sep, 35 on 16 Sep. 10 Blackness 7 Oct. 50 Stonehouse Fm, Powfoulis 25 Nov.

C   Twenty-five Forestmill 5 Jan. 16 in unspecified locality in Alloa and 15 Haugh of Blackgrange 12 Feb. Breeding season: recorded from Tullibody (16); Fishcross; Longcarse, Alloa; Kennet (23); Kennetpans; R Devon, Alva and Allaleckie, Forestmill.

S   Ten Callander 7 Jan. 12 Brae of Boquhapple Fm, Thornhill 16 Jan and 27 Jan, 8 Feb and 7 Mar. 15 Blairdrummond Carse 22 Jan with 10 there 5 and 25 Feb. 20 Keir, Dunblane 28 Jan. 10 Flanders Moss E and 20 Craigforth, Stirling 5 Feb. 30 in unspecified locality in Doune 19 Feb with 15 there 4 Mar. Breeding season: recorded from Boquhan, Kippen; Blaircessnock, Flanders Moss; Carse of Lecropt, BoA; Cromlix; Frew; Brae of Boquhapple Fm, Thornhill; Keir and Ochiltree, Dunblane (M feeding 2 chicks); Lanrick and L Watston, Doune; Blairdrummond GPs and Carse; Argaty and Bows, BoD; Lake of Menteith; Bracklinn, Callander; G Beich; Ardeonaig, Killin; Youth Hostel, Crianlarich and Braentrian, L Tay. 50 Waterside and Hutchison, Ashfield 9 Sep. 10 Argaty, BoD 9 Sep and 23 Dec. 30 Blairdrummond Carse 30 Nov. 40 Ashfield 1 Dec.

EURASIAN TREE SPARROW *Passer montanus* (B, W)

Very few large flocks again this year. BBS: recorded at 0.1 b/lkm.

F   Five Dunmore 14 Jan. Bo'ness: 2 Bo'mains Meadow 28 Jan; juv with metal ring Liddle Drive 11 Jun with 1 there 13 Oct and 2 on 1 Nov. Skinflats: 2 on 28 Feb with 20 on 26 Sep, 2 on 12 Oct and 23 on 16 Nov; in village 12 on 9 Jun with 20 there 19 Jul, 10 on 6 Aug, 10 on 7 Oct and 15 on 19 Oct. 10 S Alloa 1 Mar. 25+ Powfoulis 21 Apr with 20 there at Stonehouse Fm 25 Nov. 6 Glensburgh, Grangemouth 13 May with 2 there 13 Oct. 4 Blackness 7 Oct.

C   Cambus: 30 on 22 Jan with 20 there 31 Jan. Kennetpans: 16 on 30 Jan with 25 there 9 May and 21 on 12 Jun. R Devon, Alva: 1 on 19 Feb with 1 there 11 Nov.

S   Blairdrummond Carse: 6 on 6 Jan with 15 there 22 Jan, 40 on 28 Jan, 18 on 5 Feb, 10 on 25 Feb, 35 on 28 Feb, 40 on 4 Mar, 12 at S Kirklane on 7 Apr, 10 on 26 May, 20 on 10 Nov, 45 on 30 Nov and 20 on 26 Dec; 1 at Quarry 8 Jul. Dunblane: 17 Ashfield (Hutchison to Waterside) 9 Jan with 8 there 7 Oct as well as 2 on 25 Dec; 25 Keir 28 Jan with 1 there 19 Jun and 15 on 28 Dec; 10 Hill of Row 29 Jan; 7 Lanrick 1 Feb; 13 Stockbridge to Greenyards 5 Feb; 6 Woodend Cottage 14 Apr; 4 Kippenross 2 Nov and 25 Glenhead 13 Nov. Thornhill: 4 Brae of Boquhapple Fm 11 Jan and 8 Feb with 5 there 23 Feb and 7 Mar, 6 on 28 Mar and 2 on 5 Apr; 45 Whirrieston 5 Feb; 25 Easter Poldar 28 Nov. 12 Flanders Moss E 5 Feb with 10 there 19 Feb. Carse of Lecropt, BoA: 50 on 5 Feb with 52 there 12 Feb, 15 on 28 Mar, 2 on 9 May, 6 on 16 May and 38 on 19 Dec. 15 Craigforth, Stirling 5 Feb with 10 there 27 Mar. Doune: 2 L Watston 13 Feb with 6 there 11 Mar; 2 in unspecified locality there 11 and 21 Mar. 4 Frew 26 Feb. 4 Argaty, BoD 27 Feb with 2 there 23 Apr and 24 Nov and 1 on 1 Dec. 8 on feeders Gartincaber 23 Mar.

CHAFFINCH *Fringilla coelebs* (B, W)

BBS: recorded at 4.1 b/lkm.

C   Two hundred and twenty Gartmorn Dam 28 Oct.

S   Dunblane: 450 Dykedale 28 Jan; 150 Hill of Row 29 Jan; 800 Greenyards 5 Feb with 490 there 6 Mar; 250 Stonehill 18 Dec. 130 Craigforth, Stirling 5 Feb with 150 there 11 Feb. 300 Blairdrummond Carse 30 Nov.

BRAMBLING *Fringilla montifringilla* (W)

Yet another good year for the species.

F   Singles Skinflats 14 Oct, Blackness 3 and 4 Nov and Strathavon Fm, Slamannan 3 Dec.

C   Four Gartmorn Dam 28 Oct. 1 Dollar 9 Dec.

S   Blaidrummond Carse: 1 on 8 Jan with 30 there 28 Jan, 7 on 1 Feb, 8 on 5 Feb, 10 on 4 Mar, 2 on 30 Nov; 18 at Quarry 10 Nov with a massive 250 there 1 Dec and 50 on 7 Dec. Dunblane: 2 Greenyards 12 Jan with 4+ on 5 Feb, 1 on 6 Mar and 100 on 13 Dec; 7 Barbush Estate 29 Jan; 6 Hill of Row 29 Jan and 35 there 28 Dec; 1 Ochiltree 9 Apr; 1 Laighhills 13 Oct; 2 Rylands 20 Nov; 1 Ashfield 25 Dec. Male in unspecified locality in Doune 4 Feb. 2 Craigforth, Stirling 5 and 11 Feb. 1 Whirrieston, Thornhill 5 Feb. 1 Manse Rd, Aberfoyle 8 Feb. 3 in unspecified locality in Callander 12 Feb. 12 Killin 4 Nov and 2 Dec. F at feeder Kirkton Fm, Tyndrum 3 Dec with 1 there 10 Dec. 2 Carse of Lecropt, BoA 7 Dec. 1 L Earn 27 Dec.

EUROPEAN GREENFINCH *Carduelis chloris* (B, W)

Widespread but under-recorded. BBS: recorded at 0.6 b/lkm.

F   Twenty-five Glensburgh, Grangemouth 13 Oct with 30 there 4 Nov. 70 Skinflats 14 Oct with 30 there 3 Nov, 95 on 16 Nov and 35 in mixed flock in village 25 Nov.

S   One hundred and thirty Carse of Lecropt, BoA 5 Jan.

EUROPEAN GOLDFINCH *Carduelis carduelis* (B, W)

BBS: recorded at 0.5 b/lkm.

F   Twenty Bo'ness 27 Aug. 40 Kinneil 14 Sep with 35 there 23 Sep. 20 Skinflats 14 Sep and 6 Oct with 70 there 7 Oct. 40 Muirdyke Burn, Powfoulis 21 Oct. 50 Airth 25 Oct. 90 Kincardine Br 15 Dec.

C   Twenty Woodland Park & Drove Rd, Alva 1 Jan.

S   Dunblane: 40 Hill of Row 26 Aug and 80 Ashfield 9 Sep.

EURASIAN SISKIN *Carduelis spinus* (B, W)

BBS: recorded at 0.5 b/lkm.

F   Falkirk: 35 Kingseat Place 11 Jan with 19 there 17 and 23 Jan, 30 on 10 Feb, 15 on 2 and 10 Mar and 15 to 18 at Major's Loan 16 to 26 Jan. Up to 30 Liddle Drive, Bo'ness in Dec.

C   Thirty Gartmorn Dam 2 Dec.

S   Fifteen Brae of Boquhapple Fm, Thornhill 16 Jan. 45 Newton Crescent, Dunblane 11 Feb and 8 Mar. 20 Aberfoyle E 19 Feb. 15 Gart GPs, Callander 14 Apr. 70 G Finglas 16 Jul. 35 Cromlix Br 17 Sep. 50 Argaty, BoD 28 Dec.

COMMON LINNET *Carduelis cannabina* (B, W)

F   Seventy Kinneil 9 Feb. 120 Skinflats 17 Nov.

C   Sixty Gartmorn Dam 28 Oct with 105 there 2 Dec.

S   Fify-five Lanrick, Dunblane 1 Mar. 90 Drumloist, BoD 14 Jul. Blairdrummond: 100 on Carse 10 Nov with 120 there 30 Nov; 150 at Quarry 10 Nov with 450 on 1 Dec. Ca. 150 Carse of Lecropt, BoA 27 Nov.

TWITE *Carduelis flavirostris* (b, W)

F   One Skinflats 5 Feb with 5 there 29 Dec. 60 Airth were feeding on Sea Aster heads 25 Oct. 1 Bows, BoD 1 Apr. 4 Ardeonaig, Killin 4 Jun. 3 Kirkton Fm, Tyndrum 25 and 26 Sep. 3 Blairdrummond GPs 10 Nov with 4 there 1 Dec.

C   Five Haugh of Blackgrange 15 Apr.

LESSER REDPOLL *Carduelis cabaret* (b, W)

BBS: recorded at 0.1 b/lkm.

F   Breeding season: 6 Carronshore, Stenhousemuir 14 Apr and 2 at Kingseat Place, Falkirk 30 Apr. Winter: 15 Skinflats village 25 Nov. 4 Skinflats 29 Dec.

C   Ten Gartmorn Dam 16 Nov with 400 there 2 Dec.

S   At least 10 Auchlyne Rd, G Dochart 28 Jan. Breeding season: up to 8 recorded from many localities, including Flanders Moss W and Blaircessnock; Blairdrummond GPs; Kilbryde; central Dunblane; L Rusky; Bracklinn, Gart GPs and Crags, Callander; Cromlix; Argaty, Drumloist, Rosehall and Bows, BoD; Buchany; L Mahaick; Lanrick and Daldorn, Doune; L Watston; G Finglas; Tigh na Blair; Kenknock and central G Lochay; Inverlochlarig; Auchtertyre, Strathfillan; Auchlyne Rd, G Dochart; G Beich; Edinample and Edinchip, Lochearnhead; head of L Tay, Ardeonaig and Kirkton Fm, Killin; Bein Dubhchraig, Alt Core Dubchraig, Ben Our and Stuc Mhor. Winter: Carse of Lecropt, BoA: ca. 20 on 21 Nov with 60 there 5 Dec. 30 Blairdrummond GPs 23 Dec.

RED CROSSBILL (COMMON CROSSBILL) *Loxia curvirostra* (b, W)
BBS: recorded at 0.1 b/lkm.

F   Fifteen, including ad feeding Y, Torwood, Larbert 13 May. 5 Liddle Drive, Bo'ness 29 May. Juv ringed Lionthorn, Falkirk 3 Jun.

C   Castlebridge Business Park, Forestmill: 1 flying over 8 May with ca. 35 flying over 7 Jun, 7 flying over 8 Jun and 1 calling 3 Jul.

S   Tyndrum: 13 Kirkton Farm 1 Jan with 17 there 30 Jan, 26 on 6 Feb, 5 on 28 Feb and 1 on 16 Oct; 5+ community woodland 12 Feb; 13 in unspecified locality there 13 Apr and 3 on 12 May. Callander: 12 Ben Gullipen track 5 Jan; 5 Coilhallan Wood 11 Feb; 2 Gart GPs 14 Apr. 8 Auchtertyre Glen Gorge Woodland, Strathfillan 6 Jan and 1 there 6 Feb. 23 Torrie Forest 22 Jan. 2 F Milton of Cambus 26 Jan. 2 Sheriffmuir 1 Feb. Doune: 2 Lanrick 12 Feb, 11 Mar and 27 Mar with 4 there 5 and 16 May; unspecified locality: 2 on 4 and 10 Mar, 15 on 15 Apr and 7 on 9 Nov; 7 Daldorn 15 May with 4 there 23 Jun. 4 Kilmahog 12 Feb. Killin: 1 at Marshes 18 Feb; 1 flying overhead L Tay 24 Mar and 1 there 1 Dec; 2 Ardeonaig 4 Jun. Dunblane: 1 in unspecified locality there 19 Feb; 8 Newton Crescent 24 Jun with 6 there 6 Aug; 1 Ashfield 10 Nov. 9 Invertrossachs car park, L Venachar 26 Feb. 8 L Ard Forest, Aberfoyle 29 Feb. BoD: 4 Drumloist 17 Mar with 4 there 17 Apr, 10 on 29 Apr, 4 on 6 and 21 May, 2 on 26 May and 5 on 3 Jun; 2 Bows 1 Apr and 21 May; 5 Argaty 23 Apr with 4 there 25 Jun and 2 on 1 Dec. 4 Cromlix 17 Mar and 30 Apr with 2 on 5 May, 3 on 21 May and 8 on 17 Jun. 5 Touch 17 Mar. 4 Blairdrummond GPs 13 May with 2 there 26 Dec. 5 Loch Watston 16 May with 2 there 26 May. 1 Flanders Moss W 26 May. 3 Kenknock, G Lochay 4 Jun. 5 Kilbryde 17 Jun. 10 Stuc Mhor 19 Jun. 7 Edinchip, Lochearnhead 19 Jul.

COMMON BULLFINCH *Pyrrhula pyrrhula* (B, W)
BBS: recorded at 0.1 b/lkm.

F   Five Kingseat Place, Falkirk 17 Apr.

S   Ten L Mahaick 26 Jan. Dunblane: 6 Hill of Row 29 Jan; 8 Laighhills 13 Oct; 8 in centre 7 Dec. 6 Blairdrummond GPs 1 Feb with 8 there 5 Feb. 10 Brig o' Turk 19 Feb. 8 Falls of Leny, Callander 21 Feb. 5 Airthrey, BoA 9 Oct. 10 Argaty, BoD 1 Dec.

SNOW BUNTING *Plectrophenax nivalis* (W)

S   Auchtertyre G, Strathfillan: 31 flying over 28 Jan with 29 there 2 Feb. Gleann a' Chlachain: 1 in woodland 28 Jan; 13 Cam Creag face 29 Nov; 1 Kirkton Glen Park 21 Dec. 5 Ben Tulaichain 18 Mar. 18 Ben Challum 28 Apr. 1 Sheriffmuir 11 Nov.

YELLOWHAMMER *Emberiza citrinella* (B, W)
BBS: recorded at 0.5 b/lkm.

F   Twelve Glensburgh, Grangemouth 28 Jan. 10 Skinflats village 25 Nov.

C   Forty Alloa Rhind 12 Jan. 63 Kennetpans 30 Jan. 16 Gartmorn Dam 2 Dec.
S   Dunblane: 20 Greenyards 12 Jan with 52 there 5 Feb and 37 on 13 Dec; 45 Keir 28 Jan; 25 Hill of Row 29 Jan; 54 Dykedale 1 Mar; 12 Rylands 20 Nov. 40 Blairdrummond Carse 22 Jan with 20 there 28 Jan and 25 on 5 Feb, 15 on 11 Feb, 35 on 19 Feb, 15 on 28 Feb and 4 Mar, 10 on 2 Apr, 18 on 10 Nov and 10 on 30 Nov. 10 Flanders Moss E 5 Feb. 15 Craigforth, Stirling 5 Feb. 15 Whirrieston, Thornhill 5 Feb. 24 Carse of Lecropt, BoA 12 Feb with 21 there 5 Dec and 20 on 28 Dec.

REED BUNTING *Emberiza schoeniclus* (B, W)
    BBS: recorded at 0.2 b/lkm.
F   Twenty Glensburgh, Grangemouth 28 Jan. 7 Skinflats 7 Oct with 24 there 4 Dec. 12 Gartmorn 2 Dec.
C   Nine Blackdevon Wetlands 12 Jan with 8 there 22 May. 32 R Devon, Alva 12 Feb. 5 M Cambus 16 Jun.
S   BoA: 38 Carse of Lecropt 5 Jan with ca. 40 there 16 Jan and 14 Feb, 23 on 12 Feb and ca. 24 on 18 Nov; ca. 40 Netherton Marsh 14 Feb. 10 Keir, Dunblane 28 Jan. 25 Flanders Moss E 5 Feb with 35 there 19 Feb. 16 R Forth, Cardross Br-Ladylands 18 Feb. 6 Blairdrummond Carse 28 Feb.

ESCAPED AND INTRODUCED SPECIES

LESSER CANADA GOOSE *Branta canadensis*
S   One in unspecified locality, Doune, 29 Jan (DOE).
    This is believed to be the 1st record of this species in the recording area within what is a complex and evolving taxonomic grouping.
WOOD DUCK *Aix sponsa*
F   Union Canal: ad M Camelon 28 Jan and 4 Feb (EM, JFi); M Polmont 18 Jan, 16 Feb and 13 Mar (CM): M Falkirk 11 Feb. Forth and Clyde Canal: M Falkirk paired to F Mallard 11 Feb (SPM).
    These sightings are likely to all relate to the same individual. This is the 8th documented record (omitting multiple sightings of a long-staying bird in 2004-2006) of this species for the recording area. This may have been the same bird as the one present on the Union Canal in Mar and between Sep and Nov 2010 and at Kingseat Place, Falkirk in Dec 2011. It is thought that 4 different individuals may have been involved altogether.
WHITE STORK *Ciconia ciconia*
S   One Blairdrummond Safari Park 24 Feb. 1 Cromlix 8 Apr. 1 Carse of Lecropt, BoA 9 May. 1 in unspecified locality in Stirling 1 Jun (NB, BG, DOE).
    These sightings constitute the 8th to 11th records of escaped birds for the recording area - there are three records of assumed wild birds - but are all likely to refer to just one individual recorded at Blairdrummond from May to Dec 2008, in April and July 2009 at Blairdrummond and environs and in Falkirk and in 2010 in Dunblane.

Report of the *Forth Naturalist and Historian* Man and the Landscape Symposium Saturday 17th November 2012

How Green Is my Valley: Environmental Health Then and Now in the Forth Valley

Environmental health can mean many things. Firstly, the environment needs to be in good health, physically. We can forget that there have been and are plenty of ways in which individuals and institutions have maintained and improved this. Secondly, the environment gives us good health. Access to and enjoyment of the countryside gives us innumerable physical and mental benefits. We wanted to explore in this conference how our landscape has, over centuries, been given back to us, its custodians.

To begin, local archaeologist **Stephen Digney** discussed recent work by Stirling Local History Society and Stirling Field and Archaeological Society, with Richard Jones (Glasgow University) at the King's Knot, a pleasure garden for some in the Middle Ages. King's Park was founded by William I (1165x1175) a century or so prior to the creation of the New Park, established by Alexander III in *c.*1265. It was the Great Garden of James IV from 1493, planned along continental lines, with the construction of ditches, the planting of over 1100 young trees planted and fish ponds dug. A fence excluded Stirling citizens. For James VI this was his *special park and garden*, described as part of the fine view which made the palace of Stirling "the best and most pleasant situation of any of his highness's palaces". By 1625, however, a *skilfull and well experimented gardener in England [was instructed] to go and reside at Stirline for reparation of the orchard adjoining his Majestys Park of Stirline*, which he is informed has *for lack of attendance become wilde and overgrown with bushes and brambles,* and which state of matters *being an imputatioun to that wholle kingdome* he thinks should be remedied. William Watts spent over £5500 between 1627 and 1629 on provisions, materials and the wages of workmen that worked *at the platting and contriving of his Majesties new gairden and orcheard park of Stirling.* But Daniel Defoe (*c.*1720) was disapppointed: *In the park adjoining the Castle were formerly large gardens, how fine they were I cannot say; the figure of the walks and grass-plats remains plain to be seen, they are very old fashion'd.* Decay set in, but there have always been hints, by Froissart and Barbour in the 14th century, for instance, of a much earlier construction, perhaps a 'round table'. Stephen described the new archaeological and geophysical surveys to 'see' beneath the King's Knot itself, the details of which can be found as an article in volume 36 of the FNH Journal.

Landscape historian **John G. Harrison** explored the processes by which the bio-diverse raised mosses of the Carse of Stirling have been in parts reduced to a monoculture of spruce trees. Moss clearance commenced in the 'improvement' period after 1720, though late 16th century testaments show a 'fertile fringe' along both shores of the Forth, growing wheat, peas and beans and probably protected by sea walls. Parts of the Carse, such as at Kersie, were cleared from at least 1715, much earlier than the celebrated attempts of Lord Kames at Blairdrummond after 1766, and Kames adopted techniques that were used prior to his work. The Blairdrummond wheel was novel, but was impractical in most situations and was not imitated. Moss clearance ended as land values fell from the 1820s. Tenants with capital chose to intensify production with subsoil drains rather than continue to clear the mosses. The 'improvers' created new, regular fields and actually increased diversity, with ploughed land, margins and ditches, fallow periods, new crops and weeds, small woodlands, areas of residual peat, and ponds, streams and marshy areas within fields (Harrison, 2009). But only Gartrenich Moss (West Flanders) was identified as a Nature Conservation Area in 1949 as afforestation and industrial-scale moss clearance commenced. Of 14,257 ha of raised bog identified in specified study areas in Britain in the 1850s only 1,803 ha (13 %) remained unconverted in 1978.

Christopher Smout (Emeritus Professor, St. Andrews University) asked us to consider the remarkable improvements in controlling polluted waters in the Forth Valley over the past 150 years (Smout and Stewart, 2012). Moss clearance itself introduced a pollutant, in turning opaque formerly clear waters. In Georgian and early Victorian towns, there were always too few sewers, with waste thrown into burns. Cholera, typhoid and typhus outbreaks led to a major public health crisis in the 1830s. To urban sewage was added waste from traditional industries like tanning and from new industries: paper manufacture in the catchments of the North Esk and Water of Leith, and oil-bearing shale along the Almond. Visionaries like Edwin Chadwick and Thomas Crapper alleviated the risks of town-living and waterborne diseases declined, a Royal Commission in 1872 acknowledged. But still, industrial polluters assumed that pollutants would be carried to sea, and thus not their problem. There was for a time in the later 19th century only one inspector of rivers for Scotland. Despite pleas to shoulder more responsibility, to become 'stewards', manufacturers argued that such costs would damage productivity and hinder exports.

By the early 20th century there was an alarming 'cocktail' of toxins, alkalis and acids in most rivers draining to the Forth. Of these, the Teith was by far the healthiest, reflecting its non-industrial catchment. Anaerobic conditions led between 1860 and 1910 to a fall in fish landed at Stirling of around 80 %. The Scottish Fisheries Board became concerned for the survival of salmon and sea trout populations. In 1923 poisoning or suffocation of fish was an annual occurrence. Conditions improved only after World War II, and specifically the Rivers Purification (Scotland) Act of 1951. Improvements in discharges from the 1970s led to the recognition of the large residue of historical contaminants, a legacy of our past.

From past indiscretions, we moved to a review of present and future prospects. **Kenny Auld**, Senior Access Adviser for the Loch Lomond and

Trossachs Park (LLTP) described the first ten years of our nearest National Park. The park covers around 1,865 sq km (720 sq miles) within Argyll Forest, Loch Lomond, The Trossachs and Breadalbane. Around 15,600 people live in the park and more than 50 % of Scotland's population live within an hour's travel time. There are 7 million visitor days per year, with some £247 million spent by tourists each year. The National Park Authority employs c.150 people with a vast range of skills and expertise across conservation, rural development and visitor experience. Its aims are to promote the heritage of the area, sustainable use of natural resources, public understanding and enjoyment of the area, and to promote sustainable economic and social development. The well-being of local communities is helped by individual projects like 'Walk in the Park', a health walking scheme where volunteer leaders take groups of people who would otherwise struggle to get out on short walks around Callander, and a second initiative is the 'Step in the Right Direction' scheme. Some 72 % of women and 59 % of men are not active enough for their health. Physical inactivity is the most common risk factor for coronary heart disease. Currently only 46 % of men and 35 % of women meet the recommended levels of physical activity of 30 minutes on 5 days of the week or 150 minutes in total over the week. The park now has 350 active volunteers, contributing to practical conservation or maintenance tasks, biological surveys, organising and delivering events and producing V – the volunteer newsletter for the park. What do the next 5 years hold? The park will have a reduction in Grant-In-Aid. In the long term, it cannot be known what the financial future is. But the park has a clear set of goals that all work to enhance it.

Zoe Kemp of Scottish Natural Heritage (SNH) introduced the *Carse of Stirling Project*, a new project run by the Scottish Environmental Protection Agency (SEPA) and SNH with collaboration from partners across the Stirling Environment Partnership, including Stirling Council, Forestry Commission Scotland and the RSPB (http://www.snh.gov.uk/publications-data-and-research/publications/search-the-catalogue/publication-detail/?id=1966). It seeks to demonstrate how to balance the concerns of local communities and wider policy makers. It stems from the SNH Land Use Strategy, which envisions a Scotland where "we fully recognise, understand and value the importance of our land resources, and where our plans and decisions about land use deliver improved and enduring benefits, enhancing the wellbeing of the nation". The project draws on the idea of ecosystem services: ecosystems provide us with a range of services; land provides us with a range of benefits; so understanding these benefits should help guide the way the area is managed, and how policies and incentive schemes are tailored to reflect local needs and opportunities. Benefits from the land include jobs, income and food, of course, but also a sense of cultural heritage, bio-diversity, landscape character, and spirituality. Zoe described how the project tries to make links and to support people in their local area to bridge these gaps and find common ground for the future of land management, including what land managers want, need and are willing to do. The *Carse of Stirling Project* is a local project, with a focus on real life management, use and enjoyment of the land.

Roger Crofts concluded the day with some personal reflections. A geographer and geomorphologist, Roger spent 17 years in The Scottish Office actively involved in advising on the policy and administration of development in rural Scotland. He was appointed the first Chief Executive of Scottish Natural Heritage in 1992, and since has been Chair of the IUCN World Conservation Union UK Committee, Chair of its World Commission on Protected Areas European Region, and a Council and Board member of the National Trust for Scotland and Convenor of its Conservation Committee. Roger explored the current interest in restoration ecology, arguing that restoration itself is unachievable because our understanding of past ecosystems can never be complete: "you can never go back". Instead, you can learn from the past and it can in part inform future choices. Prehistory and history gives the Forth valley a deep, multi-layered landscape which we need to treasure and protect. Over-management of our landscapes is also a concern. We regulate rivers and catchments, often reacting to change by using negative feedbacks, 'keeping nature in its place', when nature should be allowed to take its course. We might, in the future, think and act holistically, integrating land use and conservation strategies, both natural and cultural. We might do away with monoculture forests and re-introduce new native woodland, but use these sustainably. We are losing many of the skills needed to do this. There needs to be a more effective infra-structure to our lives, more joined-up thinking, clearer approaches to preventing pollution, reclaiming floodplains to serve as temporary water stores for flood water, and greater use of renewable resources, including in the Forth Estuary, tidal energy capture. We have finite resources and we need to plan knowing this.

References

Harrison, J.G. 2009. East Flanders Moss, Perthshire, a documentary study. *Landscape History* 30, 5-19.
Smout, T.C. and Stewart, M. 2012. *The Firth of Forth. An Environmental History.* Edinburgh: Birlinn.

Richard Tipping

Plate 1. *Saxifraga nivalis.*   (Photo: D.K. Mardon)

Plate 2. *Woodsia alpina.* (Photo: D.K. Mardon)

Plate 3. *Gentiana nivalis.* (Photo: Sarah Longrigg)

Plate 4. *Carex microglochin.* (Photo: D.K. Mardon)

Plate 5. Two adult powan caught at spawning time in Loch Lomond: male, top; female, below (Photo: Peter Maitland).

Plate 6. The first powan caught by the authors at Loch Sloy, representing three age groups – see Figure 2 (Photo: Alex Lyle).

Plate 7. A fine specimen of powan caught by angler James Kirkland in Carron Valley Reservoir. This fish is probably at least fourth or fifth generation from the fry originally stocked in 1988 and 1989 (Photo: David Ogg).

Plate 8. Typical otter 'spraint' on an exposed rock in a burn (upper) and footprint or 'spore' on river bank mud (lower).

Plate 9.

The only surviving colony of Scheicher's Thread Moss in the British Isles grows on the Touch Hills in the flush shown in the foreground above. The area around the colony has been kept clear of the invasive rushes seen carpeting the moor behind the figure.

Plate 10. The former Caledonian Vaults on Baker Street with Weavers' arms above first floor windows (author's photo).

Plate 11. The doocot or former gun bastion on the town walls at Allan's School (author's photo).

Plate 12. Gardener's gravestone of 1724 with gardening tools (author's photo).

Plate 13. Bean Geese with GPs collars (Photographs: John Simpson).

GARDENS AND GARDENERS IN EARLY-MODERN STIRLING

John G. Harrison

Evidence from Stirling suggests that gardens were an important aspect of Scots towns of the sixteenth to eighteenth centuries. Some of the grander gardens, such as the famous King's Knot area, the less-well known garden in the adjacent Haining and the institutional garden of Cowane's Hospital, have received some attention from historians and archaeologists. But little is known about the garden of 'Scotland's grandest town-house' Argyll's Lodging and still less of the gardens of the less affluent inhabitants. Together, gardens occupied more urban space than did buildings, streets and markets, though the proportion gradually decreased as buildings encroached. Urban gardens, whatever their status, provided food (particularly fruit and vegetables) but they were also used to grow flowers; they were about delight, as well as utility. Whether they were rented to commercial gardeners or managed for family and domestic use they had a significant economic value. Gardens competed with other uses for space and so were a significant influence on the development of the town[1].

The map of Stirlingshire by Charles Ross of Greenlaw, dated 1780, includes an inset plan of the town of Stirling (Figure 1). Though not very detailed or accurate, it is a reasonable guide to the layout of gardens. The Bowling Green is labelled beside the church and the adjacent Cowane's Hospital Garden is shown but unlabelled. [Spittal's] Hospital Garden is labelled towards the left margin (on the south side of modern Spittal Street, the site now occupied by the Highland Hotel). 'Gardens' are labelled further down that road. Nursery Ground is labelled to the bottom right (the area between modern Barnton St and the railway station). Other eighteenth century plans show gardens between the Castle and the Gowling [Gowane] hill. There were substantial gardens associated with the Earl of Mar's Lodging [Mar's Wark]; these had once extended well beyond the mapped area of Figure 1, at the top left of the plan, joining up with the royal gardens around the King's Knot[2]. Facing Mar's Wark and shown as three sides of a square, was the former Duke of Argyll's Lodging which also had a large garden. And, throughout the town, long, narrow burgage plots run from houses back to the walls, almost all including garden ground. But, on the Meal Market [King Street] and the lower end of Baxter Wynd [Baker Street] at the lower end of the town, an area rapidly developing by 1780, Figure 1 shows that buildings are encroaching onto former garden areas.

But, clearly, there is little space for gardens between the houses on the south (left) side of the Baxter Wynd [modern Baker Street] and those houses back to back with them, on the north side of the parallel street. That parallel street is unnamed on the plan. Its lower section is now called Spittal Street; its older names have included Back Raw [Row] and *Vicus Australis* [South Lane]. Two case studies of properties in this area suggest ways garden layout can reveal elements of urban development.

On modern Baker Street is the eighteenth century facade of a pub now known as Nicky Tam's, previously the Caledonian Vaults. Over a century ago, Cook noted the Arms of the Stirling Incorporation of Weavers on the facade of the Caledonian Vaults. They are still there, though sadly no longer picked out in colour (Plate 10). Manuscript sources confirm that, as Cook says, the property was bought by the Incorporation of Weavers of Stirling in 1705, though the deal was rather complex as several people had had interests in it. Earlier in the seventeenth century, it had belonged to the Craigengelts of that Ilk, important figures in sixteenth and seventeenth century Stirling and Stirlingshire[3]. In 1705 it had the lands of Adam Jack on the west (uphill) the back tenement of Harry Livingstone and the fore tenement of John Donaldson on the east and the Back Raw on the south. But, as the dispositions and sasines show, the property also included a garden on the south side on the Back Raw where there was a doocot [dove cote or pigeon house]. The doocot is still there, a round tower, entered from within the grounds of Allan's School and dominating this section of the town wall (Plate 11)[4].

William Houston was one of the people with an interest in the property prior to its sale to the Weavers; as a professional gardener he continued to occupy the garden for some years to come, evidently as a tenant of the Weavers. In 1706 he claimed that stocks of gillyflowers, boars' ears [probably *Primula auricularia*], cowslips and other flowers had been taken from his yard in the Back Raw by John Wands, weaver though Wands could show he had obtained them from others[5]. In 1707 it was alleged that Houston had removed flowers, syboes, carrots and other roots from his garden whilst poinded for debt[6]. Houston later became the Cowane's Hospital gardener (see below). Meanwhile, the Incorporation of Weavers continued to lease their garden. In 1719 Thomas Thomson succeeded Richard Rae as tenant, paying £40 for 9 years; he was to keep up the numbers of doves and return a like quantity of dung at the end of his lease. The dung and the 100 or so pairs of doves it housed (which could be harvested for meat) must have added considerably to the overall value of the garden[7]. In 1736 William Black leased the garden and doocot for £6 sterling. the Weavers agreeing to replace any old and barren fruit trees. And in 1759 it was leased again, this time to William Simpson, the rent now £4 sterling (£48 Scots) with similar conditions[8]. The doocot seems to have been built as a sixteenth century gun emplacement on the town walls and converted for the pigeons at some later time[9].

In 1765 the Weavers sold the property to Nicol Bryce and Duncan Campbell and in 1797 (after passing through various other hands) the garden on the south of the Back Raw was sold to Allan's Mortification for construction of the first Allan's School[10]. In 1797 the garden area was described as the west-most part of the yard of James Adam (merchant) and his spouse, yard being the usual word for urban gardens throughout the period. It was then said to be 60 feet (18.288 m) wide and extending from the street to the town wall. And, the documents state, it had at one time belonged to Dame Helen Murray (Lady Polmaise) and Sir Alexander Craig, chaplain of St Andrew's Altar in the parish church and others, who had disponed it to Thomas Craigengelt of that Ilk through whose family it had eventually passed to the Weavers. A Thomas Craigengelt was succeeded by his son, John, about 1520 whilst Helen Murray, Lady Polmaise, is on record at the same period. A property between Nicky Tam's and Spittal Street, now the Old Town Coffee House, had also been part of the Craigengelt property. Its sale by the Weavers to Bryce and Campbell is confirmed by title deeds relating to its sale in 1894[11]. So, from the early sixteenth century (or earlier) the property fronting Baker Street had a garden 'across the road' to the south of Spittal Street and extending to the town wall.

The second case-study is a site further up Spittal Street, Spittal's House on the north side of the street and its former garden on the south side, on the site of the former High School, now the Highland Hotel. This garden corresponds to the area labelled as Hospital Garden on the plan (Figure 1). The seventeenth century Spittal's House was built on the site of the former house of the Grey Friars of Stirling, an institution founded and supported by James IV. During the reformation period, like so much other church property, the house and garden passed into private hands. In 1584 there were gardens on both the east and west sides of the former Grey Friars' Yard[12]. By 1604 both house and garden, still a single unit, were fully established as private property and the proprietor built a new house in the north west part of this garden, after negotiating arrangements about potential encroachments on his neighbor's light. He gave title of the new house to his sons, perhaps as their own homes[13]. Both houses and the yard remained in this family's ownership until sold to Spittal's Hospital, one of the town's charities, in the early 1660s. The charity leased the substantial house and the garden (which included an orchard) to a series of prestigious tenants whilst the 'litle friers yaird hous' (apparently the one built in c. 1604) was converted to house the Hospital's pensioners in 1665-6[14]. The charity's records reveal occasional glimpses of the garden; for example, in 1672-3 William Stevenson, gardener, supplied grafted apple, pear and cherry trees for the garden[15]. As with other rented gardens, the trees were seen as long-term assets, the responsibility of the proprietor; presumably, the tenants planted their own vegetables and flowers. There was also some new building within the yard, including the erection of a small Trades Hall. However, as will be seen later, the garden survived in some form into the nineteenth century, long after the charity had sold the associated house on the north side of the street.

Other garden properties are documented on the south side of Spittal Street in the eighteenth centuries and are further suggested by the run of 'gardens' on Figure 1. In light of the two case studies, it seems very probable that, in the first stage of the town's development, Baker Street was the only route up the hill, houses on either side having gardens extending to the wall; at some later stage, a back lane developed, parallel and to the south, cutting the houses off from their gardens and later developing into a street in its own right. Such a road existed by 1388 when two houses are recorded *in vico australis* [in the south lane]. In 1432, houses further up the road (modern St John Street) are described as on the road leading to the south gate (street) called the Back Raw[16]. The 'new house' of 1604 was part of the process of developing a new street frontage on the south side of the Back Raw and indicates that, at that time, this particular proprietor was prepared to sacrifice some garden ground for more residential space, a reminder that gardens would only survive if, in the long term, they were valued more than other potential uses[17].

Industrial and commercial developments competed for garden space. William Lorne had been a pipe maker but in 1717-8 he leased 'a little laigh [low] house' in his back yard, where he had formerly worked his clay; the tenants used it to store lime[18]. Tan pits are recorded in back yards until about the mid seventeenth century but thereafter they were transferred to the Tanners' Mailing outside the town, removing a noxious industry from the immediate vicinity of the houses. Tallow rendering and storage of coal, peat and chaff were forbidden in close proximity to the houses because of the fire danger so were best located at the far ends of the plots. Stables, storage and a range of other infilling buildings are recorded from time to time in the yards[19].

The value of gardens is obvious from the high rents. In summer of 1611 Thomas Murray, a bow-maker and burgess, sold most of the fruit and gooseberries in his garden in Mary Wynd to James Wilson; the payment was £13 6s 8d Scots (£1 sterling was around £12 Scots). A garden in the Back Raw was leased for £24 p.a. in 1630. In 1725 Robert Burn rented a garden in Mary Wynd from Edward Luckison, except some small parts for Luckison's own use including space for his bee skeps but Burn was still to pay £33 6s 8d per year for seven years; quite detailed arrangements were made for Burn's access to manure and work the garden which had fruit trees and bushes[20]. The highest of these sums are comparable with the rent of a house of several rooms and all these expensive gardens were probably commercial operations.

Some of the largest gardens were outside the town, but close enough to benefit from its manure supply and the market opportunities. The Blackfriars had a garden and orchard close to their Friary which, with interests in other gardens in the town, slipped into private hands at the Reformation. Their gardens are marked as Nursery Ground on Figure 1 and gave rise to the later street names Spring Gardens and Orchard Place.[21]

There had long been gardens associated with Argyll's Lodging[22]. An eighteenth century plan indicates the kitchen garden, the walled garden, the green (lawn) and the cherry garden amongst other areas.[23] In the early 1700s Argyll's Gardens were divided by walls into a number of enclosed, lockable gardens some of which were rented out to inhabitants of the town. In 1704

James Campbell, the earl's factor, claimed that Alexander Watson and his wife were shaking down apples from his trees and damaging the walls, a charge denied by Watson. In 1706 the earl's factor pursued 30 people for rents for yards there; most were around £1 10s to £2 but the range was from 13s 4d to £16 Scots and the total was just over £70. Eight of the tenants were soldiers in the castle, six lived in the adjacent suburb of Castlehill, James Stevenson was a gardener, one was Lady Argyll herself and one was Robert Mushet of Glassingall. Two years later, Neil Glass (another castle soldier and keen gardener) had a furious dispute with Mushet about the right to use of this garden[24]. Like this one, most urban gardens were enclosed, either with walls or hedges, sometime both. Access gates were locked. Security was an issue!

The value of urban gardens was increased, compared with rural land, by the abundance of manure such as household, byre and stable wastes of which residues can still be detected in Scots urban gardens. Also present are minerals such as mortar and lime residues; lime (mainly for building) was fairly readily available in early modern Stirling and would have had a significant impact on soil quality[xxv]. The Weavers' Yard, with its doocot, is a particularly clear-cut example of a concern about manuring expressed in all the garden leases; landlords, concerned for long-term fertility, complained if it was inadequate.

Most of the value of gardens derived from the food crops grown. Grains were not widespread by the seventeenth century with only a single crop of bear barley noted as growing in the Baxter Wynd in 1660[26]. Fruit, vegetables, salads and herbs were the most valuable produce and these were grown in gardens of every sort, with apples, pears and other tree fruits particularly prominent in the higher-status and larger gardens.

The Haining (adjacent to the King's Knot) had been planted as a royal orchard in the 1490s and assigned to the earls of Mar in the 1580s. In the later seventeenth century the earls' gardeners grew herbs, vegetables and particularly fruit, to supplement what was available from the original Mar's Wark gardens and also for sale[27]. In 1726 a report found that the fruit trees in the Haining (199 apple and pear trees, 86 plums, 2 geans [cherry trees] and 46 others) were all neglected as were the timber trees whilst the hedges and stone walls were so decayed that horses and cattle could get through[28]. Thereafter the Haining was mainly used for pasture and the neglected trees slowly vanished.

In July 1720 Dr Johnston was in his house when he saw youthful hands appear over the garden wall and reach for his ripening cherries. Sending his servant round the outside, he himself ran down the garden, shouting. It was the servant who caught and brought back a loudly-protesting boy, one of the two brothers involved. Then the boys' mother, Janet Faichney, appeared demanding to know if Johnston was murdering the lad. She was not appeased when he told her the boys had done this before as well as breaking glass in the close; he told her she should skelp her sons herself for such behaviour. He admitted, in court, that he had hit the boy through his clothes, but protested that he had done no harm. Fascinatingly, the case was not brought by Johnston, complaining of the theft but by Faichney, who complained of his assault on her son. The court absolved him, saying the case was frivolous and he could have gone further. But cases brought by aggrieved parents for assaults on their children are more plentiful than reports of ripe cherries[29]. Gooseberries and currants are the most-commonly mentioned fruit in smaller gardens, gooseberry bushes perhaps sometimes doing double duty as hedging[30].

Probably all gardens also had a limited range of vegetables. John Edmondstone and his wife, late seventeenth century tenants of the Haining and of the adjacent Mar's Wark garden were to supply their landlord, the earl of Mar, with kale and herbs for the kitchen as well as fruit for the earl's table when he was in Stirling[31]. Leeks, cabbages, kale and related types were the 'default assumption' when gardens were rented as when, in 1631 the tenant of a garden had right to plant leeks, kale and other herbs in it. These were hardy and easy to grow and were a key part of the diet (providing valuable Vitamin C). Beets, kale and herbs were planted in a garden in Friars' Wynd in 1631[32].

On Halloween in 1701, Andrew Mitchell's children were alleged to have pulled up their neighbour's whole crop of 'boukale' (cabbage), which he claimed was worth £2 Scots. This Stirling incident is perhaps the earliest record known of the Halloween ritual of pulling cabbage or kale plants to examine the roots, which foretold ones fate in marriage. As Robert Burns wrote towards the end of the century, they 'burn their nits, and pou their stocks/ and haud their Halloween'[33]. Less often mentioned are carrots, onions and syboes. Dr Johnston's fears about his garden were heightened as his peas were also maturing, though that was a rare record, peas and beans being more often grown as field crops and milled for meal. Syboes and onions were allegedly taken by some boys who broke through Marion Luckison's garden hedge in August 1678[34].

Disputes and disagreements are amongst the most useful sources for gardens. In 1629 Mr David Drummond, a local landowner, verbally agreed to lease his yard in the Back Raw to Alexander Whitebrow for five years, the rent not specified. They both had a key. Whitebrow, thinking his lease secure, planted four score fruit trees including apples, pears and cherries in addition to the 12 apple trees which had been planted some years earlier. Whitebrow also sowed vegetable seeds, including leeks, lettuce, 'neeps', half a pound of beet seeds, a pound of stewing kale and planted 1500 cabbages; he also put two bee skeps into the garden. But, Whitebrow complained, the bees were lost through Drummond's carelessness and, since Whit last, he had taken Whitebrow's key and refused to readmit him, enjoying the fruits of the garden himself. The court agreed with Whitebrow and awarded him £1 each for the grafted trees, 13s 4d each for the others, 6s 8d for each hundred kale, 40 merks for the growth of the seeds and £10 for the lost bees, a total well over £100 Scots[35].

Like many other garden tenants, Whitebrow was a professional gardener. He had been admitted a burgess of Stirling in 1611 and appears occasionally in other records, including supplying 'fronnes, tyme and levander' for the king's chamber for the return visit of James VI in 1617[36]. He – and other professional gardeners – presumably rented numbers of gardens round the town as they had need. Richard Rae, gardener (and former tenant of the Weavers' Yard) died in 1730. He rented a yard from Dr Bachop for £20 pa and at the time of his death had 200 pear and apple trees, 7 plum trees, some gean and cherry trees, thorn bushes, hollies, yews with some wood and some timber trees; he also had leeks worth £1 12s, young kale worth £2, cabbage plants and bushes worth £8 8s and a rake, barrow, spade and shovel (all old) worth £2 8s. The total of £88 3s was greatly exceeded by his liabilities of £254[37].

Gardening (like many occupations) sometimes ran in the family. Hercules Hudston, gardener in Haining and Thomas Hudston, gardener in Stirling, both owed sums of money to David Stevenson when he died in 1638[38]. John Watt, gardener, had admitted fornication with Margaret Hudston before marriage in 1635 and the couple, described as 'in the garden' (probably the Haining) owed John Stevenson money (perhaps for seeds) at his death in 1645[39]. In 1661 John Edmondstone, gardener in Haining, was married to Jean Hudston and it was their son, the next John Edmondstone and his wife Jean Paterson, who had a lease of the Haining which ran from the 1680s into the 1720s[40]. Robert Cunningham, gardener, was married to a Jonet Whitebrow[41]. The Cunninghams had been overseers of the King's Park for much of the sixteenth century.

There could be several gardeners in the town at any one time and the testament of David Stevenson (above) in addition to the two Hudstons, mentions Robert Cunningham, gardener in Stirling and 11 other gardeners, scattered across the rural hinterland of Clackmannanshire and Stirlingshire, most owing him sums of money. The merchant John Stevenson (David's son) who died in 1645 was owed money by six gardeners including by Alexander Lennox, in Dirt Raw of Stirling, specifically for seeds. Hew Nicol, another merchant, died in 1637; he was owed 58s 6d by Jon Thomson, mason in Stirling, for onion seeds, a sum which would buy a commercial quantity of seeds[42]. Seventeenth century merchants were rarely true specialists but it is clear that, for some, seeds were a significant line.

A few men were described as gardeners when admitted as burgesses including Mungo Forsyth who entered in 1604 though no more is heard of him in the burgh records. About 1616 Hew Clerk was the earl of Mar's gardener in the Haining but by 1625 he was the earl's gardener in Cambuskenneth. John Clerk, gardener, admitted burgess in 1643 was presumably a relative[43]. Many gardeners were employed by local landowners and there was a constant flux between town and country. William Stivenson, gardener at Wester Polmaise, was appointed Cowane's Hospital gardener about 1667 and held the post for some years. He was later described as gardener at Jordanhill but he returned to the Hospital in 1695 probably holding the post till his death about 1710[44]. William Houston was admitted burgess in 1681 and though sometimes described as a cordiner (shoemaker) he seems to have worked as a gardener throughout his long career. He was described as gardener to the Laird of Ardincaple in 1695. In 1699 he was back in Stirling, occupying a part of Craigengelt's House and keeping the associated garden on the south side of the Back Raw which he was reproved for tending on the Sabbath. As noted, he sold his property interest in the house and garden to the Weavers but continued to occupy the garden as a tenant until, in 1710, following William Stevenson's death, Houston was appointed gardener to Cowane's Hospital, a post from which he was pensioned as old and infirm in 1735 [45].

Neil Glass, whose argument with Mushet of Glassingall about the Argyll gardens was noted above, was first and foremost a soldier though he had appeared before the kirk session in 1699 for tending the trees in his garden on the Sabbath. His argument with Mushet was in 1704, the year he became a burgess of the town. Twenty years later, after his death, he was described as a gardener and burgess[46]. So, like other gardeners, he was a man of recognised skills and status. Gardening skills are depicted in stony form on the gravestone of John Simpson, recorded as a gardener in Cambuskenneth from 1709 and who died in 1724. On the west side (Plate 12) the stone has the tools of the gardener, the spade, shears and rake; on the eastern side is a pruning hook within a coiled serpent (symbol of eternity). The couplet on the west face says;
AS SEEDS WHEN SOWN DO DIE BEFORE THEY LIVE
I DIED IN HOPES THIS BODY WOULD REVIVE

This is clearly based on John, 12, 24 *Except a corn of wheat fall into the ground and die, it abideth alone; but if it die, it bringeth forth much fruit;* lines and symbols are relevant to Simpson's occupation but are not personal to him[47].

The Cambuskenneth gardens were, more properly, orchards. Simpson's rent partly depended on the quantity of fruit produced each year though his payment for 1714-5 was reduced as he had planted 31 young apple and pear trees in that year. But his rent also included a fixed payment of £120 for the pasture, the overgrowth and the undergrowth of the orchards[48]. Orchards were actually quite widely scattered across rural Stirlingshire. In the early seventeenth century many were at sites which had formerly belonged to monasteries, for example Throsk had belonged to Cambuskenneth and in 1600 the laird there sold all pears, apples, plums and bullaces to John Hudston, goldsmith; in 1602/3 Hudston bought up the fruit of Cambuskenneth, Throsk, Kersie, Manor and Tullibody and it cannot be chance that, as seen above, the Hudston family were gardeners in the Haining in Stirling. In 1608 Marion Mather confessed her adultery with David Ewing in West Grange (on the former Cambuskenneth lands) 'about Michaelmas when the pears was laid doun'. In 1627 Cunningham of Polmaise leased the fruit of his orchards to another Cunningham, burgess of Stirling for a year for 40 merks[49]. There was an orchard at Halls of Airth in 1489, one at Orchardhead in 1526, at Bothkennar in 1630 and as many as 12 orchards in Bothkennar parish and nine in Airth by the eighteenth century[50]. It might be that the decline of the Haining orchard was partly attributable to this spread of rural sources for fruit – somewhat less subject to the depredations of a dense urban population and better placed to benefit from use of the pasture. Both in town and country – and nicely complementing the orchards – was bee-keeping in gardens; bees produced wax as well as honey and a strong colony was very valuable. There are remains of bee-boles in which skeps could be kept, at Cowane's House on St Mary's Wynd.

In the 1580s, the views of the gardens from the palace at the castle were one of its attractions as a royal residence[51]. Mr. David Drummond, whose dispute with the tenant of his garden has been noted above, had kept the key of the garden 'for cumming and ganging to the said yaird for his awin recreatioun'. Like many other gardens, this one with its fruit and bees, was a source of pleasure and relaxation as well as of cash and food, though Drummond, whose title of Mr or Master, indicates that he was a university graduate and whose wife's testamentary inventory includes a substantial collection of books, globes, musical instruments and an astrolabe, was not a 'typical' inhabitant of the town. When Robert Gibb, a wealthy merchant died about 1689, he had 'three painted pigs for floures'[ornamented, pottery flower vases] valued at £1 8s,[52]. Several examples of flowers grown in gardens – for delight but given some monetary value – have been given. Gardens were also sometimes venues for diplomatic or business meetings, sometimes taking advantage of the comparative privacy[53]. But, for most of the burgesses' gardens, the emphasis was on utility. Cowane's Hospital garden, as originally conceived and as it has existed for most of its long life, was entirely about delight. Fortunately, there is published work available, based on the Hospital's extensive and very detailed records, so that only a few points need be made here[54].

The hospital building was completed about 1650. Though intended as an almshouse it was not occupied by the pensioners until 1673 (and even that proved to be a short-lived experiment). There had been a previous house on the site and perhaps elements of its garden survived or were incorporated into the design laid out and planted by Robert Cunningham, gardener, in 1649 at a cost of £133 Scots[55]. Perhaps this was just a simple 'yard' with some grass, geometrical flower beds and pavements; maintenance may have been patchy in the difficult years till the 1660s. It seems probable that the appointment of William Stevenson in 1667 signalled a new phase of more active concern. There are payments for trees, seeds and flowers and mention of a summer house. Stevenson must have left at some stage but, in July 1695, James Stirling was dismissed and William Stevenson reappointed. Stevenson found the garden in such a bad state that he needed workmen to assist him for a time[56]. New flowers were provided and nails were bought to fix cherry trees to the wall[57]. In 1702 new plants were ordered from Holland, included double yellow roses, jasmine and pinks, all clearly for show; but, surely, so too were the apricot, peach and almond trees, all likely to flower but none to produce harvestable produce, given the impact of climate and boys.

There was certainly a garden hedge (both holly and thorns are mentioned in the accounts from time to time) and the garden was clearly intended as an exclusive space. The grass was cut on a regular basis; new balusters were put into the high and low walks in 1700-1. That, like the laying out of the bowling green in 1711-2, is a reminder that the design was fluid but it is striking that all the changes are to do with taste, pleasure and fashion[58]. The sun dial, moved and redesigned from time to time, should also be seen as an elegant anachronism as most gentlemen would have carried a watch for the prosaic business of telling the time whilst any change of alignment would require major work to ensure continued accuracy – even when the sun shone.

In 1735 William Dawson asked to be appointed Cowane's Hospital gardener as he had some knowledge of botany which the local medical men thought might be useful to their apprentices. He must have been less than delighted to be offered the job without the salary (which was to continue to be paid to William Houston). Robert Sibbald and Andrew Balfour had established a new physic garden in Edinburgh in 1670 followed by the Chelsea Physic Garden founded in 1673[59]. So, whilst not an innovation on the wider scale this proposal was an innovation for Stirling; however, this element of practicality does not seem to have endured for long. There are regular records of maintenance thereafter (a new summer house in 1770, new regulations for the gardener in 1779, new keepers appointed from time to time, a hot bed and 'necessary house' (toilet facilities) proposed in 1785[60]. And, of course, the bowling-green continued in use until very recent times whilst the terrace, garden and green remain amongst Stirling's least appreciated assets.

From 1772 Stirling gained another public or semi-public garden when it was decided to allow people who provided themselves with a key to have access to the Spittal's Hospital Garden, further down the road, the one in the old Gray Friars' Yard. It was to be newly enclosed (presumably to ensure that 'undesirable' elements were kept more securely out) but those admitted were to be 'free to walk in the said yard'. The Hospital Yard continues to be mentioned thereafter. Indeed, as late as the 1920s it was recalled that there were still fruit trees (including cherry trees) growing in the yard in the early 1850s before the High School was built[61]. Like the Back Walk, a pioneering urban walkway, outside the walls and initiated in the 1720s, the two hospital gardens reflect a new unease about the urban milieu, a nostalgia for the rural life amongst educated people living in the increasingly crowded and industrial town[lxii]. That they were enclosed, locked and exclusive places was integral to their appeal to the well-to-do. As such people moved out of the town, to suburban houses with their own gardens, the public and the private gardens within the old town and its suburban areas were under increasing pressure of development; there are few survivors within the town today.

Acknowledgements

This paper has benefitted from discussions with Marilyn Brown, Stephen Digney and with members of the Garden History Society who accompanied me on a walk, many years ago. The former proprietors of the Old Town Coffee House kindly allowed access to their old titles. Thanks to them all; errors are my own.

Bibliography

Brown, M. 2012. *Scotland's Lost Gardens; From the Garden of Eden to the Stewart Palaces,* Edinburgh: Royal Commission on the Ancient and Historical Monuments of Scotland.

Campbell, J.W. 1924. Some Recollections of Stirling and its Vicinity 70 years ago, *Transactions of the Stirling Natural History and Archaeological Society,* **44**, 94-116.

Cook, W.B. 1898. Notes for a New History of Stirling; Part II, *Transactions of Stirling Natural History and Archaeological Society* **20**, 65-92.

[DSL] *Dictionary of the Scots Language* http://www.dsl.ac.uk/dsl/

Digney, S. and Jones R. 2013, Recent Investigations at the King's Knot, this volume.

Ewart, G., Gallagher, D. and Harrison, J., 2010. Argyll's Lodging, Stirling: recent archaeological excavations and historical analysis, *Proceedings of the Society of Antiquaries of Scotland,* **140**, 179-206.

Fraser, W. 1872. *The Cartulary of Cambuskenneth AD 1147-1536,* Edinburgh: Grampian Club.

Green, C. 2000. The Garden at Cowane's Hospital (The Guildhall) Stirling: A Brief History, *Forth Naturalist and Historian,* **23**, 123-130.

Gallagher, D.B. & Harrison, J.G. 1995, Tobacco Pipemakers in 17th-century Stirling, *Proceedings of the Society of Antiquaries of Scotland,* **125**, 1131-1142.

Golding, K.A., Davidson D.A. and Wilson C.A. 2010. Antiquated rubbish: the use of urban waste as a soil fertiliser in and near to historic Scottish Burghs. *Antiquity,* **84**, (325) http://www.antiquity.ac.uk/projgall/golding325/

Harrison, J.G. Solving the Mysterious History of Spittal's House, *Stirling Observer,* 10 Aug 1988, p.11.

Harrison, J.G. 1999. Public Hygiene and Drainage in Stirling and other Early Modern Scottish Towns, *Review of Scottish Culture* **11**, 67-77.

Harrison, J.G. 1990. Some Early Gravestones in the Holy Rude Kirkyard, Stirling, *Forth Naturalist and Historian,* **13**, 79-96.

Harrison, J.G. 1991. *Stirling Burgess List, 1600-1699,* Stirling: Central Scotland Family History Society.

Harrison, J.G. 1993. Lime Supply in the Stirling Area from the 14th to the 18th Centuries, *Forth Naturalist and Historian* **16**, 82-89.

Harrison, J.G. 2011. Stirling Castle, The Army And The Town c.1640-c.1900, *Forth Naturalist and Historian,* **34**, 129-143.

Harrison, J.G., 2013. Houses in Early Modern Stirling: Some Documentary Evidence, *Review of Scottish Culture,* **25**, 42-59.

Imrie, J. and Dunbar, J.G. 1982. *Accounts of the Masters of Works, 1616-1649,* Edinburgh: HMSO.

Logie, A. 2003. *Doocots of Stirlingshire,* Stirling Council Community Services.

Macdougall, N. 2006. *James IV; The Stewart Dynasty in Scotland,* Edinburgh: John Donald.

NADFAS Garden History Group, Stirling, 2007. *Cowane's Hospital Garden in Stirling,* privately published.

Page, R. and Page, C. 1996. The Blackfriars of Stirling, *Proceedings of the Society of*

Antiquaries of Scotland, **126**, 881-898.
Paton, H.M. 1957. *Accounts of the Masters of Works, 1529-1615,* Edinburgh; HMSO.
[RMS] *Register of the Great Seal of Scotland,* various dates, Edinburgh.
Reid, J. 1993, The Carselands of the Firth of Forth, *Calatria,* **4**, 1-32.
Renwick, R. 1884. *Charters and Other Documents Relating to the Royal Burgh of Stirling,* Glasgow: Burgh of Stirling.
Ronald, J. 1902. 'The Crafts of Stirling' *Transactions of the Stirling Natural History and Archaeological Society,* **24**, 51-88.
[RCAHMS] Royal Commission on the Ancient and Historical Monuments of Scotland, 1963. *Stirlingshire,* Edinburgh: HMSO.
Thomas, K. 1983. *Man and the Natural World; Changing Attitudes in England, 1500-1800,* London: Penguin.

Manuscript References

AP – Argyll Papers, Inveraray Castle.
FRC - Fife Record Centre, Rothes Papers
NRS- National Records of Scotland
    CC21/5 Stirling Commissary Court, Register of Testaments
    CC21/6 Stirling Commissary Court, Vouchers of Testaments
    GD124/ Mar and Kellie Papers
    SC67/49 Stirling Sheriff Court, Register of Deeds
SCA – Stirling Council Archives
    B66/ Records of the Burgh of Stirling
    CH2/ Kirk Session Minutes
    PD7/11 Incorporation of Weavers of Stirling
    SB5/ Cowane's Hospital Records
    SB6/ Spittal's Hospital Records
    SB8/ Allan's Hospital Records

---

[1] Brown, 2012, p.200-109 for an overview of urban gardens.
[2] Digney & Jones, 2013, in this volume.
[3] Cook, 1898, p.69; SCA B66/9/11 f. 254 r.; PD7/11/4 2nd June 1705.
[4] SCA B66/2/5, p.43-46; RCAHMS, 1963, p.305.
[5] SCA B66/25/779/1 bundle 5 item 49, Feb 1706.
[6] SCA B66/16/23 f. 93v-94v.
[7] SCA B66/9/14 p.181-184.
[8] SCA B66/9/18 p.10-13; NRS SC67/49/24 p. 312.
[9] RCAHMS, 1963, p.305; Logie, 2003, p.31.
[10] SCA SB8/3/2 p.460-3; PD7/11/5 26th Oct 1765 p.106.
[11] Cook, 1898, p. 65-9; Fraser, 1872, p.395, entry 207; SCA B66/5/68 p.76-9; documents in private hands.
[12] Renwick, 1884, p.92-99; MacDougall, 2006, p.217; SCA B66/15/4 Dec 1560; B66/1/7 p.115-6; B66/25/151 9th Dec 1584. See Page and Page, 1986 for how the Blackfriars' lands similarly ended up as private property.
[13] SCA B66/25/155 and B66/25/169; B66/1/8 f. 141 r.-v; ibid f. 163 r.-v;; B66/16/1 f. 157v; Ronald, 1902, p.71-3; RCAHMS, 1963, p.303; Harrison, 1988, p.11.
[14] SCA B66/25/615/1-14; SB6/3/1A writs in end papers, particularly numbers 5 and 33.
[15] SCA SB6/3/1A f. 196r.
[16] RMS I entry 755; SCA B66/25/34.

[17] Harrison, 2013, p.48 for more on the street development.

[18] Gallagher and Harrison, 1995, p.1133.

[19] SCA, B66/9/9 f 115-6; B66/16/17, f. 70v; B66/16/11 f. 152v.; B66/16/13 f. 134v.

[20] SCA B66/9/2 f. 263r-264v; B66/9/15 p.301-303.

[21] Page and Page, 1996, p.881-898.

[22] Ewart *et al.*, 2010. p.181-188.

[23] AP, NRAS 1209, bundle 3206 (c.1743-1764).

[24] SCA B66/25/779/1/ bundle 1, 3, 4, 5.

[25] Golding, *et al.* 2010; Harrison, 1993, p.82-7.

[26] SCA B66/16/12 27 Aug 1660.

[27] RCAHMS, 1963, p. 285; Brown, 2012, p.62-70; ibid p.98; ibid p 176-182; RMS V, 390; RMS VII 2125; NRS GD124/1/641; GD124/1/639;; SCA B66/16/6 31 May 1626; SCA B66/9/6 p.32 r; NRS CC21/5/5 p.23-9; ibid, p.367-376.

[28] FRC A/AAF40/30/3 Item 22; SCA, B66/25/779/3 bundle 1726; NRS GD124/6/205

[29] SCA B66/16/27, f. 75v-76r.

[30] DSL 'grosar'; SCA B66/16/15 f. 114v.

[31] SCA B66/9/14 p.331-2.

[32] SCA B66/9/2 f. 57v-58r 19 Jan 1631.

[33] SCA B66/25/779/1 bundle 4 item 1, 1701; 'burn their nuts and pull their root-stocks and hold their Halloween'.

[34] SCA B66/16/15 f. 114v; B66/16/16 f. 217r.

[35] SCA B66/9/2 f. 52r.-53r.

[36] Harrison, 1991, p.76; SCA CH2/1026/2 p.314; Imrie and Dunbar, 1982, p.445.

[37] NAS CC21/6/24/1022-4.

[38] NAS CC21/5/5 p.23-9.

[39] CH2/1026/3, 2 May 1635; NAS CC21/5/5 367-376.

[40] SCA B66/9/6 f. 32r-v.; B66/9/9 f. 12 r.; B66/9/10 p.61-2; NRS SC67/49/3 f. 117.

[41] NRS CC21/5/5 p.537-8.

[42] NRS CC21/5/5 p.367-376; CC21/5/5 p.45-6.

[43] NRS CC21/5/2 p.164-6; SCA CH2/1026/2 p.297.

[44] SCA B66/20/5 f. 63v; SB5/3/2 passim.

[45] SCA CH2/337/2 13 June 1695; CH2/1026/5 p.182; SCA B66/9/11 f. 254 r.; SB5/1/1 29 Nov 1710; ibid 20 Oct 1735.

[46] Harrison, 2011, p.132.

[47] Harrison, 1990, p.87; SCA SB5/1/1 13 Oct 1709; ibid 18 Aug 1715.

[48] SCA SB5/6/47, Lease to Simpson, August 1715.

[49] SCA CH2/1016/1 p.222; B66/9/1 f. 38 9 Feb 1627

[50] Reid, 1993 p.18.

[51] Paton, 1957, p.310-1.

[52] NRS CC21/5/5 p.453-6; CC21/5/10 p.744-753.

[53] Brown, 2012, p.210.

[54] Green, 2000, *passim*; NADFAS, 2007, *passim*.

[55] SCA SB5/3/2 discharge July 1649.

[56] SCA SB5/3/2 1668-1670 discharge f. 4; SB5/3/2 27 July 1695; ibid 24 Feb 1696.

[57] SCA SB5/3/2 accounts 1694-5; SB5/3/4 crop 1695; NADFAS, p.41.

[58] SCA SB5/1/1 Cowane's Minutes 29 Nov 1710; ibid 8 Nov 1712; SB5/6 loose papers.

[59] SCA SB5/1/1 20 Oct 1735; http://www.rbge.org.uk/about-us/history; http://www.chelseaphysicgarden.co.uk/; http://www.rcpe.ac.uk/journal/issue/journal_38_4/doyle.pdf

[60] SCA SB5/1/4 minutes 5 May 1770; Ibid 5 July 1779, SB5/1/5 7 Feb 1784; ibid 5 April 1785.

[61] SCA SB6/1/1 15 Sept 1772; Campbell, 1923-4, p.104-5.

[62] RCAHMS, 1963, p.306; Thomas, 1983, 252-3.

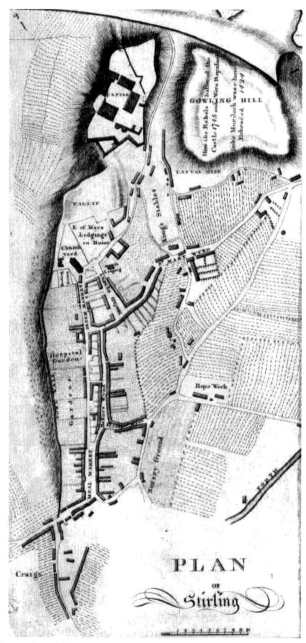

Figure 1. Inset plan of the town of Stirling from Ross of Greenlaw's Stirlingshire, 1780.
(http://bvpb.mcu.es/es/consulta/registro.cmd?control=BVPB20101045145)

THE HISTORY OF BOTANICAL DISCOVERIES AROUND BEN LAWERS

Dan Watson

The background

By the time botanists were beginning the earliest explorations of the Highlands in the late eighteenth century, the floras of the mountainous areas of England and Wales, in particular the Lake District and Snowdonia, had been explored over a century earlier. Why was this? To the well-travelled Thomas Pennant, Scotland in the 1760s 'was as little known to its southern brethren as Kamschatka' (the Kamchatka Peninsula, in the Russian Far East). Highland Scotland was a wild place even to lowland Scots as well as to those south of the border.

It was arguably the Hanoverian Government's counter-insurgency response to the Jacobite rebellions of 1715 and particularly of 1745 which helped open up the Highlands to adventurous travellers. After the rising of 1715, the construction of roads progressed rapidly under the direction of Major General George Wade. In 1724 he was sent to Scotland by George I and recommended the building of roads, bridges and barracks. Between 1725 and 1737 Wade directed the construction of some 250 miles of road, plus 40 bridges. These routes often followed ancient drove roads, but made travel by foot or horse much more efficient. The building continued after the '45, with the road from Stirling to Fort William completed by 1752. By the late eighteenth century Patrick Stuart, the minister of Killin, could write: *The military road from Stirling passes through a great part of the parish and the improvements made lately on that line of road, with the great order in which it is now kept, serve to render the communication of this country with the south of Scotland, and the west and south-west Highlands, easy and agreeable* (Stuart, 1796).

More local roads, for example along the north and south shores of Loch Tay, were also improved in the latter half of the eighteenth century. In 1774 Kenmore Bridge was built over the River Tay at the eastern end of the loch. This work was carried out through statute labour, in effect work in kind, by the tenants of the Earl of Breadalbane.

The earliest map showing Scotland in any detail was that created by Timothy Pont in the 1580s-90s. It was of little use by the eighteenth century, and following the '45, the Hanoverian commanders in Scotland found themselves in need of an updated survey of the country. As a result, in 1747 Lieutenant Colonel David Watson proposed the compilation of a map of the Scottish Highlands. In response, King George II commissioned a survey which resulted in the Duke of Cumberland's Map. This was largely the work of General William Roy, the resulting maps being compiled between 1747 and 1755. They mapped Scotland with a detail never before seen, although there is a noticeable difference in detail between the glens and the mountains; after all, their primary purpose, as with the military roads, was, once again, to facilitate swift and accurate troop movements. On the map of Ben Lawers, for instance, the hill named as such is actually Beinn Ghlas, recognisable from the distinct corrie facing the loch.

James Robertson

There was also a desire to assess the agricultural and mineralogical potential of Highland Scotland. In 1767 Professor John Hope was the King's Botanist for Scotland and Superintendent of the Royal Botanic Gardens of Edinburgh as well as Joint Professor of Botany and Materia Medica at Edinburgh University. He managed to obtain a grant from the Commissioners of the Annexed Estates to pay an annual grant of £25 (later £50) towards the employment of an itinerant botanist to make a botanical survey of the distant parts of Scotland.

It appears that Hope could spot the potential in fledgling botanists. James Robertson had been an assistant gardener at Edinburgh Botanic Gardens. Hope recognised him as a young man of promising genius though then illiterate. He trained him to carry out surveys, and Robertson then spent the summers from 1767 to 1771 making a general survey of Scotland, not just confined to the annexed estates. He would collect plants in different regions from April or May until the end of October then spend the winter arranging specimens and writing reports. His journal gives some idea of the challenges facing a traveller at that time. It seems he usually relied on the hospitality of common people during his travels, and wrote of the Highlander that they possessed *a quality in which they are outdone by no people on earth ... During five summers I have travelled among them, I was never once used unkindly; on the contrary I have oftener than once received a portion of the last morsel of bread, even when my entertainer was ignorant how he could obtain any new supply.*

The loneliness of his travels in remote areas is summed up in the following passage, where he talks of his journey through Strath Oykel: *I wandered for three days all alone till night fell, scarcely knowing whither I went. The night, which I was obliged to pass in one of the miserable huts, ill compensated the fatigue of my lonely straying thro' the day... he who accompanied me could not speak English, so that I was obliged, without an interpreter, to live among people whose language I did not understand.*

He visited Killin in August 1771 and climbed Creag na Caillich with John Stuart, son of the minister. He described it as: *A high mountain which contains many rare plants. In examining this hill, I was much assisted by my companion, who was an ingenious gentleman, and an accurate botanist.* The implication is that Stuart already knew the hill well, and it seems he had been botanising the local hills for a few years before Robertson visited.

1771 was Robertson's last year botanising in the Highlands. He left the job in debt and went on to join the British Navy. After what must have been a successful career, he settled near Cupar in Fife in 1789, building a mansion house costing £14,000. He died in 1796.

At the time of Robertson's visit to Killin, it appears that Breadalbane was one of the more 'civilised' areas of the Highlands, which is perhaps not surprising owing to its relatively close proximity to lowland Scotland. Robertson remarked on this, speaking favourably about Killin as being *a small village pleasantly situated at the head of Loch Tay. This village is adorned with wood and cornfields which are more highly cultivated than any that I have yet seen in the North. The common people have decent houses and furniture.*

Social change was proceeding apace. Going back to the First Statistical Account, Patrick Stuart stated that *towards the beginning of the present century, the people of the country were rather averse to industry..: the man who could best handle his sword and his gun was deemed the prettiest fellow; and the attentive industrious man was a character held in a degree of contempt... The people of Breadalbane are now sober, regular and industrious.*

Gaelic was still the first language of the majority of inhabitants of Highland Scotland, but many could also converse in English. Around Breadalbane, it had become common for families to send their sons to the low country for several years to work on farms there, both to pick up new agricultural skills and also to learn English. Of course, not all of them returned.

John Stuart

Compared to the start of the century, by the time the first lowland botanists were exploring Ben Lawers, there was a road network, the country was mapped, conversation with locals was possible to non-gaelic speakers without an interpreter and travel was safer than it had ever been. With all that in mind, it is somewhat gratifying to know that the earliest botanist of the Breadalbanes was a local resident. This was John Stuart (1743-1821), already mentioned as having accompanied James Robertson on Creag na Caillich. Stuart had studied for the ministry in Edinburgh, and it seems likely that he had attended the botany classes of Professor Hope. There is no direct evidence for this, but it seems likely, especially as the first record for a plant on Ben Lawers came from Hope's note-book catalogue of his now lost herbarium. From the note it appears that Stuart sent him a specimen of Alpine saxifrage *Saxifraga nivalis* (Plate 1) during or just before 1768. Unfortunately Stuart never published any records himself, so his contribution to the knowledge of Scotland's montane flora has been pieced together from surviving correspondence with and herbarium notes of contemporary botanists.

In 1772 Stuart accompanied Thomas Pennant (1726-98) on his tour of Scotland. Pennant, a wealthy Welsh landowner, had first toured Scotland in 1769. He was an antiquary, geologist and zoologist rather than a botanist, but his companion was the Reverend John Lightfoot (1735-88), an Anglican curate and a keen botanist and conchologist. Professor Hope introduced Stuart to Lightfoot, and he travelled with them, ostensibly as a translator. In *A Tour of Scotland* (1774), Pennant acknowledged Stuart *for a variety of hints, relating to customs of the natives of the Highlands, which by reason of my ignorance of the Erse or Gaelic language, must have escaped my notice.* However, Lightfoot used the trip to explore the flora of Scotland, and in the resultant *Flora Scotica* (1778), he wrote *to the Rev Mr Stuart, late of Killin in Breadalbane, now of Luss ... I am indebted for every assistance ... The young gentleman, a most accurate observer of Nature's works ... I had the good fortune to share as a fellow traveller.*

Along with Moses Griffiths, Pennant's illustrator, the party travelled widely through Highland Scotland. It seems that Pennant, being of a higher social class than Robertson had been, was able to arrange accommodation with the local gentry. When staying at Arnisdale in Invernesshire, their hostess plied them with several glasses of rum cordialized with blaeberries, with the effect (as Pennant observed) that Lightfoot and Stuart sallied forth to botanise Beinn Sgritheall *in high spirits. Flora Scotica* also revealed Stuart as having made the first recorded probable ascent of Bidean nam Bian in Glencoe during the course of his botanising. If so, this is the most impressive ascent of any Scottish mountain until that of An Teallach some half a century later.

During the course of their travels for the tour, it seems that little time was spent in the Breadalbanes. Studying their itinerary it appears that, once again, Creag na Caillich was the only hill visited. This was on 16 August 1772. Pennant apparently chose to climb the slopes of Sron a Clachain to get a view down Loch Tay, while from the records in *Flora Scotica* it seems that Lightfoot and Stuart made a swift ascent of Creag na Caillich, this being the closest hill to Killin with a good flora, as had been noted by Robertson the previous year. This was a Sunday, so the lure of a good day's botanising must have been strong to draw two men of the cloth away from attending church. Strangely, Ben Lawers is never mentioned by name in *Flora Scotica*, although many other hills in the Breadalbanes are. Apart from Creag na Caillich, these include Meall nan Tarmachan, Meall Ghaordie and Ben Heasgarnich. Stuart must have supplied records for these locations to Lightfoot in time for the publication of *Flora Scotica.*

It seems that Stuart had been at liberty to spend the summer of 1772 travelling, as although he had been licensed by the presbytery of Edinburgh in 1771, he had yet to be given charge of a parish. In 1773 he was appointed as Assistant Minister in the parish of Arrochar in Dunbartonshire, transferring to Weem in Perthshire in 1776. In 1777 he moved back to Dunbartonshire to the parish of Luss where he remained for the rest of his life. Stuart continued to botanise the Scottish mountains into his sixties. He also established a fine collection of arctic-alpines in the manse garden, and his home became a regular stopping off point for scientifically minded travellers on the military road on the west side of Loch Lomond. Apparently the local inn-keeper threatened to hang his sign over the manse door in protest against the amount of trade he was losing. Another achievement of Stuart's was the first Gaelic version of the Old Testament. He also revised his father's New Testament of 1767. A successor of Stuart's at Luss, the Rev. Duncan Campbell, collected memories from older members of the congregation when he began at the parish in 1852, thirty one years after the death of Stuart. They spoke affectionately of their previous minister as the absent-minded old scholar. In 1977 members of the British Lichen Society visited Stuart's grave in Luss in recognition of his contribution to the knowledge of Scotland's lichen flora. He is credited with having discovered the beautiful *Solorina crocea* for the first time on Ben Lawers.

James Dickson

Following on from Stuart, it was the turn of the nursery men to explore Ben Lawers, particularly John Dickson (c.1738-1822) and George Don (1764-1814). Dickson was the son of a gardener, born in Traquair in Peeblesshire. By 1772 he had set up as a nurseryman and seedsman with his own shop in Covent Garden. In 1788 he became a founding member of the Linnean Society. In 1804 he attended the foundation of what became the Royal Horticultural Society, later becoming the society's vice-president.

Dickson visited Ben Lawers twice, the first time in 1789 with his 18 year old brother-in-law Mungo Park who later gained fame as an African explorer, and the second time in 1792. He listed the plants which he discovered on these two

© Linnean Society of London
www.linnean.org

trips in the 1794 volume of *Transactions of the Linnean Society*, along with records from Ben Nevis and elsewhere. Undoubtedly this did much to bring Ben Lawers to the attention of contemporary botanists.

A major incentive for Dickson's visits to the Highlands was, of course, to collect specimens of arctic-alpines for his nursery, leading Raven and Walters (1956) to comment that *not only the owners of private herbaria have impoverished Ben Lawers; the owners of private rock-gardens are a greater threat still. They can unfortunately claim for their predatory practices the spurious respectability of a long lineage.* We can but wonder at the damage such collectors inflicted. In 1841 a professional botanical collector from Dundee, William Gardiner, wrote a

letter to his wife from Lawers Inn, telling her that *I have already collected between seven and eight thousand specimens and hope to double that number if all goes well.*

Dickson was also a keen bryologist, and in 1785 published the first of four parts of *Fascicularis plantarum cryptogamaricum Britanniae* (1785-1801), many of the bryophytes described being new to Britain. He collected bryophytes from Ben Lawers, presumably the first person to do so. He died a wealthy man, leaving £3,500 to his wife, £2,000 to each of two daughters and his half of the business in Covent Garden to his son.

George Don

In the preface to Don's *Herbarium Britannicum* he wrote of himself: *Since the editor first began his botanical excursions into the Highlands of Scotland, in the year 1779, he is confident (and he hopes he may mention it without the imputation of vanity) that he has traversed more of the Caledonian Alps than any other botanist has ever done.* This was no idle boast. He made many botanical discoveries in the Cairngorms, Clova, Ben Nevis, Ben Lomond, Ben Vorlich, Schiehallion and Lochnagar, as well as Ben Lawers and more widely in the Breadalbanes.

Don grew up in Forfar but went to Dunblane to learn the trade of horology. He developed an interest in botany, and gave up watch-making in 1779 to take a position as a gardener at Dupplin Castle near Perth. From here he began to explore the Ochil hills and the Grampian mountains on his days off, a passion which was to continue for the rest of his life. He moved south of the border in 1780, gardening at several large houses before returning to Scotland in 1788. By 1797 he had leased two acres of land at Doo Hillock near Forfar and established a nursery, finding a home for the rarities he collected on his still frequent excursions to the Scottish hills. A brief stint as head gardener at the Royal Botanic Garden followed from 1802-1806, whilst Don left his elderly father in charge of the nursery. It seems the restrictions of such employment did not suit Don, as he left the job to return to his nursery and the freedom that gave.

He must have looked peculiar stomping the hills wrapped in a plaid with a vasculum slung over one shoulder and carrying a strange tool in the other hand. This was an ash rod, fifteen feet in length, with a notched iron spaddle, which served as a hook, to pull down plants from inaccessible crevices in rocks.

Don was a hardy individual: *He occasionally absented himself for a week a time, his plaid, and a bag of oatmeal or some bread and cheese, sufficing him for shelter and sustenance; and he lost count of the days in these toilsome expeditions ... For these long rambles he was especially fitted, being stalwart and blessed with great powers of endurance, often journeying thirty or more miles without breaking fast.* (Druce, 1904). Apparently he would often take employees from his nursery along on these expeditions. Most were far less up to the task than was Don, and it seems some left his employ shortly thereafter.

A Dr. Patrick Neill visited the nursery at Doo Hillock and wrote: *On reaching Forfar towards evening I soon found Don's garden and on entering enquired of a very rough looking person with a spade in his hand whom I took for a workman, whether Mr.*

Don was at home. The answer was Why sir, I am all that you will get for him (Luscombe, 2007).

Don visited Ben Lawers numerous times, possibly as early as 1784 but certainly from 1793 until 1809, adding several plants to the Ben Lawers list. In 1793 he was accompanied by his friend John Mackay (1772-1802), the brother of James Townsend Mackay, a distinguished botanist whose name will always be associated with the flora of Ireland.

Don and Mackay *spent several days in exploring the great mountain of Ben Lawers in Breadalbane. Here Mr Dickson of London had already found the* acrostichum ilvense, [*Woodsia alpina*, Plate 2] lichen croceus [*Solorina crocea*] and fuscoluteus [*Brigantiaea fuscolutea*] *& c, all of which occurred to our travellers. They likewise picked up* Carex rigida [*C. bigelowii*] *... They found, also, several plants of the very rare* gentian nivalis [*Gentiana nivalis*, Plate 3]; *and the* arenaria saxatilis [*Minuartia rubella*] *and* cerastium alpinum *were for the first time added to the British Flora by this expedition. On this occasion, also, Mr. Don discovered a new species of grass, which has not yet been scientifically described: it seems to rank under the genus* elymus, *and he has given it the trivial name of* alpinus. *Of this rarity he could find only two plants.* This grass later came to be known as Don's twitch *Agropyron donianum*, and was one of the species which visiting botanists would seek out. However, it has since been 'demoted' to a variety of bearded couch *Elymus caninus* var. *doniana*, and accordingly it seems far fewer botanists are now interested in it.

Mackay became the Principal Gardener of the Royal Botanic Garden of Edinburgh in 1800 but his health deteriorated and he died in 1802 at the age of 30, cutting short what could have been a botanical career as illustrious as that of his brother. Apparently Don often visited Mackay on his death-bed, bringing bryophytes which he would spread out in reach of his ailing friend in an attempt to revive his spirits. Following Mackay's death Don began his short-lived occupancy of the Principal Gardener post.

In contrast to Dickson, Don died in poverty, apparently neglecting his business in favour of a passion for finding plants. He died in January 1814, having returned from an expedition the previous autumn suffering from a heavy cold. Through necessity he continued working, but his health deteriorated and he died aged 49 from a "putrid sore throat". Don's friends raised money to help his widow and family, and five surviving sons went on to work as gardeners, two of them graduating to distinguished botanical careers.

Controversy has since surrounded some of Don's records, with the list of his 'reputed discoveries' at the end of Hooker's *Students' Flora* (1870) doing much to tarnish his reputation. Some of his disputed finds were later rediscovered. For example, scorched Alpine-sedge *Carex atrofusca* was not seen again on Ben Lawers for eighty years. Others of his most controversial 'reputed discoveries' have since been fully substantiated, including purple colt's-foot *Homogyne alpina*, which was rediscovered in Glen Clova in 1951. Others do seem unlikely, such as *Ranunculus alpestris* and *Potentilla tridentata*, but there may be other explanations than that Don was being deliberately duplicitous. Possibly he was a better botanist than he was a recorder, and that after returning to his nursery with a vasculum full of plants, these may have been planted out and mixed up with plants from other parts of the world, leading to confusion when the records were published. Maybe there is even the slim possibility that some more of these plants are waiting to be rediscovered. In 1912 George Druce said of Don that *his discoveries of new plants are probably larger and more important than those made by any other British botanist.*

After the pioneers

By the turn of the century most of the plants for which Ben Lawers is renowned today had been discovered. The coming of the railway during the second half of the nineteenth century facilitated far easier access than had ever been available. Despite increasing numbers of botanists visiting the hills few new finds were made, although one of Ben Lawers' rarest plants, snow pearlwort *Sagina nivalis* remained undiscovered until 1863 when it was found by John Hutton Balfour. One of the most exciting late discoveries was that of bristle sedge *Carex microglochin* (Plate 4), found in July 1923 by Lady Davy and Gertrude Bacon during a visit by the Botanical Society and Exchange Club of the British Isles, the forerunner of the BSBI. *On this excursion two members of the party, Lady Davy and Miss Gertrude Bacon, became separated from the others and each found in a different boggy place a sedge which resembled* C.pauciflora, *but which Lady Davy felt was not that species. On returning home she compared her specimens with the figures in Coste's Flore de France and in Blytt's Norges Flora, and concluded that the sedge was not* pauciflora *but* microglochin (G.C. Druce, 1924). Although this sedge can be quite extensive in some of the flushes where it occurs, it has still not been found anywhere else in Britain.

By the late twentieth century Ben Lawers and its surrounding hills had been so well botanised that it seems remarkable that some species still awaited discovery. One of these was Arctic mouse-ear *Cerastium nigrescens*, which can be tricky to separate from the slightly more common Alpine mouse-ear *C. alpinum*. This was discovered by Sandy Payne in 1981 during a detailed survey of Ben Lawers' rarer plants. The most recent native plant to have been added to the list is tall bog-sedge *Carex magellanica*, found in 1984 by David

Mardon near Lochan na Lairige. Since then, the only additions have been the non-native plants prickly heath *Gaultheria mucronata* and slender rush *Juncus tenuis*. Thankfully, neither of these poses a threat to the magnificent flora of Ben Lawers, which has been in the care of the National Trust for Scotland since 1950.

Appendix 1

First records of the nationally rare and nationally scarce plants of Ben Lawers

Alpine saxifrage *Saxifraga nivalis*   John Stuart, c.1768
Prof. Hope's herbarium catalogue showed that Stuart had collected this from the 'Hill of Lars'.

The following nine species are mentioned in *Flora Scotica*. As mentioned above, it seems probable that only Creag na Caillich was visited by both Stuart and Lightfoot during the course of the tour, therefore some of the records may have been shared between the two. Others were attributed solely to Stuart, as mentioned below. The date is given as c.1772 as this was the date of the tour. However, some records may have been sent from Stuart to Lightfoot after this date, and some may have been recorded previously, so the only certainty is that they were made before the publication of *Flora Scotica* in 1778:

Northern rock-cress *Arabis petraea*   John Stuart, c.1772
Upon moist rocks and by the sides of rivulets, near the summits of the highland mountains in many places, as upon Creag-Cailleach, in Breadalbane.

Black Alpine-sedge *Carex atrata*   John Stuart, c.1772
A number of locations are mentioned for this in *Flora Scotica* including Meall Ghaordie and Meall nan Tarmachan. The records are unacknowledged, but given the locations they are almost certainly from Stuart.

Hair sedge *Carex capillaris*   John Stuart, c.1772
Upon the highland mountains, as on Benteskerny, Craigneulicht, and Malghyrdy, in Breadlabane. Mr Stuart.

Mountain avens *Dryas octopetala*   John Stuart, c.1772
Upon the highland mountains in many places ... in Breadalbane.

Alpine meadow-grass *Poa alpina*   John Stuart, c.1772
On the sides of Craig-challeach, above Finlarig, in Breadalbane. Mr Stuart.

Mountain willow *Salix arbuscula*   John Stuart, c.1772
Upon the Highland mountains, as upon ... Mal-ghyrdy, in Breadalbane and on Craig-vore, a high projecting rock on the west side of Loch-Laraig-an-lochain, a small lake between Loch-Tay and Glen-Lyon, Mr Stuart. In *Flora Scotica* these records are referred to *S. myrsinites*. However, doubt has been cast upon Stuarts' identification of this species by Meikle (1984), where the author suggests that all Stuart's records for *S. myrsinites* should be referred to *S. arbuscula*. Stuart did certainly find *S. myrsinites* on Schiehallion in Sept 1776 and according to Mitchell (1987) he had both plants established in his garden at Luss by the turn of the century.

Net-leaved willow *Salix reticulata*   John Stuart, c.1772
It grows upon many of the Highland mountains, in a talky soil, as upon Creg-chailleach, Mal-ghyrdy, and Mal-grea mountains, in Breadalbane. Again, given the locations, it can be assumed that the records were made by Stuart.

Downy willow *Salix lapponum*   John Stuart, **c.1772**
On the Highland mountains, as on Creg-chailleach and Mal-ghyrdy, in Breadalbane, &c. Mr. Stuart.

Sibbaldia *Sibbaldia procumbens*   John Stuart, **c.1772**
Upon many of the highland mountains, as on Ben-mor in Breadalbane &c.

Alpine fleabane *Erigeron borealis*   John Stuart, **1787**
This was found in the clefts of a high rock on the east side of Ben-Lawers by Mr Stuart, who communicated fair specimens 1787 (annotation in Lightfoot's personal copy of *Flora Scotica*). This predates Dickson's Ben Lawers record by 2 years.

Rock speedwell *Veronica fruticans*   James Dickson and Mungo Park, **1789**

Rock Whitlowgrass *Draba norvegica* James Dickson and Mungo Park, **1789**

Drooping saxifrage *Saxifraga cernua* Dr. Robert Townson, **1790**

Highland saxifrage *Saxifraga rivularis* Dr. Robert Townson, **1790**

Alpine gentian *Gentiana nivalis*   James Dickson, **1792**
Dickson described this as *concealing its eye of blue in the ledges of the steep crags.*

Alpine woodsia *Woodsia alpina*   James Dickson, **1792**
This plant has been made a new Acrostichum *by my friend Mr. Bolton, under the name of* A. alpinum. *I believe it is a* Polypodium, *but at the same time I am confident it is no other than the Linnean* A. ilvense: *I compared it both at Sir Joseph Banks's and at Dr. Smith's, and can find no difference but in size, the Scotch plant being somewhat the smaller; but those who are acquainted with ferns will be sensible how different they appear, according to their age or places of growth. I have no doubt, therefore, but the Linnean* A. ilvense *(Hudson's) and that I found in Scotland are one and the same* (Dickson, 1794). What was once called *Acrostichum* is now known as *Woodsia.* Of the two species, *alpina* and *ilvense*, only the former occurs on Ben Lawers, so Dickson's friend, Mr. Bolton, was correct.

Alpine mouse-ear *Cerastium alpinum* George Don and John Mackay, **1793**

Mountain sandwort *Minuartia rubella* George Don and John Mackay, **1793**

Alpine pearlwort *Sagina saginoides* George Don, **1794**

Russet sedge *Carex saxatilis*   George Don, **1798**
I first discovered this plant on Ben Lomond in 1789, and on Ben Lawers in 1798, and on Ben Nevis in 1794. I sent specimens of this plant to Mr. Dickson of Covent Garden in 1794; and I have a letter of that date in which Mr. Dickson acknowledges it to be a non descript. How he afterwards considered himself to be the discoverer of this plant I cannot explain. If Mr Brown's information be correct, the Rev. Mr Stuart of Luss had been acquainted with this plant some time before.

Alpine forget-me-not *Myosotis alpestris* George Don, **1804**
Considering botanists had been visiting Ben Lawers for over three decades, this seems like a very late date for the discovery of this noticeable species.

Scorched Alpine-sedge *Carex atrofusca* George Don, **1812**
Between 1812 and 1892 *C. atrofusca* was not seen, leading some to doubt whether Don had ever seen it. However, in the latter year it was rediscovered by the Very Rev. Dr. David Paul, ex-Moderator of the Church of Scotland.

Alpine bartsia *Bartsia alpina*   William Gourlie, **19th July 1842**
Recorded *on a mountain near Killin; Proceedings of the Botanical Society of Edinburgh*, Vols. 4 & 5, p.62. A herbarium specimen collected by Wm. Gourlie and dated 19/7/1842 in the

British Museum gives no further information. The record could therefore refer to Ben Lawers or Meall na Samnha.

Mountain bladder-fern *Cystopteris montana*   J.M. Balfour, **1855**

Snow pearlwort *Sagina nivalis*   J.M. Balfour, **1863**
The difficulty in identifying this species led to it having been collected at least twice before it was positively identified. H.H. Harvey collected three specimens in 1825 but it was misidentified as *Minuartia rubella*. In 1847 Prof. J. H. Balfour collected some good and some peculiar specimens of *Minuartia rubella* from Ben Lawers. The latter were later recognised as *Sagina nivalis* and in 1863 this was announced as a species new to Britain in an article by H.C. Watson in *The Journal of Botany*.

Scottish pearlwort *Sagina* x *normaniana*   George Claridge Druce et al. **1910**
This was discovered during a visit to Ben Lawers by an international party of botanists who ascended by way of the Allt Tuira Bhric. Immediately debate raged as to its status as a full species or a hybrid, of which there is a detailed account in Payne (1983). It is currently regarded as the hybrid between *Sagina procumbens* and *S. saginoides*.

Bristle sedge *Carex microglochin*   Lady Davy and Gertrude Bacon, **1923**

Close-headed Alpine-sedge *Carex norvegica*   M. McCallum Webster, **1954**

Arctic mouse-ear *Cerastium nigrescens*   Sandy Payne, **1981**

Tall bog-sedge *Carex magellanica*   David Mardon, **1984**

I am still trying to find first records for the following and would be grateful for any assistance:

False sedge	*Kobresia simpliciuscula*
Mountain scurvygrass	*Cochlearia micacea*
Dickie's bladder-fern	*Cystopteris dickieana*
Woolly willow	*Salix lanata*
Ben Lawers dandelion	*Taraxacum cymbifolium*
A Lady's-mantle	*Alchemilla glomerulans*
A Lady's-mantle	*Alchemilla wichurae*
Mountain Lady-fern	*Athyrium distentifolium*
Water sedge	*Carex aquatilis*
Rock sedge	*Carex rupestris*
Sheathed sedge	*Carex vaginata*
Alpine tufted hair-grass	*Deschampsia cespitosa* subsp. *alpina*
Shade horsetail	*Equisetum pratense*
Variegated horsetail	*Equisetum variegatum*
An eyebright	*Euphrasia frigida*
Alpine rush	*Juncus alpinoarticulatus*
Two-flowered rush	*Juncus biglumis*
Chestnut rush	*Juncus castaneus*
Interrupted clubmoss	*Lycopodium annotinum*
Cyphel	*Minuartia sedoides*
Alpine cat's-tail	*Phleum alpinum*
Glaucous meadow-grass	*Poa glauca*
Alpine cinquefoil	*Potentilla crantzii*
Whortle-leaved willow	*Salix myrsinites*
Hairy stonecrop	*Sedum villosum*
Blue moor-grass	*Sesleria caerulea*
Alpine speedwell	*Veronica alpina*

Bibliography

Adam, M. 1933. Ben Lawers. Reprint from *The Journal of the Edinburgh Royal Botanic Garden Guild Vol. III Part I.*

Balfour, J.B. 1902 Botanical Excursions made by Professor John Hutton Balfour 1846-1878. *Notes from the Royal Botanic Garden of Edinburgh* No. 7: pp.21-497.

Dickson, J. 1794. An Account of some plants newly discovered in Scotland. *Transactions of the Linnean Society* Vol 2: pp.286-291.

Druce, G.C. 1904. The Life and Work of George Don. *Notes from the Royal Botanic Garden of Edinburgh* No. 12: pp.53-290.

Druce, G.C. 1924. *Carex microglochin*, Wahl. A species new to Scotland. *Transactions of the Botanical Society of Edinburgh* Vol. 29. pt.1: 1-3

Hope, A. 2004. John Hope, 1725-1786: Scottish Botanist

Lawley, M. George Don (1764-1818). On-line at http://britishbryologicalsociety.org.uk

Lawley, M. James Dickson (c.1738-1822). On-line at http://britishbryologicalsociety.org.uk

Lightfoot, Rev. J. 1777. Flora Scotica (2 Vol). London.

Luscombe, E. 2007. George Don the Forfar Botanist: "Man of Genius". Brechin: Pinkfoot Press.

McLeod, C.R. 2009. Letters – W.Gardiner Jnr, manuscript letters and other papers, 1834-1852. Unpublished.

Meikle, R.D. 1984. Willows and Poplars of Great Britain and Ireland. London: Botanical Society of the British Isles.

Mitchell, I. 1998. Scotland's Mountains Before the Mountaineers. Edinburgh: Luath Press Ltd.

Mitchell, J. 1986. The Reverend John Stuart D.D. (1743-1821) and his contribution to the discovery of Britain's Mountain Flowers. *Glasgow Naturalist*, 21 pt 2, pp.119-125.

Mitchell, J. 1987. The Botanical Garden of the Reverend John Stuart of Luss. *Botanical Society of Edinburgh News* No.47 pp.6-7.

Mitchell, J. 1992. Further Notes on the Reverend John Stuart's Contribution to the Discovery of Britain's Mountain Flowers. *Glasgow Naturalist* 22 pt 2 pp.103-105.

Payne, S. 1981. The status of *Sagina intermedia* Fenzl in Great Britain. Unpublished report for the Nature Consevancy Council.

Payne, S. 1983. *Sagina* x *normaniana* Lagerh, its identification and distribution. Unpublished report for the National Trust for Scotland.

Raven, R. and Walters, M. 1956. Mountain Flowers. London: Collins.

Robertson, J. 1771. Journal (Manuscript in the National Library of Scotland). Unpublished.

Pennant, T. 1774. A Tour of Scotland and Voyage to the Hebrides, 1772 (2 vols). London.

Stuart, Rev. P. 1796. Parish of Killin. Statistical Account of Scotland Vol.17 pp.368-384.

RECENT INVESTIGATIONS AT THE KING'S KNOT STIRLING

Stephen Digney and Richard Jones

The King's Knot is a familiar Stirling landmark which over the centuries has intrigued both visitors and historians alike. The grass covered octagonal mound and square parterres are the remnants of a large landscaped garden apparently constructed in the late 1620s for Charles I (RCAHMS 1963: 219). These earthworks represent the final major investment in a great royal garden originally conceived by James IV in the 1490s and laid out within the Auld (royal) Park. It served the Stewarts well throughout the 16th century when Stirling Castle was a principal royal palace. However records of it are scarce and we have no accurate description, plan, or painting of it from when it was in use. This lack of knowledge together with some features which appear incongruous to the main earthworks, such as the large ditch south of the mound, has led to much speculation on the origins of the Knot. A belief that it was concealing earlier monuments seemed to be confirmed in 1975 when aerial photography recorded the presence of a multi-ditched enclosure running around and beneath the main mound. Without excavation this only added to the mystery.

In 2011 members of the Stirling Local History Society, and the Stirling Field and Archaeological Society, together with staff and students of the Archaeology Department of Glasgow University undertook a topographical and geophysical survey of the King's Knot (Digney, Jones and Maldonado, 2011). Our goal was to investigate and research the royal garden of Stirling using non-invasive techniques, and give society members and students an opportunity to experience archaeological fieldwork. The project was jointly funded by Historic Scotland and Stirling City Heritage Trust and has been supported by the Stirling Smith Art Gallery and Museum.

Historical background

A royal garden associated with Stirling Castle first appears on record in 1453 (ER V: 597) and may have been a small garden within the castle. It is not until the 1490s, when James IV began the work of creating a 'new' or 'great garden' below the castle that some details of the royal gardens emerge. Italian Renaissance concepts of gardening as a high art form and the garden as an 'earthly paradise' were becoming fashionable in northern Europe, and James was quick to embrace them. Work on the 'great garden' began in 1493 with the digging of ditches (ER XI: 144). This seemingly continued in 1496 (AT I: 276, 277, 278) and a bank and ditch boundary was established which probably also provided some much needed drainage. In 1497/1498 over 1100 young (possibly fruit) trees were bought for the garden, peas and beans were planted, and fish ponds were dug (AT I: 367, 386, 388, 390).

The garden developed further in 1501 with the appointment of a new head gardener, George Campbell. In February of that year 400 thorn trees were bought for hedging (AT II: 81-84). Further trees were purchased including sixteen pear trees, many willows, and other unidentified trees, as well as diverse seeds. Campbell was aided by an unnamed French gardener who planted vines (AT II: 102-105). The following year 1500 plum trees were sent from Culross (AT II: 358), while other fruit trees were brought in from the Carse of Gowrie and Couper Angus (AT II: 354, 425).

As well as thorn hedges and ditches, the garden was enclosed by a pale or fence in 1502-3 (AT II: 362). By this time the garden would have been well established and filled with what seems an extraordinary number of young fruit trees, as well as flowers and herbs. Fish ponds and the nearby Park Loch were regularly stocked with perch, trout and pike. Ornamental birds such as herons, cranes and bitterns, which appear in the records of the 1530's (AT VI: 97, 206, 208), probably nested in the reeds around the loch. Peacocks (including white ones) sent to Stirling from Scone (AT II: 96, 135, 445), may have stalked the garden, unless destined for consumption at royal feasts. With his 'great garden' and park, James had created a landscape of leisure which would have been impressive by the time of his marriage to Margaret Tudor in 1503. He had the pleasure of it for a further ten years before the disastrous battle of Flodden. Among those killed with the king was George Campbell (ER XIV: 38). Their legacy was a garden which flourished throughout the 16th century as an integral part of the royal palace of Stirling.

James V took possession of Stirling Castle with its park and garden when it was transferred to him from his mother in 1531 (ER XVI: 138). He soon made his mark on the royal gardens and from the 20th of April until the 8th of June 1532, four men with four horses were set to work preparing the ground and creating turf banks, while two gardeners made banks, cast knots, and sowed the garden with flowers (MWI: 109-110). This work may have taken place in the smaller garden within the castle (Brown 2012: 77).The two gardeners may have been Sir James and Sir Walter Clement (Clemat) who are named as (master) gardeners at Stirling in 1533 and 1534 (AT VI: 102, 205, 212). Their social status suggests the position as royal gardener was held in high regard. We can imagine the garden was kept in excellent condition during the reign of James V (1513-1542), especially after his visit to the royal palaces and gardens of France in 1537-1538, and with the income of two large wedding dowries, but the surviving records provide no details.

In 1583 a review of the costs for the repair and improvements of Stirling Castle for James VI described the park and garden as part of the fine view which made the palace of Stirling *the best and most pleasant situation of any of his highness's palaces* (MW I: 310). When James VI inherited the English throne in 1603 the royal focus switched to the palaces of England. James made one more visit to Stirling in 1617 and some work was done in the garden for that occasion (MW II: 27), but without a regular royal presence signs of decline soon became apparent.

Within a week of the opening of the first Parliament of Charles I in June 1625, a warrant was sent from Whitehall to John, Earl of Mar (Principal Treasurer of Scotland) to appoint *a skilfull and well experimented gardener in England* to reside at Stirling because the king had been informed that the garden had *for lack of attendance become wilde and overgrown with bushes and brambles; the state of which being an imputatioun to that wholle kingdome* which he thought should be remedied (MK 1904: 131).

William Watts was appointed and from 1627-1629 a considerable sum (over £1300 Scots) was spent on provisions, materials and the wages of workmen that worked *at the platting and contriving of his Majesties new gairden and orcheard park of Stirling* (MW: 230, 242, 257). Watts had the fence and dyke of the new garden repaired to keep out deer (MW II: 370), and the whole garden project may have been completed in time for Charles' Scottish Coronation and his stay in Stirling in June/July 1633.

Watts and his workmen appear to be responsible for creating the geometric earthworks we see today although a late James VI period construction is a possibility (Brown, 2012: 178, 181). What we do not see, and have no record of, is the arrangements of plants, hedges, trees, statues or other ornamental features. After the execution of Charles I in 1649, Charles II resided in Stirling in 1650 and 1651, but the threat posed by the forces of Cromwell meant that gardening was of little concern. Extensive repairs to the park dykes were made in the 1670s but we have no account of any garden work (Harrison, 2010: 41). It was probably minimally maintained, but with the death of Charles II in 1685 and the exile of James VII in 1688 the royal garden, symbolic of and dependent on the prosperity of the Stewarts, became redundant.

Visitors to Stirling in the early 18th century observed vestiges of the garden's grassy walks and parterres (Sibbald, 1707: 46; Defoe, 1991: 333), but it was in a state of decay and with only a few stumps of fruit trees remaining by the latter part of the century it was noted that through *long neglect, and the natural wetness of the soil, the place is now little better than a marsh* (Nimmo, 1777: 250). The main Knot earthworks were partitioned off and used for grazing while other parts became lost in cultivated fields. Around 1810 the Knot was truncated by the construction of the Dumbarton and Raploch roads. Despite these encroachments the historical value of the King's Knot was recognised and in 1867 the Office of Works had it carefully restored, leaving it in its present condition. It is now a scheduled monument in the care of Historic Scotland.

Antiquarian Interest

Since the abandonment of the royal garden the earthworks have attracted the attention of antiquarians and local historians. They have commonly held the view that the King's Knot has a deep and complex history. It has been suggested that the earthworks conceal a lost Roman fort (Maitland, 1757: 194; I. Orkney, pers.comm 2011), and the large octagonal mound has been suspected of being a modification of a pre-existing mound, possibly a motte or moot hill, or even a barrow (Shirra, 1888/9: 41-43; Cook, 1907: 132-133). These ideas propose long-term reuse of an ancient monument by Scottish kings.

The King's Knot has also been linked to the Round Table tradition of Stirling (Nimmo 1777: 251). This seems to have originated in the late 14th century when the identification of ancient Stirling as the Arthurian Snowdon was being propagated by David II (Loomis, 1947; 1955-56: 15-19; Kervyn de Lettenhove, 1967 II: 313-314; Diverres, 1965; Ditmas, 1974; Penman, 2004: 340-343). Snowdon or *Sinaudon*, according to Romance poetry, was where the Round Table was kept. Furthermore the following well known verses appear to indicate that there was something below the castle, possibly an earthwork, known as the Round Table:

> *And beneuth the castell went thai sone,*
> *Rycht be the Rond Table away,*
> *And syne the Park enveround thai,*
> *And towart Lythkow held in hy.*

(From Barbour's *The Bruce* (c. 1375), Book XIII, lines 378-381 in Duncan, 1997: 498-499)

> *Adew, fair Snawdoun, with thy touris hie,*
> *Thy Chapell Royall, park and tabyll round.*
> *May, June, July walde I dwell in thee,*
> *War I one man, to heir the birdis sounde,*
> *Quhilk doith agane thy royall roche redounde.*

(From Sir David Lyndsay's *Testament and Complaynt of our soverane Lordis Papyngo* (c.1529) in Williams (2000: 79).

If true this feature may have served as a focal point for the royal tournaments (with Arthurian themes) which took place during the reigns of David II and the early Stewarts (Ronald, 1890: 5; Edington, 1998: 53-54). It is not known whether this 'earthwork' was created by David II (or his predecessors) or if it was an ancient feature which attracted 14th century antiquarian interest.

Previous Archaeological Investigations

Despite being described by Cox (1935: 19) *as by far the most important garden (in Scotland) prior to 1600* the King's Knot has received very little archaeological attention. O.G.S. Crawford visited the site in 1937 in search of the Roman road and postulated a Roman fort but found nothing other than the large enigmatic ditch orientated NW-SE at the southern end of the Knot and suggested that *a few trial trenches would probably settle the matter* (Crawford, 1949: 22).

The Stirling Field and Archaeological Society dug a trench across a ditch in the Stirling Golf Club practice range in 1975. This was reportedly an extension of the large ditch referred to by Crawford and was found to be 8.23 m wide, very wet, with signs that its sides had collapsed at least twice, trapping vegetable matter (Milne, 1975: 53-54). Unfortunately no location maps, photographs, finds, or section drawings were ever published, thus keeping us in the dark.

In 2009, ahead of an upgrading and widening of the King's Knot roundabout, a linear feature was revealed in an evaluation trench which was interpreted as part of the truncated NW parterre (Cook, 2009: 177). Finally, in the same area, a further watching brief was carried out which identified more of this parterre and identified redeposited sands and gravels which may have been used in a decorative border (Ewart, 2010: 170).

Aerial photography

Aerial photography provided the first insight into the true complexity of the King's Knot. In the dry conditions of 1975 a multivallate enclosure was revealed as grass marks and photographed by Kenneth St. Joseph. It consists of three parallel ditches (3.5 m-5 m in width), forming part of an oval shaped

Figure 1. Aerial view of the King's Knot in 1975, showing multivallate enclosure beneath the mound (arrows). © RCAHMS

enclosure approximately 100 m x 125 m across. (Figure 1). Running around and beneath the existing octagonal mound, this enclosure is proof that there really had been an earlier monument at the King's Knot. From the air the circuit of the ditches appear incomplete, with the NE section either truncated or deeply buried.

These ditches are visible on the ground, particularly in the southeast, as low sunken depressions. This suggests that they were covered during the construction of the Charles I garden and that the covering material has subsequently subsided with compaction. Knowledge of the existence of this mulltivallate enclosure provided a primary motivation for our geophysical survey which we hoped would produce new insights. As an aid to our 2011 survey, the 1975 aerial photograph transcription was reproduced on our topographic plan (Figure 2). A full transcription showing other noticeable marks has yet to be done.

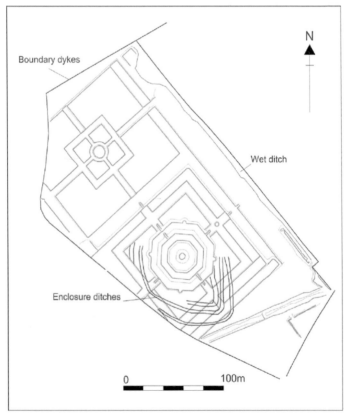

Figure 2. Reproduction of 1975 AP transcription (RCAHMS: STD/136/68) overlaid on current topographic survey.

Another aerial view (Figure 3) showing linear features in the Butt Park (top right) and a cropped field (top centre) are suggestive of a lost garden boundary. The feature in the Butt Park, heavily denuded by the hooves of cattle, may be a natural channel that has been adapted and included in this boundary system. In the crop field a ditch is accompanied by an outer bank, both have been severely ploughed.

Figure 3. Oblique aerial view from SE showing earthworks in adjoining fields to the N (arrows). © RCAHMS

The connection between these linear ditch features is obscured by the modern roads. Road widening in 2010 has further covered the linear feature in the crop field. These features are often filled with water, much of which comes from the spring at the Butt Well but also drainage from the King's Knot and surrounding slopes. The Raploch road has checked the flow or seepage of this water, causing a pool to form in the Butt Park. This suggests that prior to the construction of these roads the water carried in these ditch features probably once pooled in the lower field on the carse. The outer bank of the ditch here may have acted as a sort of dam. Also showing in the same photograph are areas of truncation and disturbance along the eastern boundary of the Knot. This probably occurred sometime after the construction of the Charles I earthwork but before the 20th century.

Topographic Survey

Using a total station a working plan of the King's Knot was produced (Figure 4) and survey grids were set out and recorded. This allowed the results of our geophysics to be displayed and overlaid on the plan accurately. While by no means perfect or complete the plan displays all detail captured during the short time of the fieldwork. Survey stations 6 and 7 are semi-permanent thus enabling the addition of future work to the plan.

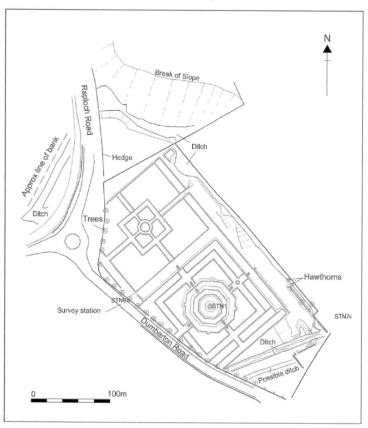

Figure 4. Topographic survey of the King's Knot.

The linear features in the adjacent fields discussed above were also included along with some basic topography. This proved useful as it showed that the ditch and bank in the crop field (to the NW) and the large ditch lying to the southeast of the octagonal mound have a symmetrical relationship. This suggests that these large ditches, including the ditch running beside the wall on the north-eastern flank of the King's Knot, are probably contemporary.

Geophysical Survey

The King's Knot is a large open grass covered field, with relatively flat areas, which provides good conditions for geophysical surveying. It offered an excellent opportunity to deploy three complementary, well-known techniques of geophysical survey (Table 1), all of which are suited to the detection of the kinds of buried man-made and natural features that were expected.

Technique	Operating conditions
Magnetometry	Bartington Grad601 gradiometers; 20 x 20 m grids; 0.5 m traverse; 0.25 m sample interval; 4.8 ha survey
Earth resistance	Geoscan RM15 resistivity meter; 20 x 20 m grids; twin-probe (0.5 m separation); 1 m traverse and sampling interval; 3.6 ha survey
Ground-penetrating radar (GPR)	Utsi Groundvue 3 GPR with 400 MHz antenna; 2000 m2 survey

Table 1. Geophysical survey techniques used at King's Knot.

The magnetic survey was extensive, encompassing most of the King's Knot field, but also a section of the grounds of the neighbouring Stirling Golf Club (Figure 5). The slower and lower resolution electrical survey was restricted to the King's Knot but covered a large area. The initial GPR work in 2011, which involved measurements in five grids to the south of the main mound allowing 3D time slices to be built up, was extended in 2012 to focus on specific targets suggested by the results of the other geophysical methods (O'Grady, 2012).

The subsoil of the King's Knot contains the sands and gravels of a glacial raised beach. However this is further complicated because as a landscaped garden monument, constructed in the form of a series of geometric platforms and terraces, it also consists of imported or redeposited material (mainly sands). These deposits have the potential to obscure underlying features depending on their depth. This is important because while the GPR is capable of sensing up to about 3 m below the ground surface, the magnetic and electrical methods can only penetrate a little over 0.6 m. Normally this would not cause any difficulty as topsoil on average is rarely much over 0.3 m in depth, but this becomes problematic when added to imported deposits of uncertain depths. Waterlogging, west of the smaller mound known as the Queen's Knot, also gave rise to particularly low values of electrical resistance. Both of these problems will be discussed in relation to the results presented below. The magnetic and earth resistance results were visualised as grey-scale plots using Geoscan's Geoplot 3.0 .

The survey results are encouraging. The resistance data (Figure 6) confirms the presence of the multivallate enclosure. On closer examination of the

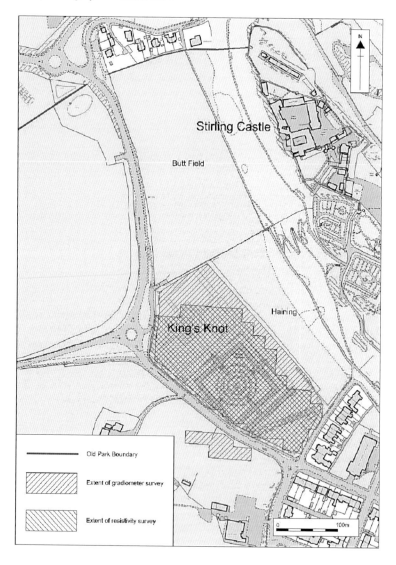

Figure 5 The extent of the 2011 geophysical surveys. © Crown Copyright/database right 2011. An Ordnance Survey/EDINA supplied service.

graphic the ditch system appears to shows a degree of complexity which hints at multiperiod construction. Immediately to the north of the stepped mound the electrical response alters due to the presence of overburden and the ditch system is difficult to see.

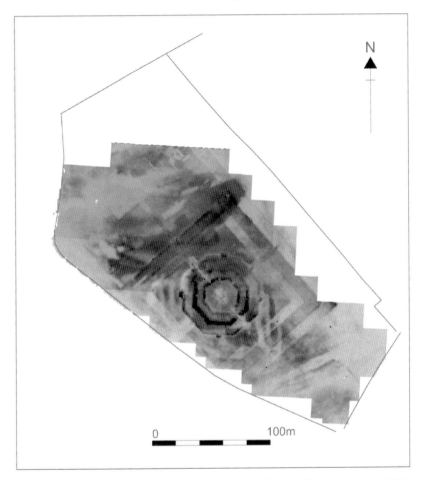

Figure 6. Results of Resistivity Survey (black and white are high and low resistivity respectively).

GPR confirmed that the level of the ground in this area has been substantially raised but the multivallate ditches are still present although severely truncated (O'Grady, 2012: 9, 11). On the lower ground of the Queen's Knot are a number of rectangular anomalies, of uncertain purpose, but which may be garden features or cuts in the ground related to drainage (Figure 7).

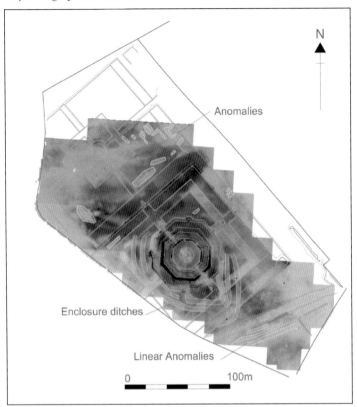

Figure 7. Some highlighted features of the resistivity survey.

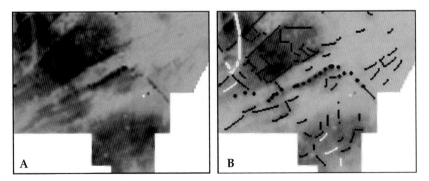

Figure 8. Detail south of the mound (A) and interpretation (B) (black and white: high and low resistivity respectively).

While the areas to the north of the stepped mound are somewhat obscured by overburden or the effects of waterlogging, the area to the south in contrast shows a wealth of detail (Figure 8).

Besides the large (low resistance) ditch many short linear high-resistance dark anomalies marked in black are evident in figure 8B. On the southern edge of the large ditch is a row of what appear to be large, independent stone blocks, possibly a stone revetment. The weak high resistance feature traversing the ditch is but one indication of building phases in this area of multiple (including recent) dates and potentially complex sequences of activity.

In the corresponding magnetic data, the main mound and its stepped structure again stand out very clearly, and around its east, south and west sides is the multivallate enclosure (Figure 9). The survey conducted on the golf course to the south east did not produce any sign of a continuation of the large open ditch (south of the Knot mound). This suggests that the ditch either terminated at, or runs beneath, the Dumbarton Road. Only stretches of (recent) field drains and an old boundary ditch were revealed on the golf range.

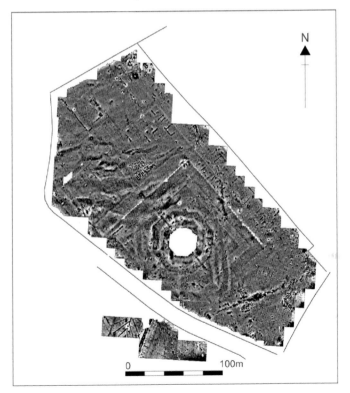

Figure 9. Magnetic survey results (black +10 nT and white -10nT).

A regular series of drains can also be seen running into the ditch on the eastern boundary of the King's Knot, while other segments of drainage are found near the Queen's Knot. The short rectangular anomalies seen in the resistivity survey are again visible. Also underlying the Queen's Knot are some irregular linear bands, running in broadly E-W directions. These can best be interpreted as natural irregular undulations in the ground surface, perhaps glaciofluvial channels. This is perhaps indicative of the lower lying area of the Queen's Knot having been scarped or truncated down into the natural during construction. One other significant feature in this area is a concentration of highly magnetic material just to the southeast of the Queen's Knot mound. Situated in what could be the very centre of the original garden there is a strong possibility that this could be the truncated base of a pond feature that has been filled with stone (Figure 10). Subsurface remains to the south of the main mound and the large E-W ditch are also evident.

The recent ground penetrating radar survey focussed on the multivallate monument and revealed good preservation of the ditches to the south and

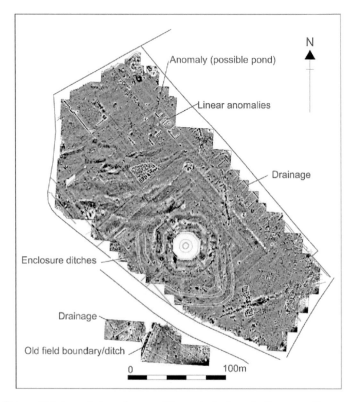

Figure. 10 Interpretation of some of the main features in the magnetic survey.

west sides of the stepped mound (O'Grady, 2012). Surviving below up to 1 m of overburden the outer ditch was found to be 3-3.5 m wide, while the inner ditches 4-5 m wide. This may indicate multi-period construction. With steep U-shaped profiles the depth of these ditches is approximately 1-1.5 m where well preserved, depleting to 0.5 m where truncated in the north. Profiles also indicate that bank remnants, accompanying the ditches, may also be present in the south. Some limited support for a possible entrance where the ditches appear to terminate abruptly on the east side of the mound was provided by the survival of historic soil horizons between the apparent breaks in the ditch system.

Interpretation

Combining the results of the geophysical and topographic surveys together with aerial photographs, historical maps and historical records it is possible to propose a sequence for the main developments of the King's Knot (Figure 11).

The earliest feature is likely to have been the triple-ditched enclosure which may have been the earthwork referred to as the 'Round Table' mentioned as early as the 14th century. It has the appearance of a prehistoric enclosure, possibly of Iron Age or early medieval date, but it is not impossible that it was a purposefully created as an archaic feature for David II in the 1360s or James IV in the 1490s. In outline, the three sets of geophysical data together with the aerial photographs collectively confirm the presence of the enclosure but at a detailed level each data set offers something different; this complex situation can only be resolved now by excavation.

The garden of James IV (1493-1513)

It seems very probable that the large southern ditch, which is mirrored in the crop field to the north, is part of a boundary ditch system which includes the eastern boundary ditch and probable ditch in the Butt Park to the north. It is possible that the northern and southern ditch were linked by a ditch now buried beneath the Dumbarton Road. Together these ditches form a large enclosure with a trapezoidal shape. The ditches and a length of linear bank may be all that is left of a bank and ditch perimeter to James IV's garden. It is also notable that the large southern ditch avoids the triple-ditched enclosure, suggesting that this monument was included as a garden feature. That the 'Round Table' is mentioned as late as 1529 would seem to support this. It is also tempting to interpret the highly magnetic feature at the very centre of the trapezoidal garden as evidence of a possible pond. The inclusion of a pond or fountain as a central feature was typical of the medieval garden. Given that the enclosed garden may have included a prehistoric monument, a pond, and wet area in the northwest, there is not a great deal of room for the rows of thousands of fruit trees reportedly planted by James IV's gardeners. It is therefore very likely that they were planted in and around the garden, on the Butt Park, Haining, and Brae, and perhaps on route to the Park Loch.

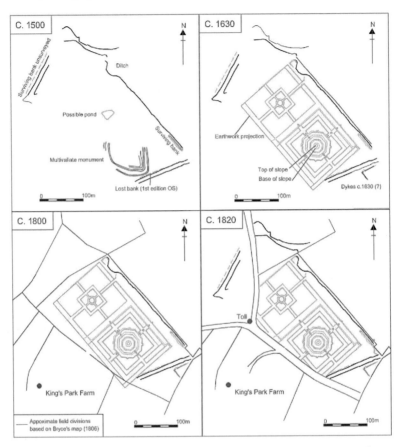

Figure 11. Interpretative scheme of main developments based on present evidence.

The garden of Charles I (c.1627-35)

The next major phase in the development of the garden that can be identified on present evidence is William Watt's geometric earthwork. This was a radical redesign but it runs parallel to the earlier eastern boundary ditch which may have acted as a baseline for setting out. The possible pond was filled in, the prehistoric monument was erased or buried, and the old ditch in the south and west would have been partially backfilled and covered by the new garden earthworks.

Abandonment, decline, and preservation (c.1690-present)

By the beginning of the 18th century the garden was reportedly in neglect, and by the end of the century the King's Knot had become part of a field system. Historic maps of this period are useful guides for building a picture of the King's Knot as it became enclosed and partly lost to cultivation. Disturbance and truncation along the eastern flank of the Knot suggest some quarrying for sands and gravels may have occurred. This could be related to the construction of the Dumbarton and Raploch Roads which dissect the western and northern edges of the Knot. Restoration in the 1860s marked a desire to protect the monument from further damage and safeguard it as a permanent feature of the Stirling landscape.

Conclusion/Future work

This survey has demonstrated the value of integrating a non-invasive approach in the field, based on geophysical, topographic and aerial survey, with study of early maps and historical records relating to King's Knot. The geophysical surveys have provided useful, interpretable results which extend what is visible in the aerial photographic record. In particular, they have been able to offer the time depth that is necessary in understanding the long history of King's Knot.

Methodologically, the geophysical survey has been a very good exercise in demonstrating the importance of adopting a multi-technique approach. For instance, both techniques detected good detail of the ditches around the main mound, yet because of the ground conditions at the northern end of the park resistivity was not performing optimally, while at the southern end this technique was more effective than magnetometry.

At the risk of generalising, magnetic survey has proven more popular and effective than resistivity in Scottish archaeology; the former usually provides more informative results than resistivity, and it is a more rapid technique. The experience at King's Knot, however, shows that where conditions favour resistivity, as they have done here, the technique works well. A comparable situation occurred at Dunkeld in the geophysical survey of the Duke of Atholl's garden estate adjacent to the Cathedral (Kellogg and Jones, 2006); whereas it was initially expected that the magnetic survey would be productive, in the event resistivity provided much more detailed information (Kellogg and Jones, 2006, Figure 22.4a-d).

Ground-penetrating radar has certainly had a role to play at King's Knot, complementing well the picture of the ditched enclosure around the main mound obtained from magnetic and electric survey. As well as supplying depth estimates GPR indicates good survival of buried ground surfaces and archaeological deposits beneath the surface earthworks (O'Grady, 2012). There is potential for further survey, notably in the area immediately south of the mound where better definition of the ditches would be valuable. This could be achieved by a combination of higher resolution resistivity survey and GPR experimenting with antennae of lower frequency. Potential building remains detected south of the Knot would also benefit from higher resolution resistivity survey.

Ultimately, however only a series of excavations to test the findings of this survey can provide detailed information on phasing, construction sequences, and former activities that took place at the King's Knot. Such a step could provide some exciting insights into the origins and a purpose of a prehistoric monument, one which may have subsequently played some significant role in the ceremonies of Scottish kings. It would also lead to an understanding of the development and uses of a High Renaissance garden and royal landscape of leisure which is of European significance.

Note: The winter storm of December 2011, brought down one of the two mature hawthorns that stood near the surviving bank and ditch east of the Knot. This provided an opportunity to test a suggestion that these may have been survivors from the 16th century garden. Dendrochronology however proved that they had in fact been planted in the late 19th century (Mills, 2012).

Acknowledgements

We thank Stirling City Heritage Trust and Historic Scotland for co-funding the project. We also would like to thank Kirsty Owen of HS for her advice and support, and especially Elspeth King and the staff of the Stirling Smith Art Gallery and Museum for providing a base for the surveys. We are most grateful to John Harrison for his enthusiastic input throughout the project. The assistance of the many local volunteers and Glasgow University students who participated in the surveys is warmly acknowledged. Special thanks go to Adrian Maldonado, Tessa Poller, Carmen Cuenca-Garcia, Oliver O'Grady, and Coralie Mills for their specialised contributions.

References

Abbreviated sources

(AT) *Accounts of the Lord High Treasurer of Scotland* I-XIII A.D.1473-1580, H.M. General Register House, Edinburgh.
(ER) *The Exchequer Rolls of Scotland* I-XXIII 1264-1600, H.M. General Register House, Edinburgh.
(MW) Paton H.M (ed) 1957. *Accounts of the Master of Works* I 1529-1615, Her Majesty's Stationery Office, Edinburgh.
Imrie, J. and Dunbar, J.G. 1982. *Accounts of the Master of Works* II 1616-1649, Her Majesty's Stationery Office, Edinburgh.
(MK) 1904. *Report on the Manuscripts of the Earl of Mar and Kellie preserved at Alloa House*, Historic Manuscript Commission 60, His Majesty's Stationery Office, London.
Brown, M. 2012. *Scotland's Lost Gardens*, Edinburgh: Royal Commission on the Ancient and Historical Monuments of Scotland.
Cook, M. 2009 King's Park and Roundabout, *Discovery and Excavation in Scotland*, New Series **10**: 177.
Cook, W.B. 1907. The King's Park of Stirling in history and record. *Transactions of the Stirling Natural History and Archaeological Society* 1907-8:110-137.
Cox, E.H.M. 1935. *A History of Gardening in Scotland*, London: Chatto & Windus.
Crawford, O.G.S. 1949. *Topography of Roman Scotland North of the Antonine Wall*, Cambridge: University Press.

Defoe, D. 1991. *A Tour Thro' the Whole Island of Great Britain*, P.N. Furbank and W.R. Owens (ed), New Haven and London: Yale University Press.

Digney, S., Jones R., and Maldonado, A. 2011. *The King's Knot, Stirling: Geophysical and Topographic Survey Report*, http://www.stirling-lhs.org

Diverres, A.H. 1965. Jean Froissart's journey to Scotland. *Forum for Modern Language Studies* **I**, 54-63.

Ditmas, E.M.R. 1974. The Round Table at Stirling. *Bibliographical Bulletin of the International Arthurian Society* Vol XXVI: 186-196.

Duncan, A.A.M. (ed) 1997. *John Barbour: The Bruce*, Edinburgh: Canongate Classics.

Edington, C. 1998. The Tournament in Medieval Scotland. M. Strickland (ed) *Harlaxton Medieval Studies VII: Armies, Chivalry and Warfare in Medieval Britain and France*, pp 46-62 Stamford: Paul Watkins.

Ewart, G. 2010. King's Knot, *Discovery and Excavation in Scotland*, New Series **11**, 170.

Harrison J.G. 2010. King of the Castle: Stirling Castle's Landscape Setting, *Stirling Castle Palace Archaeological and Historical Research 2004-2008*, Historic Scotland: Kirkdale Archaeology
http://sparc.scran.ac.uk/publications/level%20IV/level4Publications.html?current=four

Harvey J.H. (ed) 1969. *William Worcestre Itineraries*, Oxford: Clarendon Press.

Kellogg, D. and Jones, R.E. 2006. Geophysics and the management of a designed historical landscape: a case study at Dunkeld. R.E. Jones and L. Sharpe (ed) *Going over Old Ground: perspectives on archaeological geophsycial and geochemical survey in Scotland*, BAR 416, 234-245.

Kervyn de Lettenhove, M. (ed) 1967 (reprint). *Oeuvres de Froissart*, II, Biblio Verlag Osnabrück.

Loomis R.S. 1947. From Segontium to Sinadon – The Legends of a *Cité Gaste*, *Speculum* **22**, 520-533.

Loomis R.S. 1955-56. Scotland and the Arthurian Legend, *PSAS* **89**, 1-22.

Maitland, W. 1757. *The History and Antiquities of Scotland*, I, London.

Mills, C. 2012. *King's Knot, Stirling: Dendrochronology of a fallen Hawthorn*, unpublished client report for Historic Scotland.

Milne, D.J. 1975. Stirling Ditch. *Discovery and Excavation in Scotland*, The Scottish Regional Group, CBA, Edinburgh, 53-54.

Nimmo, W. 1777. *A General History of Stirlingshire*, London: Printed for William Creech, and sold by T. Cadell.

O'Grady, O.J.T. 2012. *King's Knot, Stirling: radar profile survey* http://www.stirling-lhs.org

Penman, M.A. 2004. *David II, 1329-7*, Phantassie, East Linton: Tuckwell Press.

Ronald, B. 1890. The names and localities of the old lands and crofts in and around Stirling, *Transactions of the Stirling Natural History and Archaeological Society* 1890-91, 1-32.

RCAHMS. 1963. *Stirlingshire: An Inventory of the Ancient Monuments*, I, HMSO, Edinburgh.

Sibbald, R. 1710. The History and Description of the Sherrifdoms of Linlithgow and Stirlingshire, Ancient and Modern.

Sibbald. 1739. *A Collection of Several Treaties in Folio, Concerning Scotland, as it was of old, and also in later times*, Edinburgh.

Shirra, W.L. 1888-9. The King's Knot, Stirling. *Transactions of the Stirling Natural History and Archaeological Society* 1888-9, 32-43.

LATER PREHISTORIC POTTERY FROM THE KING'S PARK, STIRLING

Nick Aitchison

The King's Park, Stirling, is both an area of great historical significance and a highly-valued local amenity. But despite belonging, together with Stirling Castle and the King's Knot, to a landscape of major national importance, comparatively little is known about the archaeology of the King's Park. The presence of a Roman road (SFAS, 1974), the embankment of a mid-nineteenth century racecourse (Aitken et al. 1984: 84) and World War I practice trenches (Cachart, 2011a) attest the potential and variety of the archaeological remains within the Park. A cup-and-ring mark carving (Morris, D.B. 1901: 91; RCAHMS 1963, Vol. 1: 65, no. 42; Morris, R.W.B. 1981: 58-9) of probably Neolithic or Early Bronze Age date is the only scheduled ancient monument in the Park. No other evidence of prehistoric activity has been recorded there. However, the proximity of Early Bronze Age cemeteries at Birkhill (centred on National Grid Reference NS 781926) (Morris, D.B. 1907; RCAHMS 1963, vol. 1: 22-4, 62, no. 18; 1979: 7, no. 8, 10-11, nos 33-7, 42-3) and Coneypark (NS 783926) (Hutchison, 1879; Thomson, 1978) indicates the presence of one or more prehistoric communities within the vicinity of the King's Park, although no settlement sites have been located.

The Site

Archaeological fieldwork within the King's Park has the potential to shed light on human activity of any period there. Unfortunately, the opportunity to examine the site of the new skate park, constructed in 2012, was missed. However, the disturbed ground around it was examined in October 2012 and February 2013, without anything of archaeological interest being noted. When the grassed area to the east of the skate park was ploughed in March 2013, the opportunity to conduct some fieldwalking was eagerly seized.

The roughly rectangular area concerned (NS 789928) measures approximately 70 m by 45 m and lies between the new skate park on the north-west and the refreshment kiosk, public toilets and disused tennis pavilion on the north-east (Figure 1). It is also bounded by a narrow strip of unploughed grass, a metalled footpath and planted borders to the south-east and the rising ground of the golf course to the south-west. The area has been disturbed on several occasions over the last century. This probably comprised part of the flat land within the east of the Park that was ploughed in an unsuccessful agricultural development in 1917 (see *Stirling Journal*, 21 February 1917, p. 4; 4 March 1943, p. 5). Tennis courts, a pavilion, band stand, putting green and public toilets were then constructed there during the 1920s as the recreational use of the Park was developed (Aitken et al. 1984: 86). The clay tennis courts were removed and the area grassed over around a decade ago. In 2012, a temporary surface was laid across this area for construction plant to access the skate park site from King's Park Road. Despite previous disturbance, the ploughing provided a rare opportunity to walk an area of turned soil.

The area was ploughed on 31 March 2013 and harrowed the same day, before it could be examined. That evening, a single rim sherd of prehistoric pottery (Sherd 1) was discovered during a casual walk around the perimeter of the broken ground. Encouraged by this, the ploughed area was fieldwalked systematically, in transects approximately 1.5 m apart, on 1 April. All items of possible archaeological interest were inspected visually but nothing of significance was found. This area was also harrowed on 2 April and walked again that evening. This yielded a second rim sherd of prehistoric pottery (Sherd 2). Further harrowing preceded grass sowing the following day. A walk around the perimeter produced another sherd of prehistoric pottery (Sherd 3) and what initially appeared to be two lumps of baked clay (Sherds 6 and 7). In fading light, and struggling to distinguish prehistoric pottery from recent rubbish, eleven more sherds were collected for closer examination.

Fieldwalking was assisted by unusually dry soil conditions but the identification of prehistoric pottery was hindered by the presence of large quantities of modern debris. Many fragments of brick, tile, field drain and blaize, as well as stones, were examined and discarded. This and other modern detritus confirmed the previous disturbance of the site. However, the presence of quantities of angular and water-rounded rocks and stones, consistent with glacial drift, indicated that ploughing had also penetrated previously undisturbed, presumably natural, levels. The soil was mostly a fine, dark loam, consistent with its cultivated state. By contrast, the soil along the south-west of the site, where the ground starts to rise, was yellow-brown in colour and did not appear to have been disturbed in the recent past. Perhaps significantly, all the sherds were found there. Because of this, it seems probable that the sherds were originally from this location or nearby and do not represent intrusive items, for example, which were imported with any topsoil that may have been brought in from elsewhere.

Further fieldwalking in late May, after the grass had taken root, yielded 22 sherds of possible archaeological interest, including another wall sherd (Sherd 4) and a wall or base sherd (Sherd 5). In addition, the only sherd of medieval pottery – from a large, thin-walled, wheel-thrown vessel with grey fabric and patchy green glaze – was found in the northern corner of the area ploughed. The rarity of medieval pottery from the site is perhaps consistent with the Park's status as a royal hunting ground, enclosed by William I and first recorded in 1165 × 1174 (see Gilbert 1979: 356).

The Ceramic Assemblage

A total of 38 sherds were recovered and, after cleaning and examination, 30 were rejected as modern, probably modern or too small to be identified or merit description. Distinguishing prehistoric from modern pottery was surprisingly difficult due to the presence of sherds of large modern vessels, probably flowerpots, with a rusticated fabric, including applied surface grits, large inclusions and the impressions of what appear to be botanical samples. The collection of as many sherds as possible enabled the prehistoric material to be differentiated on the basis of its softer and more lightly-coloured fabric, thicker wall size, irregular form, uneven gritting, evidence of construction and abraded condition. It proved even more difficult to distinguish prehistoric from modern flakes of pottery, where the full wall thickness does not survive, because of their small size and lack of diagnostic features. As flakes also tend to be less informative, they are not described here. All the sherds identified as modern have been retained in case more detailed examination reassesses any as prehistoric, as well as for comparative purposes.

The total weight of prehistoric pottery was 190 g, giving an average weight of 27 g per sherd. Each sherd was examined to produce a basic description of its fabric and stylistic attributes, including size, shape, colour, surface treatment, type of temper and residues. All these properties have implications for the function of the vessels represented and their date. The assemblage includes two rim sherds (Sherds 1 and 2), two body sherds (Sherds 3 and 4), a body or base sherd (Sherd 5), a base sherd (Sherd 6) and a possible base sherd (Sherd 7). Rim sherds, the upper part of a vessel around its mouth, usually provide more stylistic information than body sherds and enable the diameter of the mouth of the vessel to be estimated. The vessel form may be inferred from this.

Fabric analysis was undertaken only at a basic, macroscopic, level. Although convenient and inexpensive, this makes it very difficult to identify grit inclusions. Observations on inclusions, therefore, are only provisional until and unless confirmed by specialist microscopic analysis. Crushed stone was often added to wet clay by the potter as temper to reduce plasticity, making it easier to work, and to reduce shrinkage or expansion during the firing process (Gibson and Woods 1997: 213-15, 257-61; Gibson 2011: 35-9). This may explain the presence of some larger inclusions. However, very fine, possibly micaceous, inclusions may occur naturally within the clay. Similarly, it is unclear whether the softer, orange-red inclusions within some sherds are grog, crushed fragments of previously-fired pottery added as temper (see Gibson and Woods 1997: 178; Gibson 2011: 36-7), or naturally-occurring impurities in the clay.

In accordance with the Scots law of Treasure Trove, the sherds will be reported to the Secretariat of the Treasure Trove Panel for allocation to the appropriate museum.

Sherd 1

This rim sherd (Figure 2, top) belongs to a vessel with an external diameter of approximately 500 mm at its mouth. Up to 31 mm in depth of the profile and 37 mm, or approximately 2.5 %, of the rim circumference is present. The rim is simple and straight but with an irregular profile, rounded at one end of the sherd and squarish, with flat, faceted corners, at the other (Figures 3 and 4). This is consistent with what was formerly, although misleadingly, known as flat-rimmed ware (see Gibson 2011: 110, 129, 130). The rim is between 17 and 18 mm thick. No decoration is present.

The clay fabric is soft, friable and orange-pink in colour. The exterior (Figure 5, right) is uneven and its pitted surface reveals where organic material or soft grits have combusted during firing or become detached during subsequent use or deposition. A rounded inclusion of igneous rock, possibly of quartz, 1.5 by 3 mm, is impressed in the interior surface (Figure 5, left).

Evidence of the vessel's manufacture is detectable. An irregular groove, 10 to 13 mm below the exterior lip (Figure 3), may be where a strap of clay was joined to form the rim and the exterior surface was left unsmoothed. This sherd was found in three fragments. The sherd wall has delaminated, its interior and exterior faces separating along a weakness apparently created when the rim was attached and folded into the interior but not bonded properly (Figure 4). The large inclusion is associated with drag lines where the interior has been smoothed by hand while the clay was still soft, leaving drag marks in the surface. These lines are not regular enough to have been created on a potter's wheel but are consistent with hand construction.

This sherd shows no evidence of use, with no visible residues or encrustations present on its surfaces. The surfaces themselves show no signs of abrasion relating to potential use.

Sherd 2

This rim sherd (Figure 2, bottom) belongs to a vessel with an external diameter of approximately 460 mm at its mouth. As a result of the angular shape of the sherd, up to 52 mm in depth of the profile is present but only 14 mm, or approximately 1 %, of the rim circumference. The rim has a rounded profile but with a flat facet on part of the inside lip. The slightly curving rim profile suggests that the sherd belongs to a vessel with a narrower mouth than body. The rim is between 15 and 16 mm thick and the body of the vessel is between 14 and 15 mm thick. No decoration is present.

The clay fabric is moderately hard and orange in colour, with some inclusions of soft, orange-red material, up to 3 mm across. The exterior surface (Figure 6, right) is even but rough to the touch because it has been coated with fine, well-sorted, grits of white and light grey angular igneous rock, possibly quartz, 0.5 mm across. Some pitting and a Y-shaped depression 5 mm long in the exterior surface of the sherd appear to be where organic material has burned out during firing. The interior surface (Figure 6, left) is uneven and scarred. This may be a result of fire spalling, where the temperature has been raised too quickly during firing and moisture within the clay is released violently, resulting in spalls (flakes) of clay detaching from the vessel walls (see Gibson and Woods 1997: 156; Gibson 2011: 44, 48). Several small voids within the sherd wall may reveal where organic material or soft grits have combusted during firing.

Evidence of the vessel's manufacture is visible in its profile. A looped pattern is detectable in both sections, suggesting that the slightly thickened lip was formed by folding over the rim of the vessel into the interior. The unevenness of the interior surface indicates that this was not smoothed out and this may have contributed to the fire spalling.

Despite spalling, this vessel was still used. The sherd shows evidence of use in the form of a black residue or encrustation on a small area of its interior surface. This presumably represents a carbonised deposit from cooking foodstuffs over an open fire. This deposit and the surface inclusions are absent from the rest of the interior because its surface appears to have become detached. It is unclear whether this occurred during use or post-deposition.

Sherd 3

Although less informative than rim sherds, body sherds can still provide information about the form, size and manufacture of vessels. The small size (30 mm by 20 mm), uneven surface and barely discernible curvature of this body sherd make it difficult to estimate the diameter of the vessel it belongs to, but it appears to have been approximately 500 mm. The wall thickness is between 16 and 18 mm. No decoration is present.

The clay fabric is fairly hard and orange-buff in colour. The interior surface is reasonably smooth, without protruding inclusions. By contrast, the exterior surface is rough and fissured, giving a cork-like texture and appearance (Figure 7). This appears to be original, rather than having developed post-deposition as a result of the erosion of calcareous grits in certain soil conditions, as is the case with other corky-textured fabrics (see Gibson and Woods 1997: 136). Two angular inclusions, 1 mm across, of igneous rock, possibly quartz, are visible within a fissure. Softer inclusions, up to 3 mm across and orange-red in colour, are possibly grog.

Evidence of the vessel's manufacture is detectable in the rounded break to one edge of the sherd, with a slight groove and lip on the exterior edge (Figure 8). This is characteristic of coil or ring construction, where two adjacent coils or rings of clay have not been properly bonded during the manufacturing process, leaving a join void which increases in size as the clay shrinks during the drying process (see Gibson and Woods 1997: 152, 194-5; Gibson 2011: 41). Join voids create weaknesses and vessels tend to break along these, leaving rounded edges, formerly referred to as 'false rims', exposed. This has occurred in the case of Sherd 3. The inside edge of Sherd 3 has a slight lip and drag-lines are detectable in the profile, where the coils or rings have been smoothed over to create a join.

There is no visible evidence of use in the form of residues or encrustations. The surfaces show no signs of abrasion relating to potential use.

Sherd 4

This small body sherd measures 45 mm by up to 19 mm and belongs to a vessel with an external diameter of approximately 400 mm. The wall thickness is 16 mm. No decoration is present.

The clay fabric is reasonably hard and patchy in colour, but predominantly buff and orange-red. The exterior surface is orange-red in colour, possibly slipped, and is slightly irregular but has been smoothed by hand while the clay was still soft, leaving fine wipe marks (Figure 9). There are several angular inclusions, up to 1 mm across, of igneous rock, possibly quartz. A small void, 1 mm across, marks where a soft grit or organic material has combusted during firing. Only a small, abraded ridge belonging to the interior surface survives, leaving its appearance and texture unclear.

The rounded upper and lower edges of the sherd comprise false rims and, therefore, evidence of coil or ring construction. One exterior edge has a pronounced lip (Figure 10), where two adjacent coils or rings of clay have not been properly bonded. Drag-lines are also detectable in one profile where coils or rings have been joined.

There is no visible evidence of use in the form of residues or encrustations. The surfaces show no signs of abrasion relating to potential use.

Sherd 5

This roughly triangular-shaped sherd has a slightly hard orange-buff fabric with softer orange-red inclusions, up to 3 mm across, possibly grog. It appears to be from the lower wall or base of a large vessel because it was at least 36 mm thick and had an external diameter of approximately 500 mm. Only one small, apparently exterior, surface area survives, measuring up to 32 by 16 mm. No decoration is present. The surface is rough and deeply fissured (Figure 11), its cork-like texture studded with rounded inclusions, up to 4 mm across, of grey, apparently igneous, rock. Smaller white, possibly quartz, inclusions are also present. This surface has been blackened by burning. Although it has penetrated the fabric slightly, this blackening is concentrated on the surface of the sherd, indicating that it was produced while the vessel was intact, presumably in or over an open fire. However, it is unclear whether this occurred during firing or subsequent use of the vessel.

Sherd 6

This wedge-shaped sherd (Figure 12, left) has a moderately hard orange-buff fabric and measures 59 mm long, 37 mm wide and up to 27 mm thick. Its surfaces are very abraded, consistent with weathering after the vessel was broken. This sherd was initially thought to be baked clay from a kiln or furnace. However, closer examination reveals a small surface area, up to 18 by 15 mm, that has been treated in a similar manner to the surface of Sherd 2 and is coated with inclusions of fine white and light grey angular igneous rock, possibly quartz. No decoration is present. Within the body of the sherd are inclusions of a soft red-brown material, possibly grog, and several small voids, up to 3 mm across, where soft grits or organic material have been burned out during firing.

This sherd appears to belong to the angle between the base and wall of a substantial vessel.

Sherd 7

This rough, irregularly-shaped fragment of fired clay (Figure 12, right) measures 55 mm long, 33 mm wide and up to 26 mm thick. Its soft orange fabric contains some grits of dark igneous rock, up to 9 mm long, and soft red-brown material, possibly grog, up to 6 mm across. There are several small voids, the largest measuring 9 mm by up to 4 mm, within the body of the sherd where soft grits or organic material has been burned out during firing.

No surfaces are apparent, although the shape of the sherd suggests that it may belong to the angle between the base and wall of a large vessel. If this was the case, then its surfaces were very roughly finished, if at all. Fire-blackening on three sides reveals that it was exposed to heat after it was broken. Alternatively, this fragment may belong to a kiln or furnace.

Stylistic Affinities

The sherds recovered belong to large, hand-made vessels belonging to the urn tradition. Sherd 1 appears to belong to a bucket urn and Sherd 2 to a barrel urn. The other sherds cannot be identified to a specific form of urn. Bucket urns are large, flat-based, straight-sided and open-mouthed vessels (Gibson and Woods 1997: 95-6, 113; Gibson 2011: 107, 112, 130). Their height is greater than their maximum diameter, which occurs at the rim. Barrel urns are also large and flat-based but have a smooth, curving profile, their maximum diameter occurring in the upper half of the vessel. In northern Britain, both barrel and bucket urns are usually undecorated. Barrel and bucket urns do not belong to a distinctive ceramic tradition and are not indicative of date but occur widely during the Middle and Late Bronze Age (c. 1700-700 BC) and Iron Age (from c. 700 BC). It is unclear how long barrel and bucket urns continued in use (Gibson and Woods 1997: 72), but possibly into the early centuries AD (Gibson 2011: 130). Although flat-rimmed ware similar to Sherd 2 is usually associated with the Late Bronze Age, it is not confined to that period (Gibson 2011: 110, 130). Given the absence of diagnostic features, these sherds are best described as later prehistoric (c. 1700 BC-c. AD 200). The forms of pottery represented by the sherds from the King's Park are readily paralleled by those from later prehistoric settlement sites in eastern central Scotland (see Halliday 1988), including at Myrehead Farm, Whitecross, Falkirk (Barclay 1983: 58-9).

The orange-coloured fabric of all the sherds reveals that the vessels represented were fired in an oxidising atmosphere, characterised by the presence of excess oxygen, resulting in total combustion. The oxidisation of iron oxides present in the clay results in a red or reddish-brown colour (Gibson and Woods 1997: 216). This is consistent with open firing in a pit or bonfire (see Gibson and Woods 1997: 49-54; Gibson 2011: 44-5). The variation in appearance, texture and colour that can occur in large open-fired vessels makes it difficult to assess how many separate vessels are represented by this ceramic assemblage but it would appear to be at least four.

Barrel and bucket urns tend to suffer from comparison with the well-made, finer and more highly decorated ceramic traditions of the Neolithic and Early Bronze Age. As a result, they are usually described as poorly-made and their fabric as coarse (e.g. Gibson and Woods 1997: 72; Gibson 2011: 130). Nevertheless, the vessels represented here were reasonably well finished by being wiped before drying (Sherds 1 and 4), coated with fine grits (Sherds 2 and 6) and possibly slipped (Sherd 4). In addition, their large size reflects a competent ceramic technology. Moreover, the importance of these sherds lies not in the quality of the ceramic tradition to which they belong but in the evidence they provide about later prehistoric activity.

Discussion

This small surface assemblage indicates the presence of later prehistoric activity within the King's Park but the nature of that activity remains unclear. Although bucket urns from settlement sites are more familiar (Gibson 2011: 107), barrel and bucket urns are found in both domestic and funerary contexts (Gibson and Woods 1997: 71, 96). The size and number of sherds found suggest that they are unlikely to have travelled far from their original location. This implies that the pottery was turned up by the plough from sub-surface contexts. The nature and extent of the destruction of any archaeological features is unknown and can only be established by excavation. These sherds therefore contribute to our knowledge of the otherwise enigmatic prehistory of the King's Park and of Stirling in general.

This pottery not only emphasises the archaeological potential of the King's Park but also raises questions about the protection and management of the archaeological remains there. By contrast to previous work within the Park, most recently the construction of a footpath in 2010 (Cachart, 2010; 2011b), Stirling Council's archaeologist was not informed of the ploughing. It was only by chance that I spotted the operation and, fortuitously, found a rim sherd that evening. Although demonstrating that small-scale, opportunistic fieldwork can yield results, the archaeology of the King's Park deserves better and should not be left to luck. The archaeological impact of any future work within the King's Park should be assessed and, if appropriate, test excavations conducted in advance of work commencing and / or archaeological monitoring undertaken. Only such active management and intervention will enhance our understanding of the archaeology of the King's Park and its role within Stirling's wider past.

Acknowledgements

I am very grateful to Murray Cook, Stirling Council's Archaeological Officer, for his interest, to my wife Karen for commenting on an early draft of this paper and to Dr Neville Dix for his helpful editorial comments. I am also indebted to my son Blane, who played patiently while I did most of the fieldwalking: 'Dad, now I *know* you're odd'.

Bibliography

Aitken, P., Cunningham, C. and McCutcheon, B. 1984. *Notes for a New History of Stirling: Kings Park*, Stirling: the authors.

Barclay, G.J. 1983. The excavation of a settlement of the later Bronze Age and Iron Age at Myrehead, Falkirk District, *Glasgow Archaeological Journal* 10, 41-71.

Cachart, R. 2010. *Archaeological Watching Brief: New Footpath, King's Park, Stirling, ST19*, Perth, Alder Archaeology (available at: archaeologydataservice.ac.uk/catalogue/adsdata/arch-1009-1/dissemination/pdf/alderarc1-80333_1.pdf (date accessed 10.5.13).

Cachart, R. 2011a. King's Park: excavation, *Discovery and Excavation in Scotland* (new series) 11 (2010), 171.

Cachart, R. 2011b. King's Park: watching brief, *Discovery and Excavation in Scotland* (new series) 11 (2010), 170-1.

Gibson, A. 2011. *Prehistoric Pottery in Britain and Ireland*, Stroud: History Press; first pub. 2002, Stroud: Tempus.

Gibson, A. and Woods, A. 1997. *Prehistoric Pottery for the Archaeologist*, 2nd edn, Leicester: Leicester University Press; first pub. 1990.

Gilbert, J.M. 1979. *Hunting and Hunting Reserves in Medieval Scotland*, Edinburgh: John Donald.

Halliday, S. 1988. The pottery, in J.R. Sherriff, A hut-circle at Ormiston Farm, Newburgh, Fife, *Proceedings of the Society of Antiquaries of Scotland* **118**, 104-8.

Hutchison, A.F. 1879. Stone cist and skeleton found at Coneypark, *Stirling Natural History and Antiquarian Society Transactions* **1** (1878-9), 13-21.

Morris, D.B. 1901. Cup and ring marked rock surface in King's Park, *Stirling Natural History and Antiquarian Society Transactions* **23** (1900-1), 91.

Morris, D.B. 1907. Urn and supposed cist found near Cambusbarron, *Stirling Natural History and Antiquarian Society Transactions* **29** (1906-7), 79-81.

Morris, R.W.B. 1981. *The Prehistoric Rock Art of Southern Scotland*, BAR British Series no. 86, Oxford: BAR.

RCAHMS 1963. Royal Commission on the Ancient and Historical Monuments of Scotland, *Stirlingshire: an Inventory of the Ancient Monuments*, 2 Vol, Edinburgh: HMSO.

RCAHMS 1979. Royal Commission on the Ancient and Historical Monuments of Scotland, *The Archaeological Sites and Monuments of Stirling District, Central Region*, Society of Antiquaries of Scotland Archaeological Field Survey, Edinburgh: RCAHMS.

SFAS 1974. Stirling Field and Archaeological Society per D.J. Milne, Stirling: Roman road, *Discovery and Excavation in Scotland* 1974, 65-6.

Thomson, J.K. 1978. A Bronze Age cairn at Coneypark, Stirling, *Glasgow Archaeological Journal* **5**, 1-8.

Figure 1. The area fieldwalked, after ploughing and harrowing, photographed from the skate-park, looking south-east. King's Park Road is at the top of the photograph. The later prehistoric pottery was found towards the top right-hand side of this area.

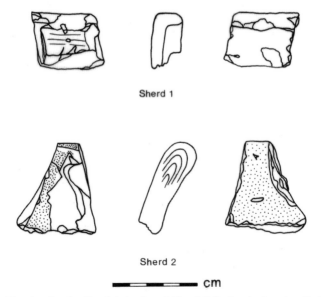

Sherd 1

Sherd 2

cm

Figure 2. The rim sherds: Sherd 1 (top) and Sherd 2 (bottom), showing their interior surfaces (left), profiles (centre) and exterior surfaces (right).

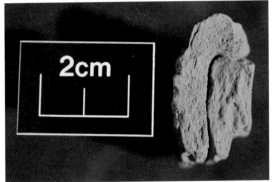

Figure 3. Sherd 1: the faceted rim with an irregular groove below the exterior lip.

Figure 4. Sherd 1: profile view, showing faceted 'flat' rim and delamination of the sherd wall.

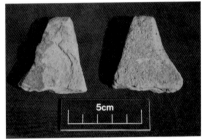

Figure 5. Sherd 1: the interior (left) and exterior (right) surfaces.

Figure 6. Sherd 2: the interior (left) and exterior (right) surfaces.

Figure 7. Sherd 3: the fissured and gritted exterior surface, showing its 'corky' appearance.

Figure 8. Sherd 3: the broken edge, showing its rounded 'false rim' with slight groove and lip on its interior edge.

Figure 9. Sherd 4: the wiped and possibly slipped exterior surface.

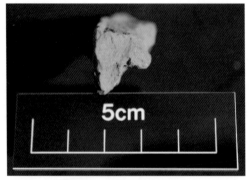

Figure 10. Sherd 4: the broken edge, showing its lipped 'false rim'.

Figure 11. Sherd 5: the fissured, gritted and possibly burnt exterior surface, showing its cork-like texture.

Figure 12. The base sherds: Sherd 6 (left), showing the small gritted surface area at the front, and the possible base sherd, Sherd 7 (right).

Report of the *Forth Naturalist and Historian* Wildlife and Landscape Forum,
Saturday 22 September 2012

The *Forth Naturalist and Historian* held its first Wildlife and Landscape Forum
in September 2011, an event which had never been attempted by the Society
previously. It was so successful that a second Wildlife and Landscape Forum
was held in 2012, and more are planned for the future. However, what were the
ingredients that led to this success?

The first Forum aimed to bring together and showcase the huge range of
activities by many societies and community groups in the Forth Valley. It
consisted of two distinct elements. At the 'fayre' there were many stalls where
each group displayed information about its activities. There was a series of
quick-fire talks, 5 minutes (or thereabouts) each, which demonstrated the
enthusiasm of so many people who undertake voluntary activities in the Forth
Valley. There were also a few longer talks which aimed to provide topics of
general interest for everyone attending the Forum. The Board of the *Forth
Naturalist and Historian* is very grateful to Stirling Council for providing funds
to support this initial Forum.

The 2012 Forum followed a similar format. Again the Board of the *Forth
Naturalist and Historian* is grateful to one of our District Councils for supporting
the Forum – this year it was Clackmannanshire Council – and the Forum was
introduced and participants welcomed by Councillor Donald W. Balsillie. He
took this opportunity to launch the revised Clackmannanshire Biodiversity
Action Plan.

David Anderson is RSPB Scotland's Inner Forth and Loch Leven
Futurescapes Officer and **Kate Studd** the Inner Forth Landscape Initiative
Project Officer. Their joint talk presented details of two exciting new
programmes taking place in the upper reaches of the Forth Estuary, defined as
from Stirling downstream to Blackness and Rosyth. The Inner Forth Landscape
Initiative is a partnership programme, which has earmarked funding under the
Heritage Lottery Fund's Landscape Partnership Scheme. Partners include local
authorities, government agencies and charities, led by RSPB Scotland. The
Initiative aims to:

- turn perceptions of the Inner Forth around and rekindle pride in the local
  environment;

- connect disparate habitats to create a landscape flourishing with wildlife;

- conserve, enhance and celebrate the Inner Forth's natural, cultural and
  built heritage; and

- create opportunities and support people to enjoy, explore and work to
  look after their landscape.

During autumn 2012 the Initiative was in its development stage. The next year-long stage will see short-listed projects being taken forward; finally some major projects will be selected. The first results are expected in 2014.

RSPB's vision for the Inner Forth Futurescape is for large scale wetland habitat creation across 2,000 hectares, centred on the Falkirk and Alloa areas. This network of wetland habitats, including saltmarsh, mudflat and reedbed, will create habitats and food for wildlife, as well as a range of benefits for people living around the Forth. This vision cannot be achieved by any single organisation working alone. Only through the creation of strong partnerships with communities, landowners, local councils, government agencies and charities, will the vision become a reality.

Roy Sexton gave a presentation which illustrated the importance of articles in the Society's journal, *The Forth Naturalist and & Historian*, in the development of wildlife conservation policy in Clackmannanshire.

In the first volume of the Journal, published in 1976, the editorial board set out its objective to increase our knowledge of a neglected part of Scotland by encouraging the missing ingredient – the enthusiastic amateur – which had been so evident in the late 19th and early 20th centuries. The aim was to do this by providing a vehicle for publication which would not only stimulate existing workers to publish their results but encourage others to take up new researches. It certainly achieved both of these goals. For instance the annual Bird Report in volume 1 involved just 10 contributing recorders, a number which had grown to 105 in 2012. The latest volumes also include similar Moth and Plant reports. These annual articles provide important archives of wildlife information. Again using the first Bird Report as an example, the Ring Ouzel's breeding was described as widespread but patchy in scrubby gullies and crags in the Ochils. Sadly a review of the modern lists shows it has not been reported in the same area for at least 11 years.

The inaugural board of the FNH had members who resided in Clackmannanshire. A quick look through the journal's on-line index (http://www.fnh.stir.ac.uk/journal/indexes_contents_page/cumulative_keyword_index_1-33.pdf) reveals a long list of articles about the county's wildlife. Mountain hares, moorland birds, sticky catchfly plants, fleas, brown argus butterflies, mayflies, hoverflies, riverine birds, alpine foxtail grass, sparling fish, whooper swans, mistletoe and many other species feature. These articles provide an archive of the numbers and sites where these organisms are found. Such information is invaluable to modern developers who are obliged to undertake Environmental Impact Assessments when they plan large projects like windfarms and quarries. The articles also serve to increase local awareness of Clackmannanshire's wildlife riches and in doing so have probably done more to protect both species and habitats than any other conservation measure. The FNH journal has articles about Clackmannashire's ponds, rivers, woodlands, bogs, salt marshes and, perhaps most important of all, the intertidal mudflats which provide the food source for our internationally important populations of waders. Landscapes are also covered by articles on the county's geology, geomorphology and mines, often written with secondary schools in mind.

The work of the Ochils Landscape Partnership was described by **Nathan Critchlow-Watton** on behalf of **Sheena Stone**. The partnership, of 19 organisations based along the Hillfoots, aims to undertake several built and natural heritage projects. During its first year of operation it initiated some of its planned 22 projects. Five examples of the projects are:

* the archaeological dig in Dollar Glen in September 2012 was run in conjunction with the National Trust for Scotland, with over 40 volunteers involved;
* a drystone bench and sensory garden in Alva Glen, and a feasibility study for a hydro scheme, and training for volunteers in path maintenance;
* the overgrown burnside scrub has been cleared in Mill Green, Dollar, so that children can again be encouraged to play by, and learn about, the burn;
* the control of various alien, invasive species along the River Devon by contractors; and
* a wildlife pond and a seating area have been created in Muckhart Nature Park, and volunteers have planted native fruit trees.

The Ochils Landscape Patnership ran its first *Ochils Festival* in June 2012, providing 20 free walks, talks and workshops on the area's built and natural heritages. Over 490 people attended. Similar *Ochils Festivals* are planned to take place in June 2013 and 2014. Training for volunteers has been provided in palaeography, oral history, and developing interpretation boards. Volunteers interested in a range of different aspects of the history of the Hillfoots area are being supported in various research projects.

The Ochils Landscape Partnership is funded by the Heritage Lottery Fund, University of Stirling, Clackmannanshire Council, EDF Energy, Clackmannanshire & Stirling Environment Trust, and the Clackmannanshire Heritage Trust.

Lewis Pate of the Scottish Wildlife Trust spoke about the conservation of the red squirrel, *Sciurus vulgaris*. Saving Scotland's Red Squirrels (SSRS) is a national conservation project focussed around the principle of proving that targeted grey squirrel control is of measurable benefit to the remaining red squirrel populations.

Scotland now has around 75 % of the UK's red squirrels (around 121,000 animals). Apart from habitat loss, the main threat to these endearing and iconic creatures is squirrelpox virus (SQPV). The disease is carried by grey squirrels in which it is asymptomatic. It is fatal to red squirrels which have little immunity and will die usually within 15 days of contracting it. SSRS is working hard to contain the disease in the Borders; however, it is constantly being pushed north into healthy populations of red squirrels in the north and west of the country. So far, the furthest north it has reached is Mauchline in Ayrshire where it was contained by rapid and extensive grey squirrel control. There is now an annual virus screening programme where blood testing is carried out in order to determine the spread of the disease.

The project has now developed significant landowner involvement with multiple schemes running across areas of the Borders, Tayside, Loch Lomond and Trossachs National Park and a few in Aberdeenshire. There has been both integrated grey squirrel control and protection of existing red squirrel populations, even bringing red squirrels back into areas where they have not been seen for many years. Robust monitoring is now in place across the country, utilising a combination of sticky hair trap feeder boxes, walking transects and motion sensing camera traps. These data provide annually comparable early warnings about changes in red squirrel abundance. SSRS is now in its final phase, on completion of which the project will be reviewed by SNH.

There was a series of nine short talks during the Forum. The titles of the talks and the speakers were:
- Buchlyvie Wildlife Garden and environmental education by Jessica Langford,
- Clackmannanshire Biodiversity Action Plan by Helen Blenkharn,
- Environmental Action Killin by John Holland,
- Falkirk Wildlife Festival by Dan Jackman,
- Friends of the Earth Stirling by Walter Atwood,
- Natural Communities by Kate Williamson,
- The Conservation Volunteers by John McFarlane,
- The Forthbank Loop woodland creation project by Guy Harewood,
- Wildlife photography by Dave Taylor.

As well as the opportunities for networking between the many societies and groups represented at the Forum, there was discussion of the future of the *Forth Naturalist and Historian* itself. Earlier in 2012 it had metamorphosed into a membership society, and it was pleasing to note that the Forum allowed the opportunity to recruit some new members. There was encouragement for those present to ensure the future of the society's journal by buying it, by reading it and by contributing articles. At a time of relative financial austerity, it was stressed that membership of the society, use of the journal and attendance at the annual series of conferences were all vital if the *Forth Naturalist and Historian* is to continue to provide its positive contribution to life in the Forth Valley.

Michael B. Usher

Book Review

The Firth of Forth – An Environmental History by T.C. Smout and Mairi Stewart. Published by Birlinn. ISBN 978-1-78027-064-7. £14.99.

For anyone who is either a Forth Naturalist or a Forth Historian, this new book, an environmental history of the Forth, is an essential addition to their library. In a series of well-written chapters, each of which is an essay in its own right, the authors place the environment of the Forth in a clear historical context and show how the impact of mankind over many centuries has produced the Forth as we see it today. T.C. Smout and Mairi Stewart cover the entire aquatic environment of the Forth from river to estuary to firth and attempt to examine the conundrum of how a vibrant fishing industry in the Firth of Forth collapsed never to be reborn, but that there are more fish-eating bird and mammals now living in the Forth that any time in the past. How could there be fewer fish caught, but more fish-eating birds and mammals about? The answer to this question is not simple and this book reveals the many facets of the answer. The collapse of the fisheries was apparently due to over-exploitation by fishermen and a failure of management and science at all levels. Early fishing had little impact, until exploitation developed after 1730 so that by the 1790s both white fish and herring were reported as scarce. The Lammas Drave was an inshore herring fishery between July and September which targeted the spawning stock and its failure is attributable to both natural fluctuations as well as to over-fishing of a comparatively small and discrete population. The winter herring stock was exploited in the 19th century through periods of boom and bust, until it too failed. For oysters the failure was due to over-fishing coupled with an almost total lack of size control, so that small immature oysters were removed for restocking other oyster bed areas such as the Thames. For white fish a sustainable line fishery was replaced by trawling and attempts to control it were thwarted by Thomas Huxley and William M'Intosh, the leading scientists of their days, who declared that the seas were inexhaustible. By the time that controls took effect the irreparable damage had been done.

Pollution of the Forth got progressively worse from 1860 to 1960, and various attempts at control were ineffective. Only with the establishment of the Forth and Lothians River Purification Boards in 1951 did matters improve, and then through subsequent legislation and control by the Scottish Environment Protection Agency much of the effects of pollution have been eliminated. Land claim on the shores of the Forth which has been undertaken for centuries for reasons of agriculture, sea defence and industrial development has removed about 50 % of the intertidal habitat. However this is now being reversed through re-naturing projects such as at Skinflats.

In contrast to the sorry story of man's destruction of the fisheries, the wildlife of the Forth has flourished in the 20th century. The numbers of gannets on Bass Rock has risen from 3000 pairs in 1904 to a total of 55,482 in 2009. The number of puffins on the May has risen from <100 in 1935 to 72,136 in 2002. The same is true for fulmar, cormorant, shag, gulls, kittiwake, guillemot and razorbills. The reasons seem to be a lack of persecution coupled with a growth in abundance of small fishes such as sand-eels and sprats. Whatever recent fluctuations in bird numbers have occurred they are small compared to their phenomenal growth over the past century. Equally dramatic has been the rise in numbers of grey seal from none in 1892, to 2 in 1935, to 3 in 1950, and then to around 2000 in the late 1990s. This rise appears to have been triggered by culling at the Farne Islands.

Throughout these accounts the authors maintain a clear perspective and show how a combination of natural fluctuations, growth in human population, the development of regulations (often ineffective at first, and sometimes only effective too late) plus changing social attitudes have created the Firth of Forth and its estuary as we see them today.

I strongly recommend this book to anyone interested in the Forth in all its forms. I hope that a future edition will however be able to correct some of the proof-reading errors which have slipped in – most annoying to this reviewer is that the Latin name of the Norway Lobster/ Scampi is *Nephrops*, not nethrops!

Donald McLusky

ROBERT KITSON

An article by C.A. Thomson and I.P. Wilkinson on the life and work of Stirling's Victorian palaeobotanist, Robert Kitson has appeared on the British Geological Survey (BGS) website.

As would be expected there are many similarities with our own publication (Edwards, 1964) and while it seems indebted to Edward's correspondence with Kitson's daughter for some of the anecdotal material, it is never-the-less recommended as an additional source of information and some photographs which do not appear in our article.

The BGS account brings out quite clearly the importance of his achievements, more is the pity then that he is not better remembered here today.

Of his huge collection of fossil plant specimens, 7500 form the basis of the national collection at BGS and are still being studied today.

Kitson is one of the few people from Stirling who have reached international fame in modern times and it is a shame that there is nothing commemorating his achievements in the city, no plaque or even a road name.

Reference

Edwards, D. 1984. Robert Kitson: the most professional palaeobotanist. *The Forth Naturalist and Historian* **8**, 65-93.

Neville Dix